OCULAR ANATOMY
AND HISTOLOGY

OCULAR ANATOMY AND HISTOLOGY
Third Edition

By

D.M. PIPE BSc (Hons), FCOptom, FBDO (Hons)

and

L.J. RAPLEY BSc (Hons), FCOptom, PGCE

THE ASSOCIATION OF BRITISH DISPENSING OPTICIANS
Godmersham Park
Godmersham
Canterbury, Kent
CT4 7DT

THE ASSOCIATION OF BRITISH DISPENSING OPTICIANS
Godmersham Park
Godmersham
Canterbury, Kent
CT4 7DT

ISBN 0-900099-21-6

First Edition – August 1984
Second Edition – June 1997
Third Edition – August 2008

Printed by :
Ashford Press, Bottings Industrial Estate, Hillsons Road, Curdridge, Southampton, Hampshire, SO30 2DY

PREFACE

Our aim in writing this book is to fill the need for students of ocular anatomy to have a text which is concise but which contains all the major features of the visual system and its associated structures. To assist students further, we have included the introductory chapters to form a bridge between general anatomy and the greater cytological detail required in the study of the eye and its adnexa.

Since many of our readers may not have easy access to additional texts or journals, we felt that the inclusion of lengthy reference lists was not appropriate to this volume but we have included a short bibliography to aid those for whom facilities for further reading are available.

At examination time students may be expected to produce sketches to illustrate the structures that they describe and, for that reason we have made extensive use of simple line drawings. In this third edition the illustrations are coloured to aid differentiation of the components of the structures depicted.

Many of the ocular tissues were described in detail in the early 1700's and we have tried to draw attention to these early contributions by giving eponyms and the date of description where possible. Unfortunately, naming an anatomical feature after a particular individual does nothing for its description and may indeed be a source of confusion, especially where the same name is ascribed to several structures (Müller and Zinn for example). Both eponyms and descriptive names are given in this text so that whichever is subsequently used the student will be able to identify the feature under discussion.

CONTENTS

INTRODUCTION

Since the terms employed in this text to describe the relative position of anatomical structures, may differ from those with which the reader is familiar, we have set out those most frequently used in this introduction and the accompanying diagrams.

Figure 1 shows an oblique view of the head and identifies the various anatomical planes.

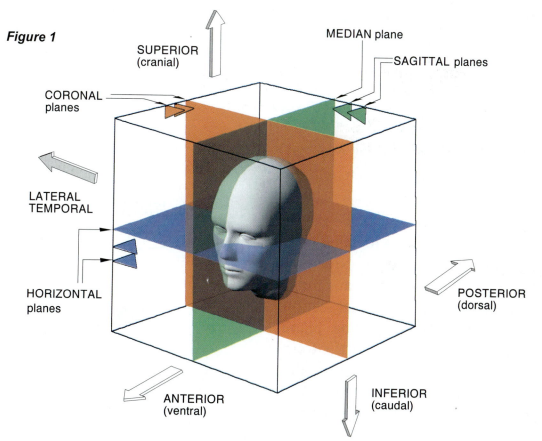

Figure 1

The use of the term 'vertical plane' to refer to either a sagittal plane or a coronal plane could lead to confusion and is not recommended. The median plane is the special case of a sagittal plane which divides the head into symmetrical sections. The bracketed terms have been carried over from those used for quadrupeds and are intended for reference only.

Superior and inferior are comparative terms used where two structures have the same name so that the superior orbital fissure lies higher in the orbit than the lower, inferior orbital fissure. These terms should not be confused with supra- and infra- which mean above and below.

Inter- means between while intra- means within. Extra- means outside. Para- usually refers to a structure that lies immediately next to another, so that the parastriate cortex lies next to the striate cortex. Peri- is used for more distant structures (the peristriate cortex is further away from the striate cortex than the parastriate).

Figure 2 shows the right eye and optic nerve seen from an antero-medial direction.

In Figure 3 the eye is shown cut in the three major planes together with the sections so obtained. Note that the sagittal section has a similar appearance to the horizontal section (except that the sectioning plane misses the optic nerve). Care should be taken when studying the diagrams later in the text to ensure that the orientation of each is fully understood.

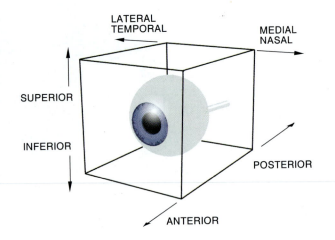

Figure 2

Figure 3

Horizontal plane

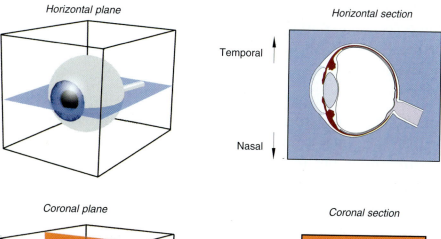

Horizontal section

Temporal ↕

Nasal ↓

Coronal plane

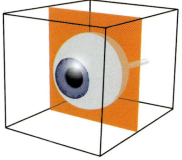

Coronal section

Sagittal plane

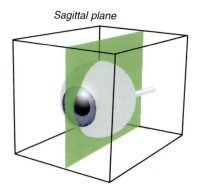

Sagittal section

Superior ↑

Inferior ↓

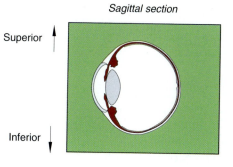

Where no orientation is stated the section may be obtained by cutting the tissue in any of the three major planes. Some sections are referred to as 'transverse'; this implies a section perpendicular to the surface as opposed to a flat section which is taken in a plane parallel to the surface. Longitudinal sections are taken in a plane parallel to the long axis of the tissue.

We have used micrometres (microns, μm) and nanometres (nm) in describing fine structure. Note that 1000μm = 1mm and 1000 000nm = 1mm. We have avoided the use of Ångstrom units but for reference 10Å = 1nm. Where practicable a marker has been included on the diagrams to give an indication of the dimensions of the structures illustrated.

Chapter 1

THE CELL

A study of ocular anatomy and histology requires an understanding of the units that are combined to form the ocular structures. To comprehend the organisation and function of the eye the form and function of its components must be studied, so before moving on to the gross anatomy of the easily visible parts of the eye, the fundamental nature of its cells (a science known as cytology) and the fibres that comprise the tissues (histology) must be reviewed. This text therefore commences with a description of the cell which is the basic structural unit of all living organisms. Cells vary greatly in size and shape so initially it is convenient to describe a generalised cell before considering specialised cells and their organisation with other components into tissues.

Individual cells are generally too small to observe without magnification and many ocular structures have cells which are less than 0.01mm across. Magnifications of between 30 and 1000 times can be achieved with a light microscope while the electron microscope provides magnification in excess of 100,000 times. The majority of cells are transparent so as well as magnification they also require treatment with stains that artificially colour their component

Fig.1.1 A GENERALISED CELL

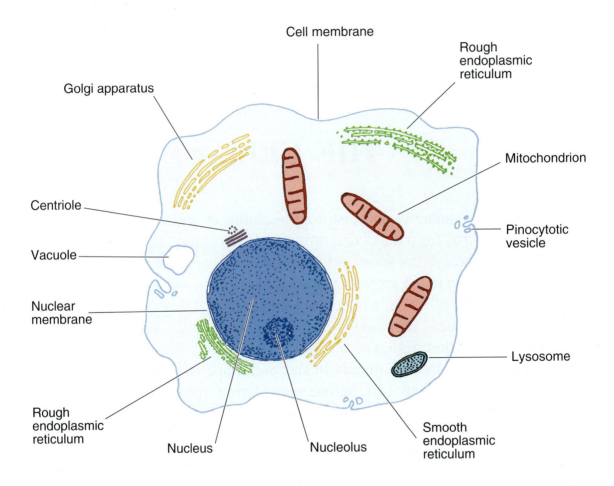

Golgi apparatus

Cell membrane

Rough endoplasmic reticulum

Centriole

Mitochondrion

Vacuole

Pinocytotic vesicle

Nuclear membrane

Lysosome

Rough endoplasmic reticulum

Nucleus

Nucleolus

Smooth endoplasmic reticulum

parts. The tissue is dehydrated and embedded in wax or resin and sectioned (sliced thinly) for microscope examination.

The structures made visible in a cell will depend on the type of stain used and the degree of magnification. With the light microscope the most distinctive features will usually be the cell nucleus and the cytoplasm. The cell membrane is not generally visible except as the boundary between the cell cytoplasm and adjacent structures, but the location of cells within the tissue is easily seen because of their nuclei. The shape and orientation of the cell nucleus also gives a guide to the shape and orientation of its cell. With electron microscopy the high magnification available allows the cytoplasmic inclusions, the organelles and the form of the cell membrane to be examined, together with details of junctions between cells.

THE COMPONENTS OF THE CELL

The cell membrane

The cell membrane is a complex phospholipid (fatty) protein structure some 7.5nm thick bounding the cell cytoplasm. The permeability and form of the membrane may be varied by the cell to allow the passage of materials into and out of the cell.

The cell membrane is often deeply folded with projections fitting into depressions in surrounding cells. The term for this is interdigitation. The free surface may also have numerous projections called villi or microvilli. Some cells have hair-like processes (cilia)

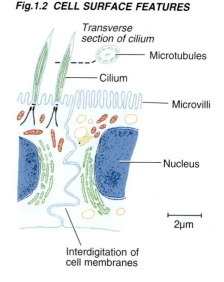

Fig.1.2 CELL SURFACE FEATURES

Transverse section of cilium
Microtubules
Cilium
Microvilli
Nucleus
2µm
Interdigitation of cell membranes

projecting from their free surfaces. In such cells the movement of the cilia is associated with the transport of substances over the surface of the cell. Structures similar to cilia may also be found within cells, as is the case in the retinal receptors.

Cell junctions

Where cells are firmly attached to each other, the membranes display specialised contact areas of several different kinds.

Desmosomes (also called maculae adherentes or macula adhesions) are regions where the normal 20nm intercellular gap widens to 25nm and filaments pass between and into adjacent cells. Hemidesmosomes, which are desmosomes on the cell side of the junction only, may appear between the cell membrane and its associated basement membrane. The cell may therefore be less firmly attached to its basement membrane than to adjoining cells.

Adhesions (zonulae adherentes or zonular adhesions) are areas where the membranes of both cells on each side of the junction are thickened and an adhesive material is found within the space between the membranes.

Tight junctions (zonulae occludentes or zonular occlusions) are regions where adjacent cell membranes are in tight contact, limiting the passage of materials between the cells. These are often found where the free surface of the cells is bathed in fluid.

Gap junctions occur where the distance between the cells is reduced to about 3nm and

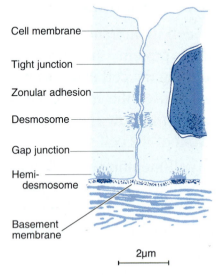

Fig.1.3 CELL JUNCTIONS

Cell membrane

Tight junction

Zonular adhesion

Desmosome

Gap junction

Hemi-desmosome

Basement membrane

2µm

this is bridged by fine channels allowing the passage of ions. These junctions are found (mainly) between smooth muscle cells and also between some cells of the central nervous system.

The specialised junctions between the membranes of nerve cells are described in Chapter 2.

Cytoplasm

This is the material that fills the cell and surrounds the nucleus. It consists of a viscous fluid that contains the organelles and inclusions of the cell. About 70-80% of the cell volume is water containing carbohydrates, lipids and proteins and also inorganic ions.

The nucleus

This is the largest of the organelles and it is the nucleus which regulates the internal activity and motility of the cell and controls cell division (mitosis). It is surrounded by a double nuclear membrane and contains deoxyribonucleic acid (DNA) in thread-like strands. These threads coalesce into dense bundles known as chromosomes when the cell is ready to divide. The nucleolus which is a small, usually spherical, body found within the nucleus contains ribonucleic acid (RNA). DNA and RNA react to give the nucleus its typical dark appearance seen with light microscopy when the cell is stained with a basic dye such as haematoxylin.

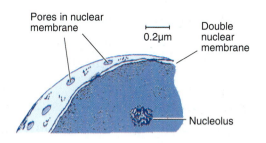

Fig.1.4 THE NUCLEUS

Pores in nuclear membrane

0.2µm

Double nuclear membrane

Nucleolus

Golgi apparatus

The Golgi apparatus appears as layers of sacs and is associated with the modification of secretory materials produced elsewhere in the cell, and also with the production of lysosomes and cell membranes.

Fig.1.5 GOLGI APPARATUS

Cisternae

300nm

Lysosomes

These are membrane-bound spherules, up to 0.8μm across (see Fig.1.9). They act phagocytically within the cell and contain enzymes used in the breakdown of damaged cells.

Ribosomes

Ribosomes are granules of about 20nm diameter which are composed of protein and RNA. These form clusters when the cell is active in protein synthesis.

Endoplasmic reticulum

This is a series of sacs or tubules. When found in association with ribosomes it is known as rough endoplasmic reticulum and is involved in protein synthesis. Without ribosomes it is called smooth endoplasmic reticulum and is found in cells involved in carbohydrate metabolism and hormone production.

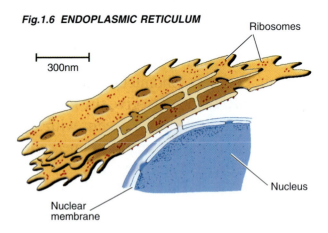

Fig.1.6 ENDOPLASMIC RETICULUM

Ribosomes

300nm

Nucleus

Nuclear membrane

Mitochondria

Mitochondria are membrane covered ellipsoids which are 0.5-2.0μm wide and up to 3μm long. They form the principal sites for energy production and they are more numerous in highly active cells. The number of mitochondria within a cell is thus some indication of the cell's potential for activity.

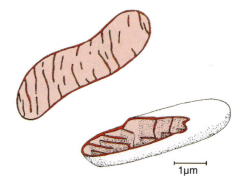

Fig.1.7 MITOCHONDRIA

1μm

Microtubules and microfilaments

These appear to give the cell rigidity or they may be involved in cell motility. They are numerous in neurones, ciliated cells and muscle cells.

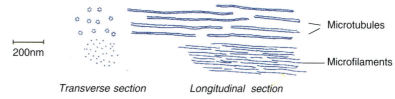

Fig 1.8 MICROFILAMENTS AND MICROTUBULES

200nm

Microtubules

Microfilaments

Transverse section   Longitudinal section

Vacuoles and vesicles

A vacuole is a membrane-bound bubble usually containing fluid. A vesicle is a small vacuole. (See also Glossary - Pinocytosis).

Inclusions

Inclusions are materials which may be produced by the cell or brought into the cell from outside. These may be crystals, lipid (fat) droplets, pigments (such as melanin giving the cell a brown colour), stored carbohydrates (in the form of glycogen), or secretions contained in large membrane-bound vacuoles or smaller vesicles.

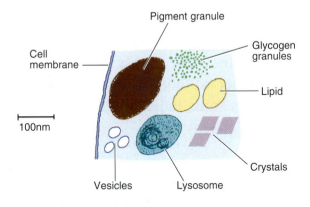

Fig.1.9 INCLUSIONS

Pigment granule

Glycogen granules

Cell membrane

Lipid

100nm

Crystals

Vesicles

Lysosome

Chapter 2

THE TISSUES

The tissues of the body are formed from accumulations of cells and their products, and these tissues are in turn organised to form systems and organs.

It is convenient to divide the tissues into four main groups.
- Epithelium
- Connective tissue
- Muscle
- Nervous tissue

EPITHELIUM

The term epithelium is applied to the sheets or layers of cells that line or cover the internal and external surfaces of the body. Epithelium (plural epithelia) may also be referred to as epithelial tissue.

Epithelial cells provide control for the passage of materials into and out of the underlying tissues, and may also be mechanically protective, secretory or of a special sensory nature. Epithelial cells that are exposed, and thus prone to damage, have great regenerative properties and can, in some cases, migrate or slide over one another to cover injured areas.

The cells are tightly packed and there is therefore little extracellular material in the epithelial layers. The deepest, basal cells rest on a basement membrane which is a layer of procollagen (the basic constituent of collagen, see page 18), reticulin and glycoprotein. The basement membrane is usually about 2μm thick but in some locations it may be considerably thicker.

Blood vessels are not found in epithelial layers and their absence means that the cells must obtain their nutrition from the neighbouring tissues, either by diffusion or by active transport.

CLASSIFICATION

The epithelia are divided into two main groups based on the number of layers of cells. Simple epithelium (unilaminar) consists of a single layer of cells resting on a basement membrane. Stratified (multilaminar) epithelium has more than one layer, the deepest cells dividing to replace those lost from the surface.

Simple epithelium

Since simple epithelium has only one layer of cells, it does not offer much protection to underlying tissues and is therefore not found on exposed surfaces of the body. However, it is well adapted to take part in absorption and secretion, because the single layer of cells is relatively thin.

Squamous (pavement) epithelium

This consists of very flat (squamous), polygonal cells forming a lining tissue. In blood vessels and lymphatic canals this is known as endothelium. The thickness of the cell may be less than 1µm so that the nucleus forms a bulge in the free surface. These cells are tightly linked by zonulae occludentes which prevent materials in the surrounding tissue fluid from passing between the cells. Substances which pass through the epithelium do so by diffusion or by active transport under the control of the cells.

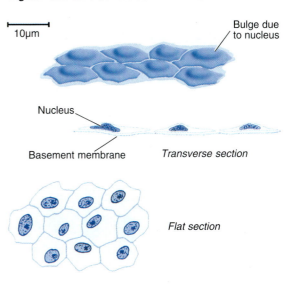

Fig.2.1 SIMPLE SQUAMOUS EPITHELIUM

10µm

Bulge due to nucleus

Nucleus

Basement membrane   Transverse section

Flat section

Cuboidal epithelium

This term is misleading since, when seen in flat section, tightly packed cells appear hexagonal. Although when viewed in transverse section some cells may seem to have approximately equal height and width, the location of the epithelium greatly affects its appearance (see Fig.2.5, glandular epithelium and the crystalline lens, Fig.10.18).

Fig.2.2 SIMPLE CUBOIDAL EPITHELIUM

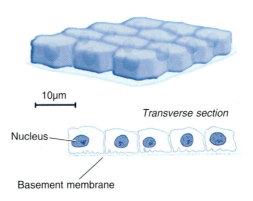

10µm

Transverse section

Nucleus

Basement membrane

Columnar epithelium

In transverse section these cells are seen to be taller than they are wide. Some carry microvilli on their free surface which greatly increases their surface area for absorption and they are thus found in areas such as the small intestine. In the Fallopian (uterine) tubes, columnar cells have cilia which help to transport the ovum towards the uterus (womb).

Fig.2.3 COLUMNAR CELLS

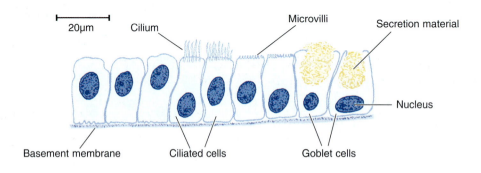

20µm   Cilium   Microvilli   Secretion material   Nucleus

Basement membrane   Ciliated cells   Goblet cells

Pseudostratified epithelium

This is simple columnar epithelium containing small immature cells and cells distorted by lateral pressure from their neighbours. The cell nuclei therefore lie at different distances from the basement membrane so that the epithelium appears to have more than one layer when seen in transverse section. However, as all the cells rest on the basement membrane, this is a simple epithelium. Pseudostratified epithelium is often ciliated and this type of cell lines the respiratory tract helping to move foreign bodies and dust particles away from the lungs.

Fig.2.4 PSEUDOSTRATIFIED EPITHELIUM

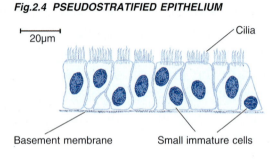

20µm   Cilia

Basement membrane   Small immature cells

12

Glandular epithelium

Glandular epithelium is formed by columnar or cuboidal cells providing the special function of secretion. Unicellular glands are formed by isolated secretory columnar cells. Because of their swollen shape when full of their secretion product, they are known as goblet cells (Fig.2.3).

In multicellular glands, the cells may be arranged around a duct, releasing their secretion into its lumen. These are known as exocrine glands. Endocrine glands have no duct and their secretion is released directly into the blood stream.

Glands may also be described by the type of secretion that they produce. Mucous cells produce a thick slimy secretion that reduces drying and acts as a lubricant. Serous cells produce a clear watery secretion.

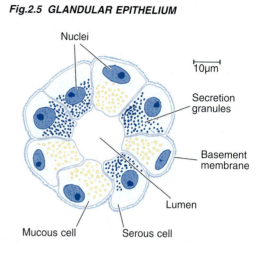

Fig.2.5 GLANDULAR EPITHELIUM

Nuclei

10µm

Secretion granules

Basement membrane

Lumen

Mucous cell   Serous cell

Pigment epithelium

The cells of pigment epithelium may be cuboidal or columnar and are packed with the brown pigment melanin. Melanin absorbs light and the greater the amount of melanin present the darker the layer of epithelium will appear to be. Pigment epithelium thus acts as a barrier to light. (Melanin is also found in other light absorbing cells, see melanocytes Fig.2.10).

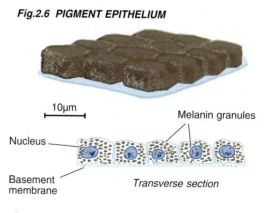

Fig.2.6 PIGMENT EPITHELIUM

10µm

Melanin granules

Nucleus

Basement membrane

Transverse section

Stratified (multilaminar) epithelium

The additional layers of cells found in stratified epithelium give protection against mechanical and chemical damage.

Stratified squamous epithelium

This is the most common and generally the thickest form of epithelium and is found where there is greatest wear and risk of damage. The basal cells resting on the basement membrane are columnar and the cells in the layers above become progressively flatter towards the surface. There are two forms of this epithelium.

In keratinising (or keratinised) stratified squamous epithelium the most superficial layers are non-living and are converted into a hard, fibrous protein called keratin. This type provides the tough outer layer of the skin of the body (the epidermis). See page 236 for a detailed description.

Within the body, moist non-keratinising (or non-keratinised) stratified squamous epithelium is found lining the mouth, the oesophagus and other internal ducts.

Fig.2.7 STRATIFIED SQUAMOUS EPITHELIUM

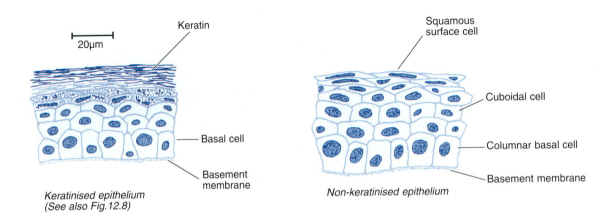

20μm

Keratin

Basal cell

Basement membrane

Keratinised epithelium
(See also Fig.12.8)

Squamous surface cell

Cuboidal cell

Columnar basal cell

Basement membrane

Non-keratinised epithelium

Urothelium (transitional epithelium)

Urothelium is found lining the urinary bladder. There are four or five layers of cells which can easily change their shape from cuboidal to squamous and back again in response to variations in bladder volume.

Fig.2.8 UROTHELIUM (TRANSITIONAL EPITHELIUM)

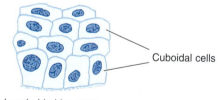

Cuboidal cells

Relaxed - bladder empty

Stretched - bladder full

CONNECTIVE TISSUE

While the cells of epithelium form sheets and cover surfaces, the cells of connective tissue are embedded in material known as the ground substance or matrix. This extracellular material may range from solid to fluid and generally contains fibres. Connective tissue forms much of the structure of the body and provides support for other tissues. Bone, cartilage, tendon and fascia and the stroma (bulk) of many organs are made of connective tissue. In addition, blood and lymph, (the circulating fluids of the body), also contain connective tissue cells.

Cellular components

Fibroblasts

These are the most common type of cell found in connective tissue. They are flattened star-shaped cells with long branching processes. The nucleus, which has several large nucleoli, produces a bulge in the centre of the cell. Rough endoplasmic reticulum, responsible for protein synthesis, is obvious in young fibroblasts but is less visible in inactive cells which are known as fibrocytes.

Fibroblasts are associated with the production of fibres (see below) and, when a tissue is injured, they proliferate to repair the wound which results in the formation of scar tissue.

Melanocytes

These are cells similar in shape to fibrocytes but they contain the pigment melanin. They are found in connective tissues where light absorption is required.

Macrophages

These cells are phagocytes forming the body's short-term defence system and are responsible for scavenging for bacteria and remnants of damaged tissue. For this purpose they contain large numbers of lysosomes. They are formed as monocytes (see page 27) in the bone marrow and can be extremely mobile.

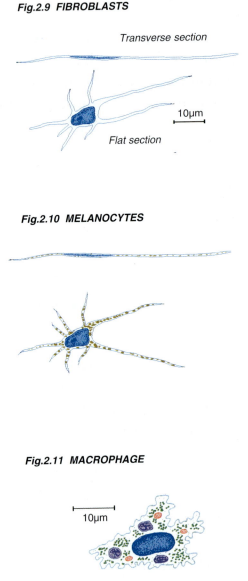

Fig.2.9 FIBROBLASTS

Transverse section

10μm

Flat section

Fig.2.10 MELANOCYTES

Fig.2.11 MACROPHAGE

10μm

Lymphocytes

These amoeboid cells vary in size from 6-16μm and are only present in large numbers in disease or in damaged tissues. They produce antibodies which bind to invading organisms to disable or destroy them.

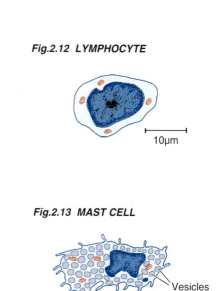

Fig.2.12 **LYMPHOCYTE**

10μm

Mast cells

These cells are round or ovoid, and have large numbers of dense vesicles in the cytoplasm. They are known to contain heparin which is an anti-coagulant, and histamine and serotonin which are both involved in inflammatory changes. However, the exact function of these cells is uncertain.

Fig.2.13 **MAST CELL**

Vesicles

10μm

Fat cells

These are large cells of 50μm diameter, having the cytoplasm and the nucleus compressed against the cell membrane by a globule of fat (lipid) stored within the cell (see Fig. 2.16).

Fibres

Collagen

The main fibre constituent of connective tissue is collagen. These fibres form straight or slightly sinuous bundles of white, flexible tissue. The individual fibres are 0.3-0.5μm in diameter and are composed of bundles of 20-100nm fibrils which in electron micrographs can be seen to be crossbanded at intervals of 64nm. These fibrils are formed of tropocollagen filaments made up of a triple helix of procollagen molecules.

Collagen is very strong and generally inelastic and inextensible, but the characteristics of tissue formed from collagen may vary considerably from site to site.

Fig.2.14 THE STRUCTURE OF COLLAGEN

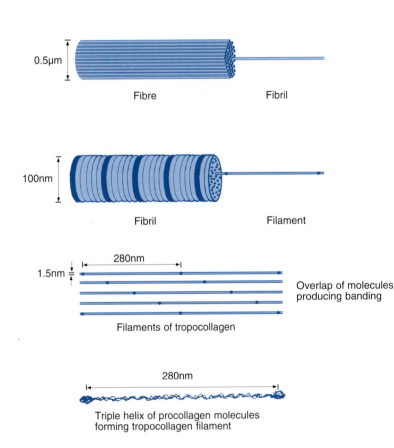

0.5μm

Fibre   Fibril

100nm

Fibril   Filament

280nm

1.5nm

Overlap of molecules producing banding

Filaments of tropocollagen

280nm

Triple helix of procollagen molecules forming tropocollagen filament

Elastin

Unlike collagen, elastin fibres frequently branch and rejoin. Tissue composed of elastin fibres has a yellowish colour and is elastic. This is due to the random orientation of the molecules making up the fibres and the readily deformed bonds that link these molecules. The tissues formed by elastin fibres become less elastic with age.

Reticulin

These fibres form the network of support for glands and the lymphatic system and are found in basement membranes. Reticulin fibres are considered to be a variety of fine collagen fibre.

The ground substance

The ground substance is a gel largely composed of water. The water may be bound to carbohydrate molecules forming a mucopolysaccharide or it may be bound to carbohydrate and protein molecules when it is known as glycoprotein.

The viscosity of the ground substance depends on the links between its component molecules and its association with cell membranes and fibres. The ground substance forms a pathway for the movement of metabolites, gases and electrolytes within the tissue.

CLASSIFICATION

The form taken by structural connective tissue shows great variation, the differences relating to the function of the tissue in a particular location. At one extreme is the rigid connective tissue, bone, providing strength and physical protection and at the other is loose (areolar) connective tissue which is found in the stroma of highly mobile structures such as the eyelids. Structural connective tissues are classified here by the 'density' of the tissue. Although containing connective tissue cells, blood and lymph have a fluid matrix and these tissues are described separately.

Structural connective tissue

Loose connective tissue

Loose or areolar connective tissue is widely distributed throughout the body and is highly extensible and elastic. Thin elastin and collagen fibres form an open meshwork in which all types of connective tissue cells are found, together with nerve fibres and capillaries. Since the components are not tightly packed and the

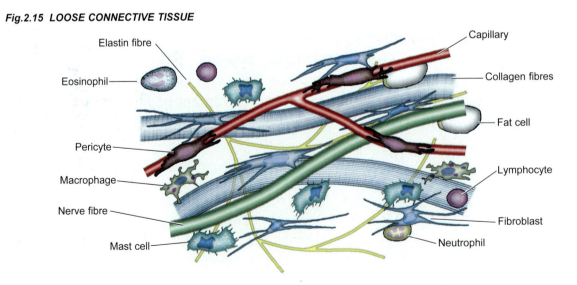

Fig.2.15 LOOSE CONNECTIVE TISSUE

Elastin fibre
Eosinophil
Pericyte
Macrophage
Nerve fibre
Mast cell

Capillary
Collagen fibres
Fat cell
Lymphocyte
Fibroblast
Neutrophil

ground substance is jellylike and semi-fluid, structures containing this tissue can be made to change shape with ease (see the iris, Chapter 8 and the eyelid, Chapter 12). This tissue is found forming sheaths around nerves and muscles, dividing glands into lobes, and in those areas of skin where little fat is present.

Adipose tissue

Adipose tissue consists mainly of fat cells grouped into lobules by vascular loose connective tissue. There are few fibres and little ground substance. The fat contained in the cells provides a source of energy that can be stored or mobilised as required. In some locations, under the skin for example, adipose tissue offers mechanical and thermal protection. In the orbit (the eye socket), fat provides a cushion behind the globe, against which the eye can rotate.

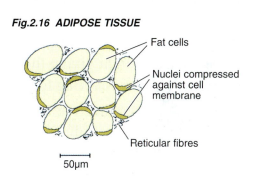

Fig.2.16 ADIPOSE TISSUE

Fat cells

Nuclei compressed against cell membrane

Reticular fibres

50µm

Dense connective tissue

The bulk of this form of connective tissue is thick collagen fibres with a variable amount of elastin. It has little ground substance and contains few cells and blood vessels. This tissue is very strong, and is used for protection and for anchoring structures within the body.

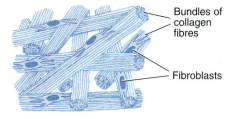

**Fig.2.17
IRREGULAR DENSE CONNECTIVE TISSUE**

Bundles of collagen fibres

Fibroblasts

In irregular dense connective tissue the collagen bundles interweave in all directions forming a very resilient structure. This tissue forms the strong outer

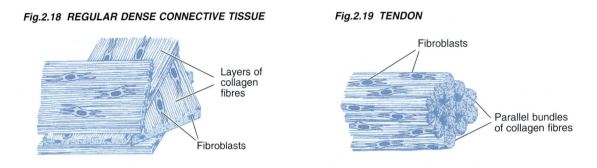

Fig.2.18 REGULAR DENSE CONNECTIVE TISSUE

Layers of collagen fibres

Fibroblasts

Fig.2.19 TENDON

Fibroblasts

Parallel bundles of collagen fibres

coat of the eye, the sclera. The randomly arranged collagen fibres scatter all wavelengths of light giving the sclera its white appearance. Irregular dense tissue is also found as a covering for muscles, nerves and bones.

Regular dense connective tissue forms tendons and ligaments and has rope-like bundles of collagen fibres with a common direction giving it a shiny silvery appearance. Tendons and ligaments are very strong, flexible and inelastic. In general, tendons are extensions from muscle tissue (see page 36) anchoring muscle to bone. Ligaments are extensions from the fibrous connective tissue covering bone which are used to attach one bone to another and to limit movement.

Cartilage

This is a dense avascular connective tissue with a highly resilient elastic ground substance. Some cartilage forms a transition stage in the development of bone. It also forms articulating surfaces and is found in the walls of the large ducts of the respiratory system and in the external ear.

The active cells of cartilage are called chondroblasts, while the resting, mature cell is the chondrocyte. These are found in spaces in the matrix called lacunae. Since the matrix is in general avascular, these cells have to obtain their metabolites by diffusion. As the cartilage ages, the ground substance calcifies, reducing the supply of metabolites to the older cells which die.

Fig.2.20 FIBROCARTILAGE

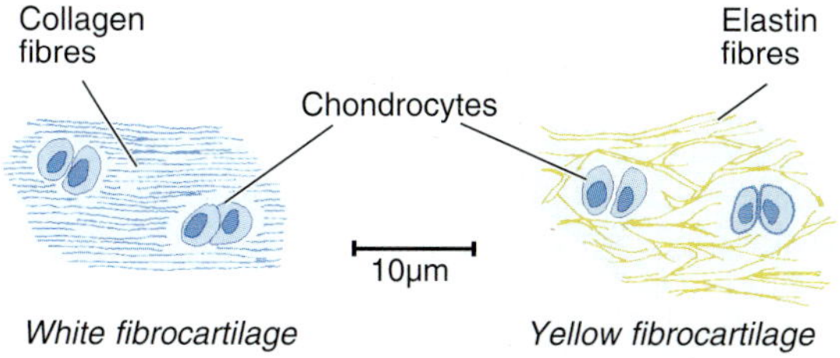

Fig.2.21 ARTICULAR HYALINE CARTILAGE

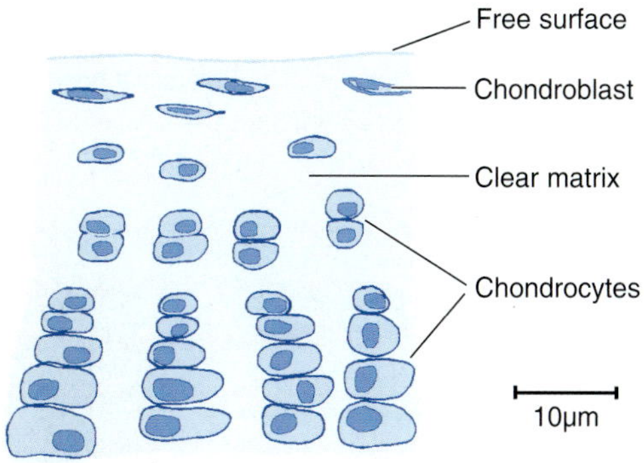

Collagen fibres

Chondrocytes

Elastin fibres

Free surface

Chondroblast

Clear matrix

Chondrocytes

10µm

White fibrocartilage

Yellow fibrocartilage

10µm

The ground substance of cartilage is a firm gel in which fibres may be visible. This is known as fibrocartilage which is classified as white if the fibres are mainly collagen as in the intervertebral discs, or yellow if the fibres are elastin as in the pinna of the ear.

If the fibres are not predominant, the cartilage is said to be hyaline (glassy) and it is this type which forms the articular surfaces of bones, the nasal, tracheal and bronchial cartilages, and is the type of cartilage that eventually develops into bone.

Bone

Bone either develops directly from primitive connective tissue cells or by changes in cartilage, a process known as ossification. It is a tissue that is strong and vascular, and has a matrix made rigid by the presence of inorganic salts, principally those of calcium and magnesium, in which the bone cells, called osteocytes, are embedded. Mature bone is easily sub-classified on the basis of its appearance. Compact bone forms the dense outer layer of a bone, while the more open inner regions are formed of spongy or cancellous bone.

Compact bone is composed of a large number of cylindrical structures forming the Haversian system (Fig.2.22). These consist of a central canal containing

Fig.2.22 COMPACT BONE

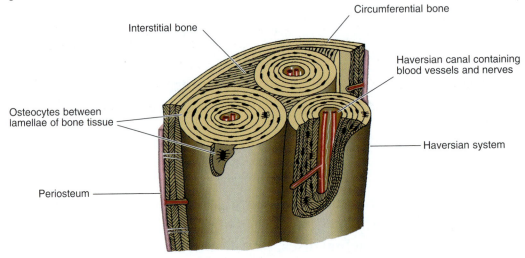

Circumferential bone

Interstitial bone

Haversian canal containing blood vessels and nerves

Osteocytes between lamellae of bone tissue

Haversian system

Periosteum

nerves and blood vessels, and this is surrounded by concentric lamellae (sheets) of bone tissue. The osteocytes are found between these lamellae, filling lacunae (spaces). The outer surface of the whole bone is formed of circumferential lamellae and this, in turn, is covered by vascular dense connective tissue, the periosteum.

Spongy (cancellous) bone is also lamellar in nature but lacks an organised, internal vascular system so that nutrition is mainly obtained from the connective tissue that surrounds the strands or trabeculae of bone tissue.

Fig.2.23 CANCELLOUS BONE

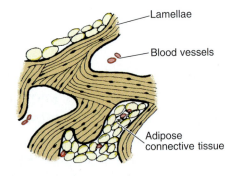

Lamellae

Blood vessels

Adipose connective tissue

BLOOD

All the cells of the body receive nutrition from, and lose waste products to, the tissue fluid in which they are bathed. This fluid is replenished by metabolites brought to the tissue by blood contained in the capillaries of the cardiovascular system. The cardiovascular system consists of the heart, the blood vessels and the circulating blood. The heart acts as a pump to drive the blood round the body in the blood vessels.

Fig.2.24 METABOLITE EXCHANGE

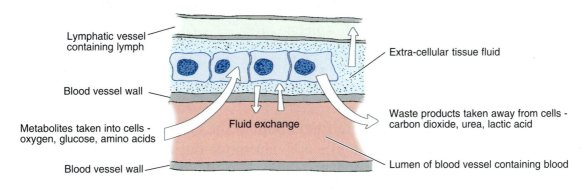

Lymphatic vessel containing lymph

Extra-cellular tissue fluid

Blood vessel wall

Waste products taken away from cells - carbon dioxide, urea, lactic acid

Metabolites taken into cells - oxygen, glucose, amino acids

Fluid exchange

Blood vessel wall

Lumen of blood vessel containing blood

Blood components

Blood plasma

This is a pale yellow fluid which is 90-93% water and which contains plasma proteins involved in blood clot formation, hormonal activity and defence against disease. It also contains sodium, chloride, potassium, calcium, magnesium, phosphate and bicarbonate ions as well as glucose and amino acids, all of which are essential for cells to function normally.

Red blood corpuscles

The red blood corpuscles (erythrocytes) contain the protein haemoglobin which is used to carry oxygen to the tissues and to remove carbon dioxide. Red blood corpuscles are non-nucleated biconcave discs 7-9µm in diameter, their size depending on their state of hydration. There are 4-6 million erythrocytes in 1 cubic millimetre (mm^3) of blood. Erythrocytes are produced in bone marrow and are broken down by the cells of the liver and spleen after circulating for about one hundred days.

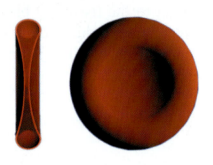

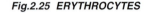
Fig.2.25 ERYTHROCYTES

White blood cells

White blood cells or leucocytes are found both in the circulating blood and in the tissue fluid, as many are very mobile and can move out of the blood vessels by forcing their way between the endothelial lining cells. There are 5-10 thousand white blood cells in 1mm^3 of blood and they have a range of defensive functions.

The leucocytes can be divided into two main groups; those having granular cytoplasm and lobed nuclei called granulocytes and those without cytoplasmic granules and having regular-shaped nuclei, which are known as the agranular leucocytes.

• Granulocytes (polymorphonuclear leucocytes)

This group consists of cells of about 10-15µm diameter and is subdivided by the reaction produced in the granules when stained.

• Basophils

The granules of these cells stain strongly with basic (alkaline) dyes such as

Fig.2.26 GRANULOCYTES

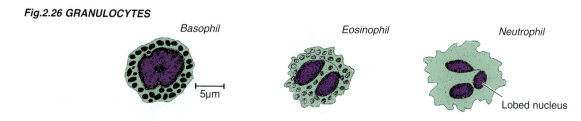

methylene blue. They form about 1% of the total white blood cell count. Their function is uncertain but they contain similar substances to mast cells (page 17).

• Eosinophils

The cytoplasmic granules of these cells stain with acid dyes such as eosin and the cells are twice as numerous as basophils. They are active in allergic disorders and respond phagocytically to antibody/antigen combinations.

• Neutrophils

These cells have granules which respond weakly to both acid and basic dyes. They form 60-70% of the white cell population. The number of lobes of the nuclei of these cells increases with age, although the lifespan of a neutrophil is only about fifteen hours. They form the first line of defence against attacking micro-organisms and move rapidly, in great numbers, from blood vessels into the surrounding tissue to ingest the invaders.

• Agranular leucocytes

• Monocytes

These are the largest type of leucocyte having a diameter of up to 20µm. They make up about 5% of the total number of white blood cells and have an unlobed, kidney-shaped nucleus. They are actively phagocytic cells and are believed to be the macrophages found in connective tissues (see page 16).

• Lymphocytes

These cells have already been described in the section on connective tissue cells (page 17). They are also found in large numbers in the lymphatic system. They form about 25% of the total number of white blood cells. Because of variations in diameter (6-16µm) they may be subdivided on a size basis, but since many lymphocytes are in a transitional phase, this is probably arbitrary. Lymphocytes move constantly between blood and tissue fluid, and their lifespan may range from days to years. Their principal function is to produce antibodies.

Platelets

These are small, non-nucleated bodies which have an irregular shape and are contained in a thick membrane. Their size is 2-4µm and there are up to 500,000 in 1mm^3 of blood. When bleeding occurs, the platelets release an enzyme (thrombokinase), which assists in the formation of a fibrous clot to seal the wound. This sealing process is also aided by the platelets sticking to one another. Platelets normally remain in the circulation for about ten days.

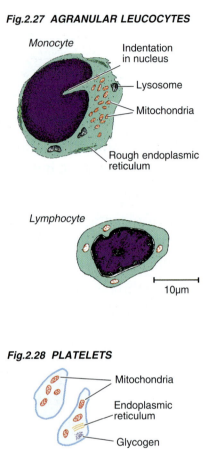

Fig.2.27 AGRANULAR LEUCOCYTES

Monocyte
Indentation in nucleus
Lysosome
Mitochondria
Rough endoplasmic reticulum

Lymphocyte
10µm

Fig.2.28 PLATELETS

Mitochondria
Endoplasmic reticulum
Glycogen

BLOOD VESSELS

Blood is transported throughout the body from the heart by vessels which progressively divide from the large arteries to form smaller vessels called arterioles and which then divide several more times to form capillaries. The blood is then returned to the heart by vessels which join and increase in size to form venules which then join forming veins.

Apart from capillaries, the walls of these vessels are all considered to be composed of three concentric layers of tissue, the outermost is the tunica adventitia, the middle layer is the tunica media and the innermost is the tunica intima.

In arteries, the tunica adventitia is fibrous connective tissue containing little elastin which blends with the surrounding tissue. In veins, this layer is relatively thick and contains a large number of elastic fibres, and in the largest veins there are many longitudinal smooth muscle cells (see page 36).

The tunica media of arteries is a thick layer of circularly or spirally oriented smooth muscle cells interspersed with elastic fibres. The relative proportion of muscle and elastic fibres varies with the function of the artery. The aorta receives blood from the heart and has very elastic walls to withstand the rapid variation in blood pressure. More peripheral arteries have a greater proportion of muscle tissue which can alter the lumen of the vessel to control the blood flow to various

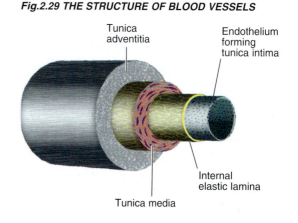

Fig.2.29 THE STRUCTURE OF BLOOD VESSELS

Tunica adventitia

Endothelium forming tunica intima

Internal elastic lamina

Tunica media

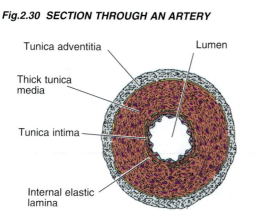

Fig.2.30 SECTION THROUGH AN ARTERY

Tunica adventitia

Lumen

Thick tunica media

Tunica intima

Internal elastic lamina

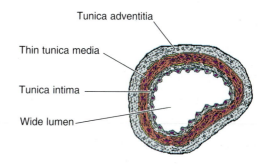

Fig.2.31 SECTION THROUGH A VEIN

Tunica adventitia

Thin tunica media

Tunica intima

Wide lumen

parts of the body. The tunica media of veins is thinner and contains more collagen and less muscle and elastin fibres than arteries of corresponding size since the pressure in the venous part of the circulation is lower.

The tunica intima of both arteries and veins consists of a single layer of endothelial (simple squamous epithelial) cells supported on a connective tissue layer lying external to these cells. This connective tissue layer is called the internal elastic lamina and in the larger arteries consists of a sheet of elastic tissue. In veins this elastic layer is more net-like and the endothelial cells are externally coated with fibroblasts. Many veins contain valves which prevent the reverse flow of blood. These valves consist of folds of the tunica intima, reinforced with connective tissue.

The capillaries, which form the junction between the arterial and venous systems, are formed by a single layer of endothelial cells. The capillaries are often less than 10µm in diameter and usually not longer than 1mm. They are formed into complex networks or beds through which the blood flow can be controlled; how this is achieved, and the role of the pericytes which are cells found surrounding some capillaries, is uncertain.

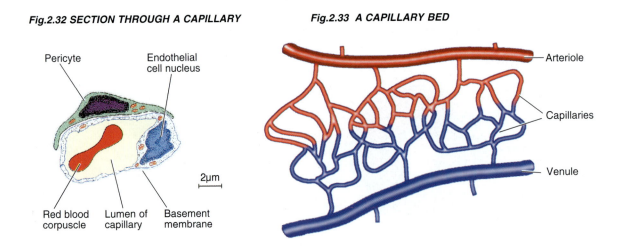

Fig.2.32 SECTION THROUGH A CAPILLARY

Pericyte

Endothelial cell nucleus

2µm

Red blood corpuscle

Lumen of capillary

Basement membrane

Fig.2.33 A CAPILLARY BED

Arteriole

Capillaries

Venule

THE LYMPHATIC SYSTEM

Some of the tissue fluid that is formed in the capillary bed is not returned directly to the venous ends of the capillaries, but is collected in the lymphatic capillaries. These vessels are similar to blood capillaries and commence in the tissue adjacent to the capillary beds. They carry fluid to lymph nodes which are small bean shaped structures occurring in groups along the course of the lymph vessels. These nodes form a filtering maze and contain phagocytic cells which remove cell debris and particles from the lymph. The filtered lymph then passes through a series of vessels of increasing size which finally deliver it back to the venous system via ducts close to the heart. The spleen and thymus are parts of the lymphatic system. The spleen contains phagocytic cells which remove debris from the circulating blood and it is a source of lymphocytes and monocytes. The thymus also produces lymphocytes.

Fig.2.34 THE STRUCTURE OF A LYMPH NODE

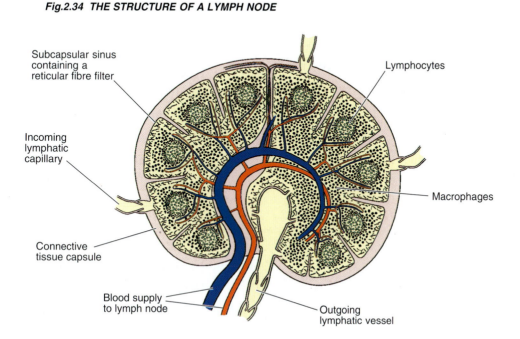

Subcapsular sinus containing a reticular fibre filter

Lymphocytes

Incoming lymphatic capillary

Macrophages

Connective tissue capsule

Blood supply to lymph node

Outgoing lymphatic vessel

MUSCLE TISSUE

All living cells have some ability to contract but some cells have contraction as their primary function. Groups of these form muscles which produce movement. The contractile ability of muscles depends upon the properties of the protein filaments actin and myosin contained within the muscle cells.

With light microscope examination, muscle cells are found to be of two main types; striated (striped) or non-striated (unstriped). In striped muscle the regular arrangement of the actin and myosin gives the cell a striated appearance but in unstriped muscle the proteins have no obvious pattern.

Striated muscle is generally related to movement of the skeleton and is therefore also called skeletal muscle. Since it is usually under conscious control it is also known as voluntary muscle. Cardiac muscle, which is a specialised type of striated muscle tissue, is however not under direct voluntary control.

Fig.2.35 STRIATED MUSCLE

20µm

Longitudinal section

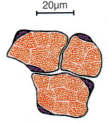

Transverse section

Fig.2.36 NON-STRIATED MUSCLE

Longitudinal section

Transverse section

The muscles formed by the non-striated cells are also referred to as smooth, unstriped or plain. Because they are not normally under conscious control, they are also called involuntary muscles. They are to be found in many areas such as the walls of blood vessels and the alimentary tract. Due to its location in the internal organs (the viscera) smooth muscle may also be termed visceral.

Some epithelial cells, which have not fully differentiated into muscle, have developed specialised contractile functions, such as the myoepithelial cells found in the salivary glands and the cells of the iris dilatator.

Striated (skeletal) muscle

The cells that form skeletal muscle are very long (up to 30cm) and have a diameter of 10-60μm. They are frequently referred to as fibres. These large cells have many nuclei which lie just beneath the cell membrane (the sarcolemma). Within the cell cytoplasm (sarcoplasm) are the 1μm diameter myofibrils composed of the contractile proteins, actin and myosin. Between the myofibrils are numerous mitochondria.

Fig.2.37 A STRIPED MUSCLE CELL

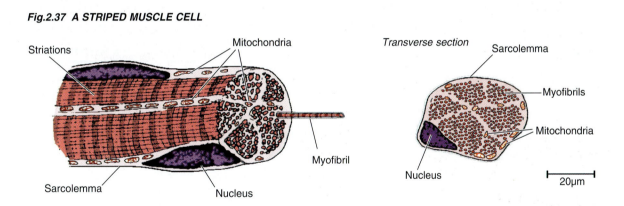

The cross-striations or bands, which give this type of muscle its name, run at right angles to the long axis of the myofibrils. These striations are classified by the way in which they react to stains and their appearance in polarised light. The light bands stain weakly with haematoxylin, are singly refracting and are known as I (or isotropic) bands. The darkly staining bands which are double refracting are the A (or anisotropic) bands. The I band is bisected by the darker Z

Fig.2.38 DETAIL OF A MYOFIBRIL

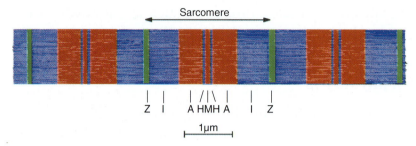

Sarcomere

| | | | /|\ | | | |
Z | A HMH A | Z

1μm

Fig.2.39 THE ARRANGEMENT OF THE MYOFILAMENTS

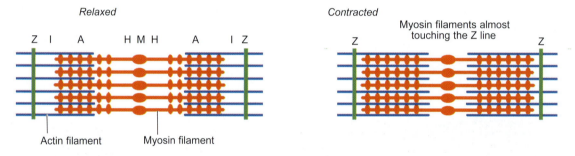

Relaxed

Z I A   H M H   A   I Z

Actin filament   Myosin filament

Contracted

Z   Myosin filaments almost
        touching the Z line   Z

(Zwischenscheibe) line while the A bands are bisected by the lighter H (helle) band. The relationship between these various bands depends on the degree of contraction of the cell.

The structures between the Z lines form the sarcomere, the contractile unit of the cell. The length of the sarcomere can change by movement of the actin filaments between the myosin filaments. The maximum extension is about 3.5μm while the minimum effective length is about 2.0μm which is when the myosin filaments are almost in contact with the Z line.

A complex system of microtubules runs within the cell. These consist of the sarcoplasmic reticulum (a modified form of endoplasmic reticulum), transverse

Fig.2.40 THE INTERNAL MICROTUBULES

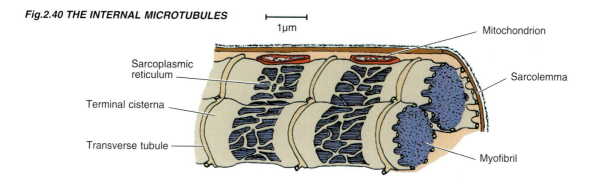

1μm

Mitochondrion

Sarcoplasmic
reticulum

Sarcolemma

Terminal cisterna

Transverse tubule

Myofibril

tubules and terminal cisternae. The microtubules appear to ensure that the effects of stimulation can be propagated almost simultaneously to all parts of the cell, enabling it to produce its characteristic rapid contraction.

Although in general striated muscle can produce rapid strong contraction, the individual cells may be of a slow twitch type, having a 75ms contraction period (twitch), or of a fast twitch type, with a 25ms contraction period. These twitch fibres have well-defined myofibrils and they are referred to as Fibrillenstruktur fibres. Human extrinsic ocular muscle has a third type which are slow (tonic) fibres. These have a smoother appearance in cross section and are known as Felderstruktur fibres.

Fig.2.41 SECTIONS THROUGH STRIATED MUSCLE CELLS

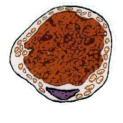

10μm

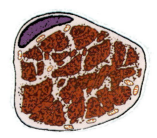

Felderstruktur

Fibrillenstruktur

35

Bundles of fibres are called fasciculi and are surrounded by a connective tissue sheath, the perimysium. Vascular loose connective tissue or endomysium fills the spaces between the cells and is surrounded by the perimysium. The fasciculi, which collectively form the muscle, are enclosed in a dense connective tissue sheath called the epimysium and this blends with the connective tissue of surrounding structures. The muscle cells may extend the whole length of the muscle, or they may be attached to connective tissue which penetrates the muscle at intervals. The muscles are anchored by tendons, the collagen fibres of which fuse with the connective tissue of the muscle.

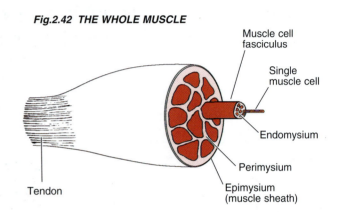

Fig.2.42 THE WHOLE MUSCLE

Muscle cell fasciculus

Single muscle cell

Endomysium

Perimysium

Epimysium (muscle sheath)

Tendon

Smooth muscle

The cells of smooth muscle are much smaller than those of striated muscle and do not show the latter's variation of diameter and length. Most cells are 5-10µm in diameter and their lengths are from 15-30µm, although in the wall of the uterus during pregnancy they may be up to 0.5mm long.

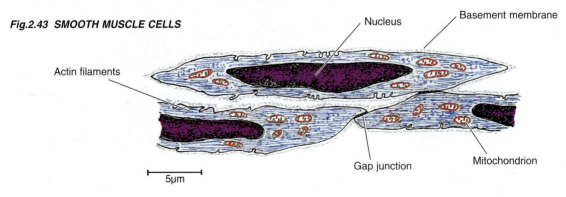

Fig.2.43 SMOOTH MUSCLE CELLS

Nucleus

Basement membrane

Actin filaments

Gap junction

Mitochondrion

5µm

These cells have numerous gap junctions providing intercommunicating pathways with adjacent cells. The cells have a single, centrally placed nucleus and the cytoplasm is packed with actin and myosin filaments as well as the usual organelles. However, the absence of a distinctive arrangement of the filaments makes the mechanism of contraction uncertain.

Cell contraction is slow and sustained and is said to be tonic.

Cells may occur singly or grouped together in fasciculi, or in sheets surrounded by loose connective tissue which is less rich in blood vessels than that around skeletal muscle.

Cardiac muscle

This type of muscle is found in the heart and is a form of striated muscle, however, its striations are less well-defined than those of skeletal muscle.

Cardiac muscle cells are about 50-100μm long and 15-20μm in diameter and in man they usually have a single nucleus. The cells branch and these branches interconnect via dense plates called intercalated discs which are formed by a line of gap junctions and desmosomes. The cells have a system of internal tubules similar to that of skeletal muscle.

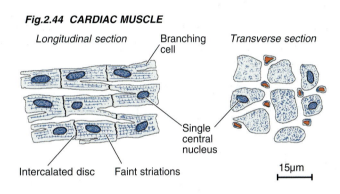

Fig.2.44 CARDIAC MUSCLE

Longitudinal section — Branching cell — Transverse section

Single central nucleus

Intercalated disc   Faint striations

15μm

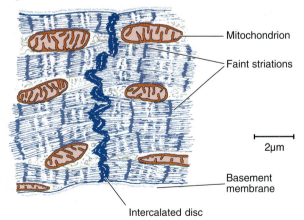

Fig.2.45 JUNCTION BETWEEN TWO CARDIAC MUSCLE CELLS

Mitochondrion

Faint striations

2μm

Basement membrane

Intercalated disc

Cells are combined into bundles of up to several hundred by a sheath of perimysium. The endomysium within the bundle is very vascular.

Regulation of muscle activity

Control may be voluntary or involuntary and may be brought about directly by the actions of the nervous system on the muscle cells or by chemical agents or hormones circulating in the vascular system. The following account of the control of muscle activity includes description of components of the nervous system, further details of which may be found later in this chapter.

The control of the contraction of a muscle varies with its type and, to some extent, its location.

In skeletal muscle, the fast (or twitch) fibres receive motor innervation from the flattened plate endings of the motor axons. The slow fibres receive the divided end of the nerve fibre as a multiple or grape ending.

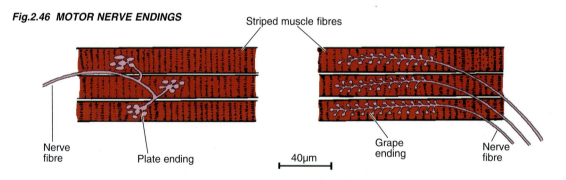

Fig.2.46 MOTOR NERVE ENDINGS

Striped muscle fibres

Nerve fibre

Plate ending

40μm

Grape ending

Nerve fibre

The muscle cell contracts when the nerve terminal releases acetylcholine, bringing about changes in cell membrane permeability. This allows positively charged sodium ions to pass into the cell causing the internal potential to move from -80mV, with respect to the cell surface, to +40mV. This change, known as

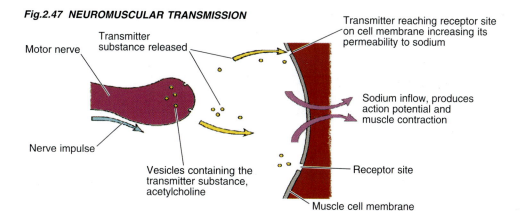

Fig.2.47 NEUROMUSCULAR TRANSMISSION

Motor nerve

Transmitter substance released

Transmitter reaching receptor site on cell membrane increasing its permeability to sodium

Nerve impulse

Sodium inflow, produces action potential and muscle contraction

Vesicles containing the transmitter substance, acetylcholine

Receptor site

Muscle cell membrane

the action potential, moves throughout the muscle cell and produces a momentary twitch or contraction lasting up to 75ms. There is then a refractory period of a few milliseconds, during which the cell will not respond.

Since individual muscle cells can only contract fully or not at all, graduated movements produced by a muscle occur by control (by the nervous system) of the number of cells stimulated. In order for actions to be controlled and co-ordinated, information about the state of contraction of the muscle and its tendons is required and skeletal muscle contains many sensory structures for this purpose (Fig.2.49).

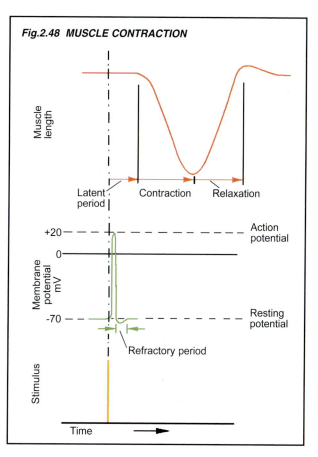

Fig.2.48 MUSCLE CONTRACTION

Muscle length

Latent period

Contraction

Relaxation

+20

0

Membrane potential mV

-70

Action potential

Resting potential

Refractory period

Stimulus

Time

Fig.2.49 SENSORY STRUCTURES IN MUSCLE

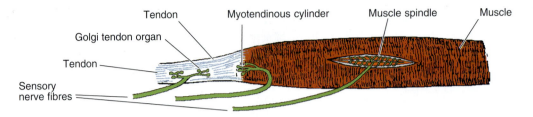

Tendon Myotendinous cylinder Muscle spindle Muscle

Golgi tendon organ

Tendon

Sensory
nerve fibres

These are of three types, muscle spindles, Golgi tendon organs and myotendinous cylinders. Muscle spindles, which lie between the muscle cells, monitor the extent of contraction of the muscle. Golgi tendon organs are compressed by the parallel bundles of tendon that surround them and communicate information about the imposed strain. A third type of receptor lies at the junction of the tendon and the muscle, and is known as a myotendinous cylinder or a palisade ending. Nerve fibres having free endings, which are normally associated with the transmission of sensations of pain, are also frequently found in the endomysium.

The nerve supply to smooth muscle is used to modify its normal spontaneous (myogenic) contraction. Smooth muscle is described as being single unit type or multi-unit type depending upon the number of contacts made by the incoming nerve fibres. The single unit type has few controlling nerve endings and this is typical of visceral smooth muscle. The electrical impulse is spread via gap junctions from one cell to another, controlling the slow rhythmic contractions.

Direct control of smooth muscle occurs in the multi-unit type where the nerve supply usually initiates muscle contraction. A large number of cells receive nerve endings producing a faster and more precise response. An example of the multi-unit type of smooth muscle is the iris sphincter.

Cardiac cells demonstrate a spontaneous rhythmic contraction with a long duration action potential. The gap junctions of the intercalated discs between adjacent cells provide a rapid transfer of excitation across the tissue and cardiac muscle cells can therefore contract simultaneously. Groups of specialised cardiac muscle cells (nodes) initiate and synchronise the contractions of the various regions of the heart. The rate of the heart beat is controlled by nerves derived from the autonomic nervous system.

NERVOUS TISSUE

Nervous tissue contains two specialised types of cells; neurones and neuroglia.

Neurones are the functional units of nervous tissue and their characteristic feature is their highly developed ability to transmit signals. Neuroglia have a supporting role. Neurones, neuroglia and their associated connective tissue coverings form the nervous system. The function of the nervous system is to carry information rapidly from one region of the body to another.

Neurones extend branching processes to make contact with other cells. These processes may be a few micrometres in length or they may stretch for tens of centimetres. Because of their appearance when examined with the light microscope, they are often referred to as fibres. Two types of process are usually described; one which conducts information towards the cell body, the dendrite or afferent fibre and one which carries information away from the cell body, the axon or efferent fibre. Both types of process may branch extensively, but while neurones may have many dendrites, they possess only a single axon.

The cytoplasm of the cell body contains many microtubules and microfilaments and these are also a feature of the processes. There are also large amounts of endoplasmic reticulum, whose associated accumulations of ribosomes are visible with the light microscope as granular masses (Nissl bodies). These granular

Fig.2.50 A NERVE CELL

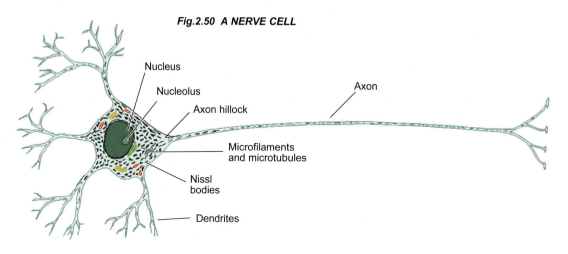

Nucleus

Nucleolus

Axon hillock

Axon

Microfilaments
and microtubules

Nissl
bodies

Dendrites

structures are generally absent from the point of exit of the axon (the axon hillock) and this can aid differentiation of the axon from the other cell processes.

Signals that travel along these conducting processes do so in the form of changes in the internal potential of the cell relative to the external potential. The potential difference between the inside and the outside of the cell membrane is normally -70mV. This is the resting potential. Suitable stimulation of the cell causes the internal potential to rise to about +40mV. This change is the action potential. Because the relative internal potential changes from a negative value through zero to

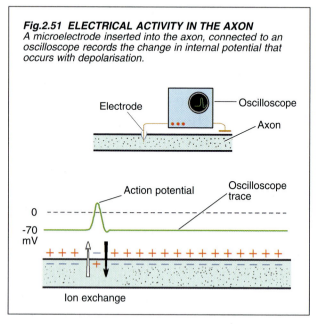

Fig.2.51 ELECTRICAL ACTIVITY IN THE AXON
A microelectrode inserted into the axon, connected to an oscilloscope records the change in internal potential that occurs with depolarisation.

Electrode

Oscilloscope

Axon

Action potential

Oscilloscope trace

0

-70
mV

+ + +   + + + + + + + + + + + + +

Ion exchange

a positive value, the effect is called depolarization. The change in potential is brought about by alterations in the cell's membrane permeability which in turn affects the internal ionic concentrations of the cell.

In the axon, this is an all or none effect. It is not possible to adjust the stimulus to produce a smaller action potential; either a stimulus is adequate to produce a full change or no change occurs at all. The cell signals the strength of the stimulus by increasing the frequency of the action potentials as the stimulus intensifies and by decreasing the frequency as the stimulus weakens. Because of the structure of the cell membrane, the permeability change moves along the axon at a given speed for a particular neurone. This conduction velocity can vary from 1m/s to about 100m/s, the faster speeds occurring in axons of larger diameter.

Dendrites and neurone cell bodies respond to stimuli by exhibiting graded potential changes. This means that the level of internal potential depends on the strength of the stimulus and also on the number of locations on the cell membrane that receive a stimulus, an effect known as summation. A suitable stimulus causes graded potential changes in the dendrites and cell body which initiates the train of impulses in the axon.

The end of the axon is divided into a number of fine branches, each of which is tipped with a swelling, the terminal bouton. The bouton has a flattened surface which lies 20-30nm from the membrane of the adjacent cell and this membrane has areas of specialised molecules called receptor sites. This specialised junction is called a neuro-effector junction if the adjacent cell is

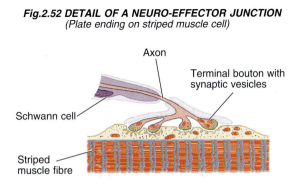

Fig.2.52 DETAIL OF A NEURO-EFFECTOR JUNCTION
(Plate ending on striped muscle cell)

Axon

Terminal bouton with synaptic vesicles

Schwann cell

Striped muscle fibre

non-neural and a synapse when contact is being made with another neurone.

When the nerve impulse reaches the axon terminal, vesicles containing a chemical transmitter substance move to the surface of the bouton and release the transmitter into the gap between the cells. If sufficient transmitter substance is released and reaches the receptor sites, a wave of depolarization will be initiated in the receiving cell. The passage of signals from one cell to another by this means is called neurohumoral or neurochemical transmission. In many instances multiple connections between neurones occur, with a cell receiving axons from several sources, some of which may be excitatory and some inhibitory.

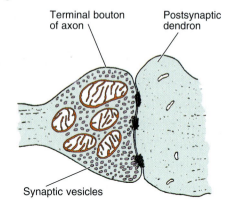

Fig.2.53 DETAIL OF A SYNAPSE

Terminal bouton of axon

Postsynaptic dendron

Synaptic vesicles

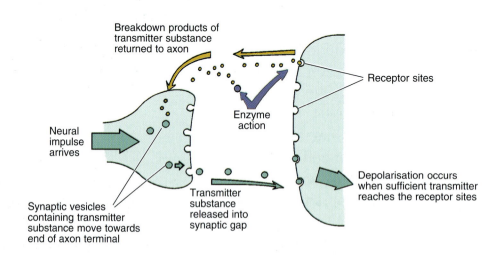

Fig.2.54 NEUROHUMORAL TRANSMISSION

Breakdown products of transmitter substance returned to axon

Receptor sites

Enzyme action

Neural impulse arrives

Synaptic vesicles containing transmitter substance move towards end of axon terminal

Transmitter substance released into synaptic gap

Depolarisation occurs when sufficient transmitter reaches the receptor sites

CLASSIFICATION

Classification of neurones is complex since cells may be grouped together in many different ways. Schemes of neurone classification may include those based on their location, their form or their function.

Location

Those neurones which form the brain and spinal cord are classed as part of the central nervous system (CNS) and are identifiable by their location within the connective tissue sheaths that enclose these two structures. The connective tissue forms the three meningeal sheaths or meninges. The outer inelastic layer is the dura mater, lining the skull and vertebrae which themselves support and protect the neural structures. Internal to the dura is a loose connective tissue layer, the arachnoid mater, and inside this, closely covering the brain and spinal cord, is the vascular pia mater. Between the dura and the arachnoid is the (potential) subdural space, and between the arachnoid and pia is the subarachnoid space, traversed by trabeculae (cords) of connective tissue, nerves and blood vessels, and containing cerebrospinal fluid. This fluid is similar to blood plasma and provides support and nourishment for the tissues it bathes.

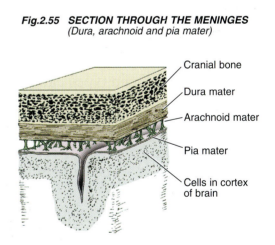

Fig.2.55 SECTION THROUGH THE MENINGES
(Dura, arachnoid and pia mater)

Cranial bone

Dura mater

Arachnoid mater

Pia mater

Cells in cortex of brain

Neurones that lie outside the meningeal sheaths are classed as being part of the peripheral nervous system (PNS). In this system, neurones are collected together in bundles to form nerves. In some peripheral nerves, groups of cell bodies are found along their path. This collection of cell bodies causes a bulge in the nerve

45

known as a ganglion. Individual nerve fibres are surrounded by loose connective tissue, the endoneurium. A connective tissue sheath, the perineurium, encloses groups of nerve fibres and their endoneurium to form a fasciculus (bundle). Between the fasciculi lies vascular connective tissue and the whole nerve is enclosed in a dense connective tissue sheath, the epineurium.

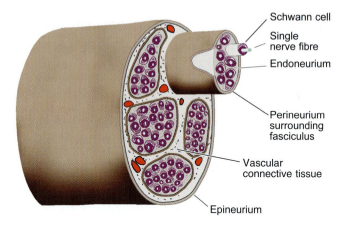

Fig.2.56 A PERIPHERAL NERVE

Schwann cell

Single nerve fibre

Endoneurium

Perineurium surrounding fasciculus

Vascular connective tissue

Epineurium

Neurone form

Neurones vary greatly in size and shape but three main types can be distinguished.

• *Unipolar*. These have a single process extending from the cell body which then splits to form a dendrite and an axon.

• *Bipolar*. Bipolar cells have two separated processes extending from the cell body.

• *Multipolar*. These are cells possessing a single axon but which have a large number of dendritic processes entering the cell body.

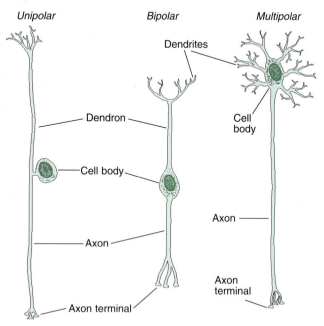

Fig.2.57 NEURONE FORMS

Unipolar

Bipolar

Multipolar

Dendrites

Dendron

Cell body

Cell body

Cell body

Axon

Axon

Axon

Axon terminal

Axon terminal

Axon terminal

While in general these cells all follow the rule of conducting the neural impulse from the dendrites to the cell body and thence to the axon, a group of retinal cells called amacrine cells have processes with bi-directional conduction.

Myelination

Some nerves appear white to the naked eye while others appear grey. The white appearance is produced by a sheath of the fatty substance myelin surrounding the fibres. This sheath is formed by the membranes of neuroglial cells (see page 52). Fibres with this covering are said to be myelinated while those without are non- or unmyelinated.

Myelinated fibres have small gaps in the myelination, these are nodes of Ranvier and they occur at regular intervals along the fibre, exposing the neurone to the extracellular fluid. Because the polarization changes appear only at the exposed surfaces of the neurone, the action potential seems to jump from node to node (saltatory conduction). The velocity of conduction of the action potential is higher in processes possessing a myelin sheath than in similarly sized fibres lacking such a sheath.

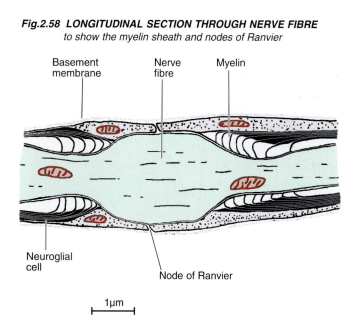

Fig.2.58 LONGITUDINAL SECTION THROUGH NERVE FIBRE
to show the myelin sheath and nodes of Ranvier

Basement membrane   Nerve fibre   Myelin

Neuroglial cell

Node of Ranvier

1μm

Function

In some circumstances, it is convenient to consider nerve fibres on the basis of the direction in which they transmit their signals relative to the central nervous system, so that fibres which bring information into the CNS are afferent and those which carry signals away from the CNS to the periphery are efferent.

Afferent fibres carry signals collected from receptors designed to inform the CNS about the outside world and about the state of the body. Some of this information reaches conscious levels in the CNS and gives rise to sensation and thus afferent fibres are also referred to as sensory fibres. Nerves which consist of sensory fibres are known as sensory nerves. The receptors that initiate these sensory signals can be divided into special or general. Vision, audition (hearing), taste and smell are examples of special senses, while general or cutaneous sensitivity includes touch, pain, heat and cold.

Fig.2.59 BASIC SENSORY/MOTOR PATHWAY

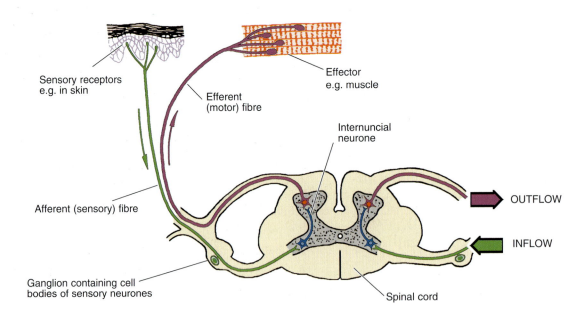

48

Efferent fibres are directed towards structures that produce physical change; muscles contract producing movement, glands secrete and capillaries constrict, so that these fibres are also described as motor fibres. Nerves containing motor fibres are known as motor nerves while nerves containing both motor and sensory fibres are referred to as mixed nerves.

Virtually all sensory neurones in the peripheral nervous system are unipolar and all motor neurones are multipolar. However, within the CNS, the vast majority of neurones are multipolar, and this includes the association or internuncial cells which communicate between sensory and motor neurones.

VOLUNTARY AND AUTONOMIC SUBSYSTEMS

Peripheral motor nerves that can be used with conscious effort to control striped muscle are termed voluntary or somatic. Other peripheral motor nerves provide innervation without conscious effort to smooth muscle, glands and the heart and these form the peripheral autonomic or involuntary motor system. In many cases the terms involuntary and voluntary can be seen to be inappropriate. Reflexes, which by definition are involuntary, often involve skeletal striped muscle, and it is possible to learn to control the heart rate or to produce pupil constriction by control of involuntary muscle. However, notwithstanding the limitations of the definitions, the terms do convey the widely accepted sense of the functions of the two subsystems.

There are identifiable differences between peripheral somatic and autonomic motor nerve pathways and the nature of some of their neurones. The autonomic nerve pathways are interrupted by a synapse which may be close to the CNS or close to the innervated structure. These synapses occur in the autonomic ganglia. The nerve fibre leading to the ganglion is called preganglionic and the fibres travelling from the cells contained in the ganglion to the neuro-effector junction, postganglionic. In general, postganglionic fibres are unmyelinated. Autonomic fibres are usually small in diameter when compared with somatic fibres.

The autonomic nervous system is further subclassified into two divisions which have generally opposed functions and also differ in organisation. These are known as the sympathetic division and the parasympathetic division.

The sympathetic division

This part of the autonomic nervous system is the larger and its preganglionic fibres are derived from cells lying in the thoracic and lumbar segments of the spinal cord. These fibres synapse with cells located in the twenty or so pairs of sympathetic ganglia which lie alongside the anterolateral border of the spinal column. The unmyelinated postganglionic fibres follow the paths of blood vessels to form a meshwork or plexus near the organ they supply.

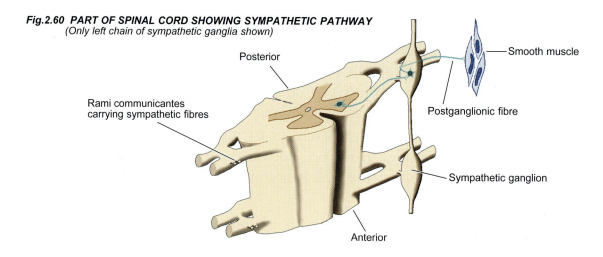

Fig.2.60 PART OF SPINAL CORD SHOWING SYMPATHETIC PATHWAY
(Only left chain of sympathetic ganglia shown)

Posterior

Rami communicantes
carrying sympathetic fibres

Smooth muscle

Postganglionic fibre

Sympathetic ganglion

Anterior

As a system, the sympathetic prepares the body for action; the heart rate is increased, as is the breathing rate, and blood is diverted from the skin to the skeletal muscles. Since these activities are associated with danger or a shock, the sympathetic is commonly termed the 'fright, fight, flight' system.

The transmitter substance released at the neuro-effector junction is noradrenaline and sympathetic stimulation also causes noradrenaline to be released from the suprarenal glands (located over the kidneys) into the blood stream. This, together with the associated substance adrenaline, circulates in the vascular system and spreads the effects of stimulation throughout the body by acting directly on sympathetic receptor sites.

The parasympathetic division

Unlike the diffuse sympathetic distribution, the parasympathetic preganglionic fibres pass in well-defined bundles to synapse with cells in ganglia lying close to the organ supplied. Thus by comparison with the sympathetic system the postganglionic course is relatively short. At the neuro-effector junctions, the transmitter substance released is acetylcholine.

The functions of the parasympathetic nervous system include slowing the heart and respiration rate and stimulating salivation and intestinal activity.

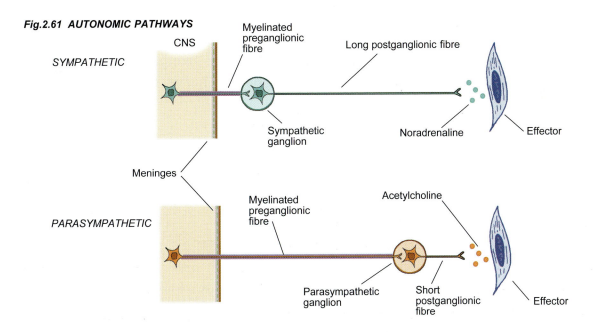

Fig.2.61 AUTONOMIC PATHWAYS

SYMPATHETIC

CNS

Myelinated preganglionic fibre

Long postganglionic fibre

Sympathetic ganglion

Noradrenaline

Effector

Meninges

PARASYMPATHETIC

Myelinated preganglionic fibre

Acetylcholine

Parasympathetic ganglion

Short postganglionic fibre

Effector

NEUROGLIA

All neurones are accompanied by non-excitable cells, the CNS having three main types: astrocytes, microglia and oligodendrocytes.

Astrocytes have some processes that end on the surface of neurones, while other processes terminate on the surface of nearby capillaries, thus forming a supporting framework for the nervous tissue. In injury, astrocytes proliferate and, aided by microglia and fibroblasts, work to repair and clear the damaged area. Microglia are small phagocytic cells often found close to capillaries and it is possible that they are monocyte derivatives. Oligodendrocytes have fewer processes and are found in rows along nerve fibres or grouped together close to the neural cell body. They may link a number of nerve fibres and form an insulating sheath around these processes.

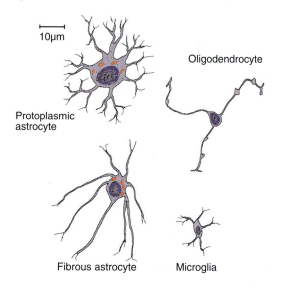

Fig.2.62 CNS NEUROGLIAL CELLS

10µm

Oligodendrocyte

Protoplasmic astrocyte

Fibrous astrocyte

Microglia

Fig.2.63 MYELINATION

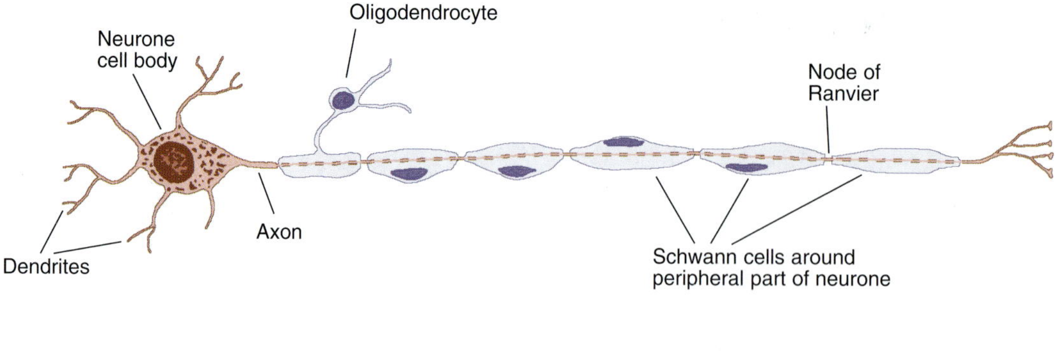

Neurone cell body

Oligodendrocyte

Node of Ranvier

Dendrites

Axon

Schwann cells around peripheral part of neurone

52

The Schwann cell is the chief non-excitable cell in the peripheral nervous system and this type of cell is found to relate to nerve fibres in two distinct ways. Fig.2.64 shows nerve fibres and their accompanying Schwann cells to illustrate these different ways of association.

Where the neurones are large, they are isolated from their surroundings by the Schwann cell membrane which is seen to wrap as a tight multiple sheath around the process. Because of the appearance of the myelin this type of neural tissue is referred to as the white matter of the nervous system.

Smaller neurones are separated from each other by being individually enfolded in the body of the Schwann cell, but without the multiple wrapping. Such processes do not appear white.

Fig.2.64 SCHWANN CELLS

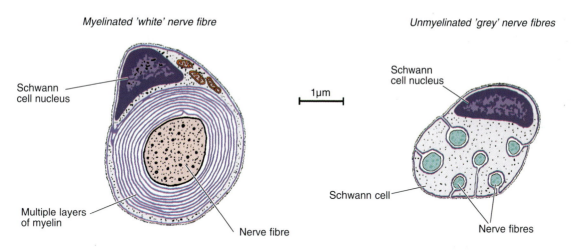

Myelinated 'white' nerve fibre

Unmyelinated 'grey' nerve fibres

Schwann cell nucleus

Multiple layers of myelin

Nerve fibre

1µm

Schwann cell nucleus

Schwann cell

Nerve fibres

Chapter 3

THE CENTRAL NERVOUS SYSTEM

The central nervous system is composed of neural and neuroglial tissue bathed in cerebrospinal fluid, enclosed in the protective meninges. This chapter describes the two main divisions of the central nervous system, comprising the brain and the spinal cord. The brain is subdivided into forebrain, midbrain and hindbrain. These terms have been retained from descriptions of the nervous system of quadrupeds in which the central nervous system is orientated along the animal's anterior-posterior axis.

Reference is made throughout this section to white and grey matter; these are traditional terms describing tissue that is largely composed of myelinated fibres (white matter) or containing large numbers of cell bodies (grey matter). Where the grey matter forms the outer layers of the brain it is called the cortex. Groups of cells forming grey matter within the brain are referred to as nuclei.

The forebrain

The forebrain is composed of the two cerebral hemispheres (the cerebrum), the thalamus, the hypothalamus and the geniculate bodies.

Fig.3.1 LATERAL VIEW OF BRAIN
  (Cerebral hemisphere shown shaded)

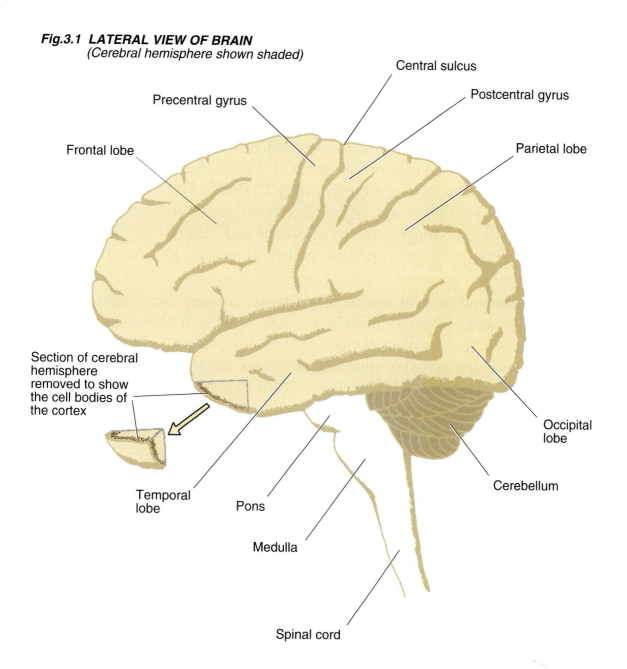

Central sulcus

Postcentral gyrus

Precentral gyrus

Parietal lobe

Frontal lobe

Section of cerebral
hemisphere
removed to show
the cell bodies of
the cortex

Occipital
lobe

Temporal
lobe

Pons

Cerebellum

Medulla

Spinal cord

The surface of the cerebral hemispheres shows numerous convolutions called gyri between which run fissures or sulci. The hemispheres are divided, for convenience of description, into lobes whose names are derived from the cranial bones that cover them. The surface of the hemispheres, the cortex, is divided into motor and sensory areas, which have themselves been subdivided to give an indication of function; a scheme popularised following work by Brodmann (1909). The average thickness of the cortex is 2.5mm (the range is 1.5-4.5mm) and it has a total surface area of approximately 2500cm^2. The work of Brodmann has also imposed a system of six layers of cells and fibres on descriptions of the cortex. However, the complex interconnections and regional variations of the cortex make such a layering scheme unhelpful except for the purposes of comparison.

The cortex is involved with intellectual activity, sensory functions (including vision) and initiating voluntary muscle actions. A division between the sensory and motor areas of the cortex is provided by the central sulcus. The gyrus anterior to this (the precentral gyrus) is generally motor and the gyrus behind the central sulcus (the postcentral gyrus) is sensory.

Within the hemispheres, myelinated (white) fibre tracts pass to and from lower areas of the brain. Some pass around the cavities of the lateral ventricles (see Fig.3.18) which are filled with cerebrospinal fluid. Others form a bridge, the corpus callosum, between the two halves of the forebrain. Below the corpus callosum and between the two hemispheres is the third ventricle in whose lateral walls lie the two halves of the thalamus. The thalamus is a mass of grey matter involved in the relay and modification of information passing between the lower regions of the central nervous system and the cerebral cortex. On the lateral surface of the thalamus lies the internal capsule (see Fig.17.25), a thick layer of white matter carrying sensory information from the thalamus to the postcentral gyrus. Motor information is carried from the precentral gyrus via the corona radiata to the internal capsule and thence in the corticonuclear tract to the

Fig.3.2 MEDIAL VIEW OF BRAIN

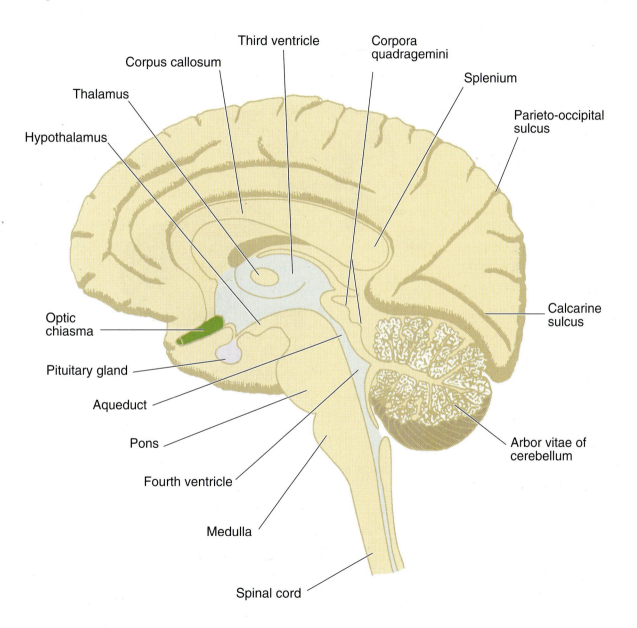

Corpus callosum

Thalamus

Hypothalamus

Third ventricle

Corpora quadragemini

Splenium

Parieto-occipital sulcus

Optic chiasma

Pituitary gland

Aqueduct

Pons

Fourth ventricle

Medulla

Spinal cord

Calcarine sulcus

Arbor vitae of cerebellum

Fig.3.3 LATERAL VIEW OF THE BRAINSTEM AND SECTIONS THROUGH IT

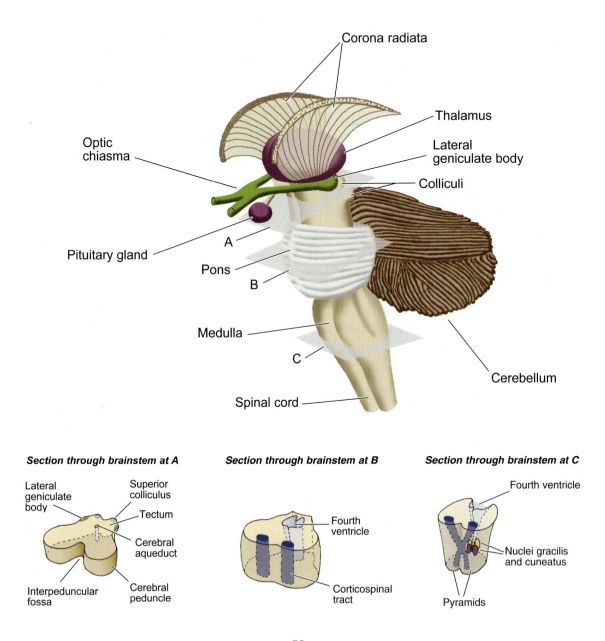

Corona radiata

Thalamus

Lateral geniculate body

Optic chiasma

Colliculi

Pituitary gland

A

Pons

B

Medulla

C

Cerebellum

Spinal cord

Section through brainstem at A

Lateral geniculate body

Superior colliculus

Tectum

Cerebral aqueduct

Interpeduncular fossa

Cerebral peduncle

Section through brainstem at B

Fourth ventricle

Corticospinal tract

Section through brainstem at C

Fourth ventricle

Nuclei gracilis and cuneatus

Pyramids

58

brainstem and in the corticospinal tract to the spinal cord. (That part of the central nervous system known as the brainstem is shown in Fig.3.3).

Behind the pituitary stalk and the optic chiasma lies the hypothalamus forming the lower walls of the third ventricle. The hypothalamus is concerned with a wide range of visceral and behavioural functions.

The medial and lateral geniculate bodies are collections of cells forming relays in the acoustic and visual pathways respectively.

The midbrain

The midbrain lies below the third ventricle, above the pons and anterior to the cerebellum; in lateral views of the brain it is hidden by the temporal lobes of the cerebral hemispheres.

The anterior part of the midbrain is formed by the two cerebral peduncles with the interpeduncular fossa lying between them. The posterior part or tegmentum is pierced vertically by the cerebral aqueduct (of the midbrain) linking the third and fourth ventricles (see Figs.3.3 and 3.18). Behind the aqueduct lies the tectum which has on its surface the four colliculi or corpora quadragemini. The superior pair of these masses contains visual reflex nuclei and the lower pair auditory nuclei.

Within the substance of the midbrain lie groups of nuclei and fibres related to control of some of the ocular muscles, with the bulk of the midbrain being occupied by fibre pathways running vertically between forebrain and hindbrain. The pathway of the fibres from the superior colliculi to the nuclei of the nerves controlling the extrinsic ocular muscles is known as the tectobulbar tract.

The hindbrain

This is composed of the pons above, the cerebellum behind and the medulla oblongata below.

The pons is continuous with the midbrain, and the medulla oblongata is continuous with the spinal cord. Like the midbrain, the pons contains major motor nuclei and nerve pathways. The anterior part of the pons is traversed by corticospinal fibres passing down to the medulla oblongata where they form elevations in its anterior surface, the pyramids of the medulla. Like the spinal cord with which it merges, the pons contains a cerebrospinal fluid-filled cavity, the fourth ventricle.

The medulla oblongata has nuclei relaying and modifying sensory information travelling up from the spinal cord, the nuclei gracilis and cuneatus.

The largest part of the hindbrain is the cerebellum linked to the pons and to the medulla oblongata by the cerebellar peduncles. These are fibre pathways which convey information from the spinal cord, hindbrain and midbrain to the cerebellum and which enable it to control and modify posture and movement. The folded surface of the cerebellum is composed of grey matter, unlike the midbrain, spinal cord and other hindbrain structures which have their grey matter internally. The grey matter of the cerebellum is about 1mm thick and covers the myelinated nerve fibre layer whose tree-like appearance gives rise to the name arbor vitae (tree of life). A major feature of the grey matter of the cerebellum is the presence of Purkinje cells which are neural cells having an unusual virtually two dimensional arrangement of their dendritic branches.

The brainstem and cranial nerves

The brainstem consists of the midbrain, the pons and the medulla and contains many of the centres responsible for essential autonomic and reflex functions.

There are twelve pairs of cranial nerves closely associated with the brainstem, the majority of which serve structures in the head and upper part of the body. The cranial nerves are numbered in sequence from the top of the brainstem to the medulla and, where several emerge from the brain at the same level, they are numbered from the midline outwards.

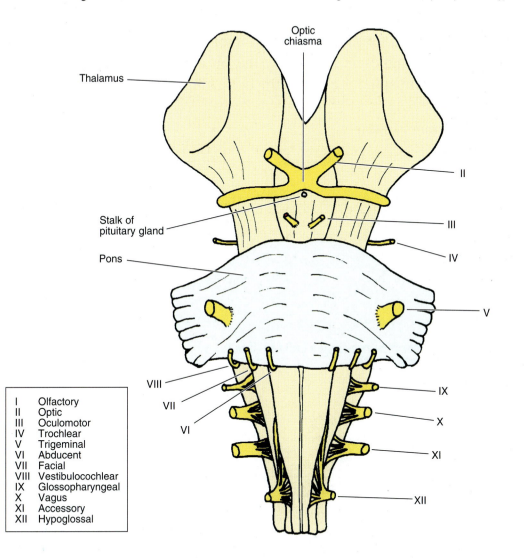

Fig.3.4 ANTERIOR VIEW OF THE BRAINSTEM *showing the cranial nerves (except olfactory)*

Optic chiasma

Thalamus

II

Stalk of pituitary gland

III

IV

Pons

V

VIII

VII

VI

IX

X

XI

XII

I	Olfactory
II	Optic
III	Oculomotor
IV	Trochlear
V	Trigeminal
VI	Abducent
VII	Facial
VIII	Vestibulocochlear
IX	Glossopharyngeal
X	Vagus
XI	Accessory
XII	Hypoglossal

Only the main functions of the nerves are given here, those cranial nerves which relate specifically to the eye, orbit and ocular functions are described in greater detail in Chapter 17.

1 Olfactory (Cranial nerve I)

These nerves serve the sense of smell and run from the nasal mucosa in twenty or so unmyelinated bundles to terminate in the olfactory bulbs. After synapsing, the modified olfactory information is carried by the olfactory tracts to the olfactory cortex of the cerebral hemispheres close to the optic chiasma.

Fig.3.5 OLFACTORY PATHWAY

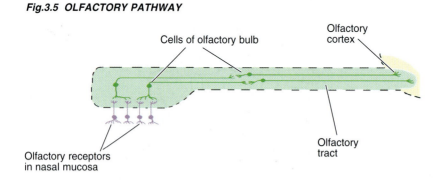

Cells of olfactory bulb

Olfactory cortex

Olfactory tract

Olfactory receptors in nasal mucosa

Fig.3.6 SAGITTAL SECTION THROUGH ANTERIOR SKULL
showing the olfactory nerve

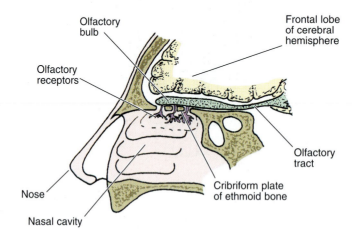

Olfactory bulb

Frontal lobe of cerebral hemisphere

Olfactory receptors

Olfactory tract

Nose

Cribriform plate of ethmoid bone

Nasal cavity

2 Optic (Cranial nerve II)

The optic nerves are sensory, carrying visual and visual reflex information from the retinae. The optic nerve axons synapse in the lateral geniculate bodies and midbrain reflex nuclei. Fig.3.7 shows the optic nerve and the other components of the visual pathway.

Fig.3.7 THE VISUAL PATHWAY

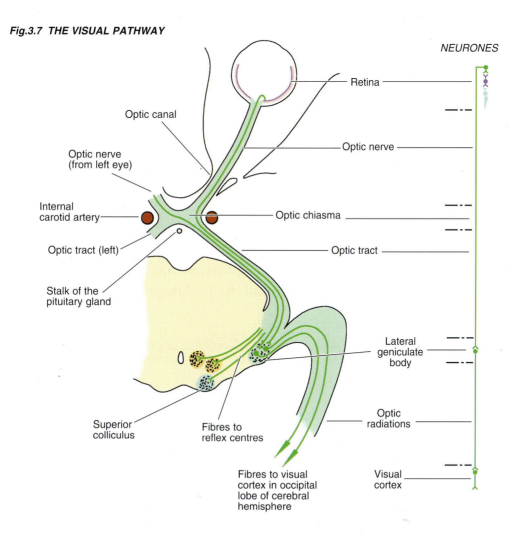

NEURONES

Retina

Optic canal

Optic nerve

Optic nerve (from left eye)

Internal carotid artery

Optic chiasma

Optic tract (left)

Optic tract

Stalk of the pituitary gland

Lateral geniculate body

Superior colliculus

Fibres to reflex centres

Optic radiations

Fibres to visual cortex in occipital lobe of cerebral hemisphere

Visual cortex

3 Oculomotor (Cranial nerve III)

These motor nerves have their nuclei of origin in the midbrain and they supply four of the six pairs of the oculorotatory muscles. They also carry parasympathetic neurones to the ciliary ganglia from where, after synapsing, the fibres pass to the intrinsic muscles of the eye.

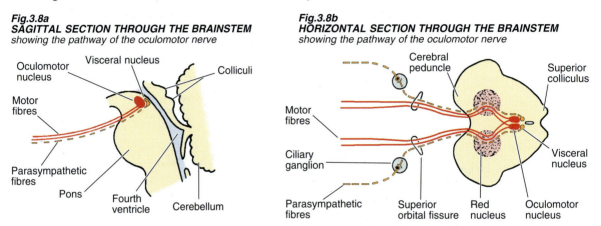

Fig.3.8a
SAGITTAL SECTION THROUGH THE BRAINSTEM
showing the pathway of the oculomotor nerve

Fig.3.8b
HORIZONTAL SECTION THROUGH THE BRAINSTEM
showing the pathway of the oculomotor nerve

4 Trochlear (Cranial nerve IV)

The nuclei of origin of the trochlear nerves are in the midbrain and provide motor neurones to the superior oblique extrinsic ocular muscles. The fibres emerge at the back of the brainstem and pass round the peduncles before travelling forward to the orbits.

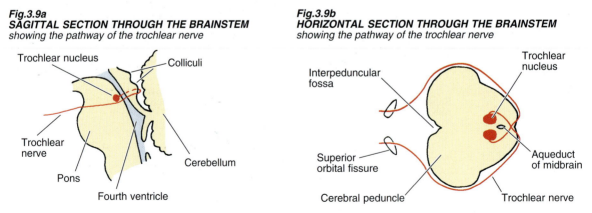

Fig.3.9a
SAGITTAL SECTION THROUGH THE BRAINSTEM
showing the pathway of the trochlear nerve

Fig.3.9b
HORIZONTAL SECTION THROUGH THE BRAINSTEM
showing the pathway of the trochlear nerve

5 Trigeminal (Cranial nerve V)

The trigeminal nerves are the largest of the cranial nerves. They are the general sensory nerves of the face, mouth and part of the scalp. The fibres have their unipolar cell bodies in the trigeminal ganglia. From here, the fibres travel to the principal sensory nucleus or to the spinal nucleus of each trigeminal nerve. The trigeminal nerves also have motor fibres which supply the digastric muscles of the lower jaw.

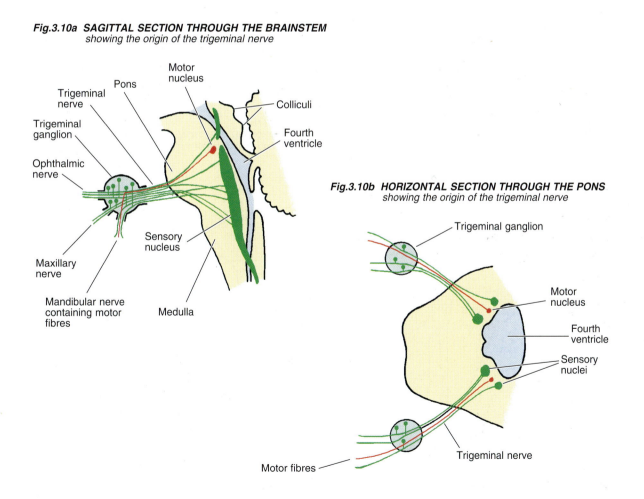

Fig.3.10a SAGITTAL SECTION THROUGH THE BRAINSTEM
showing the origin of the trigeminal nerve

Motor nucleus
Pons
Trigeminal nerve
Trigeminal ganglion
Ophthalmic nerve
Maxillary nerve
Mandibular nerve containing motor fibres
Sensory nucleus
Medulla
Colliculi
Fourth ventricle

Fig.3.10b HORIZONTAL SECTION THROUGH THE PONS
showing the origin of the trigeminal nerve

Trigeminal ganglion
Motor nucleus
Fourth ventricle
Sensory nuclei
Trigeminal nerve
Motor fibres

6 Abducent (Cranial Nerve VI)

This pair of motor nerves supplies the lateral rectus muscles of the eyes and each has its nucleus of origin close to the floor of the fourth ventricle.

7 Facial (Cranial Nerve VII)

These are mixed nerves as they contain motor, sensory and autonomic fibres. The motor nucleus is situated in the pons and supplies the voluntary muscles of the face, scalp and lower jaw. Sensory fibres carry the sense of taste from part of the tongue and palate into the brainstem. Parasympathetic fibres from the salivatory nuclei travel with the facial nerves to supply the salivary and lacrimal (tears) glands.

Fig.3.11a
SAGITTAL SECTION THROUGH THE BRAINSTEM
showing the origins of the abducent and facial nerves

Fig.3.11b
HORIZONTAL SECTION THROUGH THE PONS
showing the origins of the abducent and facial nerves

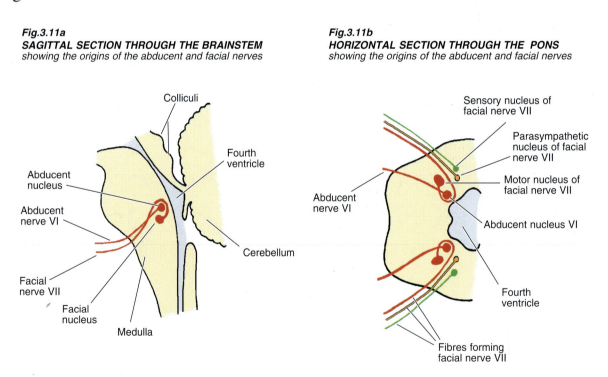

8 Vestibulocochlear (Cranial nerve VIII)

These sensory nerves have two roots; one serving to carry postural and movement signals from the gravity and acceleration sensors of the inner ear and the other root carrying the sense of hearing from receptors located in the spiral cochleae. The two vestibulocochlear nerves along with the two facial and abducent nerves have their superficial origins at the junction of the pons and the medulla.

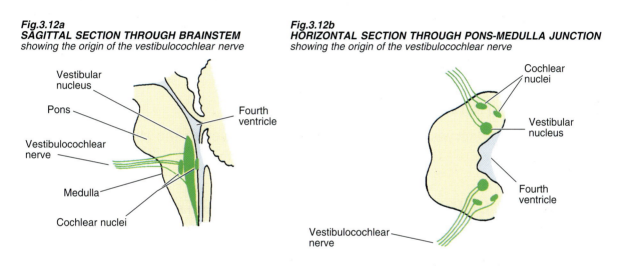

Fig.3.12a
SAGITTAL SECTION THROUGH BRAINSTEM
showing the origin of the vestibulocochlear nerve

Fig.3.12b
HORIZONTAL SECTION THROUGH PONS-MEDULLA JUNCTION
showing the origin of the vestibulocochlear nerve

9 Glossopharyngeal (Cranial nerve IX)

These mixed nerves have their motor nuclei in the medulla oblongata from which somatic motor fibres pass to the stylopharyngeus muscle (used in swallowing) and parasympathetic fibres to the otic ganglion for relay on to the parotid (salivary) gland. Sensory fibres carry general sensation and taste information from the posterior part of the tongue and mouth into the medulla.

10 Vagus (Cranial nerve X)

The vagus nerves are principally the parasympathetic motor supply to the heart, respiratory system, stomach and intestines. They also have somatic sensory fibres from the respiratory tract and the upper part of the alimentary canal and voluntary motor fibres to muscles of the soft palate and pharynx.

11 Accessory (Cranial nerve XI)

These motor nerves have two divisions. The cranial root forms part of the motor supply carried by the vagus nerve to the soft palate and is also distributed to the pharyngeal and cardiac nerves. The spinal root supplies some of the voluntary muscles of the neck.

12 Hypoglossal (Cranial nerve XII)

The hypoglossal nerves are the principal motor nerves to the striped muscles of the tongue.

THE SPINAL CORD

The spinal cord runs some 45cm from the medulla oblongata just below the foramen magnum of the skull down the vertebral canal of the spinal vertebrae to terminate as a narrow thread, the filum terminale, at about the level of the second lumbar vertebra. Its anterior surface is grooved by the anterior median fissure which with the posterior median septum, provides a line of demarcation between the symmetrical halves of the spinal cord. In each half, the grey matter is formed into an anterior and a posterior horn, and the

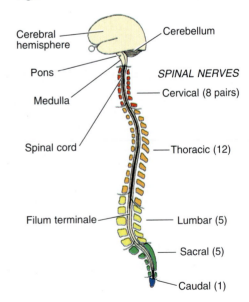

Fig.3.13 THE SPINAL CORD

Cerebral hemisphere

Cerebellum

Pons

SPINAL NERVES

Medulla

Cervical (8 pairs)

Spinal cord

Thoracic (12)

Filum terminale

Lumbar (5)

Sacral (5)

Caudal (1)

68

Fig.3.14 HORIZONTAL SECTION THROUGH THE SPINAL CORD

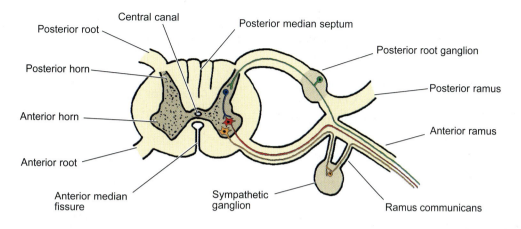

two halves are joined by a bridge of grey matter which surrounds the central canal.

The thirty-one pairs of spinal nerves are joined to the cord by their anterior and posterior roots, the latter carrying the spinal posterior (or dorsal) root ganglion.

The posterior roots of the spinal nerves contain only unipolar somatic sensory neurones whose cell bodies lie in the posterior root ganglia and which synapse with cells in the posterior horns. The anterior roots contain both somatic motor and preganglionic sympathetic autonomic fibres. The anterior and posterior roots join and then divide again to form the anterior and posterior rami of the spinal nerves which contain fibres that are both sensory and somatic motor and also contain autonomic postganglionic axons from cells in the sympathetic ganglia.

In the posterior horns of the grey matter lie the internuncial cell bodies which send their axons into the anterior horns or into the surrounding columns of white matter and then travel upwards. Some of these axons ascend to synapse with cells in the brainstem, while others may travel a relatively short distance to synapse with anterior horn cells on a different level.

The columns of myelinated fibres are the spinal tracts and these are generally referenced by their origin if descending or their destination if ascending. Hence the corticospinal tracts carry the axons of cells located in the motor cortex down to synapse with anterior horn cells, while the spinothalamic tracts carry sensory information from one side of the body up to cells located in the contralateral thalamus.

Blood supply and drainage

The blood supply to the brain is from the two internal carotid arteries and the two vertebral arteries. The vertebral arteries unite to form the basilar artery and this in turn is linked by the posterior communicating arteries to the internal carotids. At the level of the orbits the carotid arteries branch forming the anterior and middle cerebral arteries which, with the posterior cerebral arteries, supply the cerebral hemispheres.

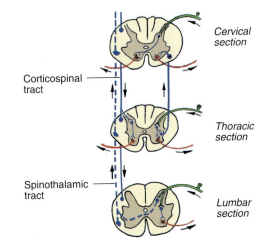

Fig.3.15 ASCENDING AND DESCENDING PATHWAYS
The arrows indicate the direction of the neural impulses

Cervical section

Corticospinal tract

Thoracic section

Spinothalamic tract

Lumbar section

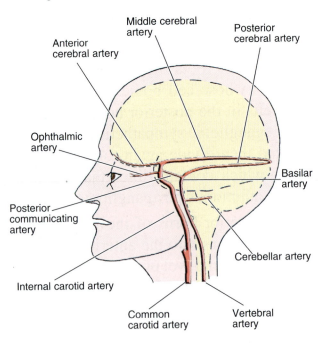

Fig.3.16 BLOOD SUPPLY TO THE BRAIN

Middle cerebral artery

Posterior cerebral artery

Anterior cerebral artery

Ophthalmic artery

Basilar artery

Posterior communicating artery

Internal carotid artery

Cerebellar artery

Common carotid artery

Vertebral artery

Venous drainage from the brain passes to large venous sinuses lying enclosed in dura mater between the skull and brain. The sinuses communicate with the cerebrospinal fluid via projections of arachnoid mater covered in endothelium. These projections are the arachnoid granulations, which protrude through the dura into the sagittal and transverse sinuses. The sinuses finally drain into the internal jugular veins. The spinal cord is supplied via the anterior and posterior spinal arteries and by spinal branches of local arteries. Drainage is through a complex system of intercommunicating (anastomosing) veins formed from valveless venous plexuses.

Fig.3.17 VENOUS SYSTEM OF BRAIN

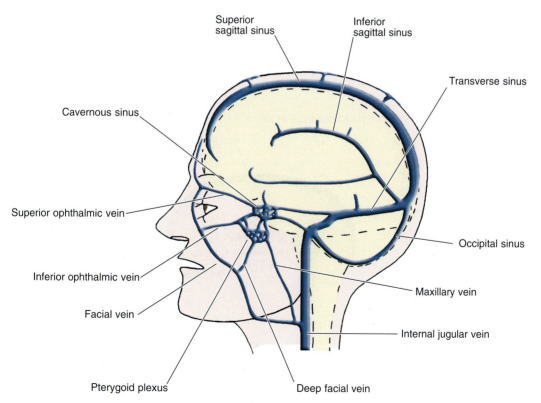

Superior sagittal sinus

Inferior sagittal sinus

Transverse sinus

Cavernous sinus

Superior ophthalmic vein

Occipital sinus

Inferior ophthalmic vein

Maxillary vein

Facial vein

Internal jugular vein

Pterygoid plexus

Deep facial vein

Cerebrospinal fluid

The ventricles, aqueducts and canals within the brain and spinal cord and the associated meningeal spaces all communicate with each other. They are filled with circulating cerebrospinal fluid which is produced by the choroid plexus of the lateral and third ventricles. This plexus is a highly vascular region where the

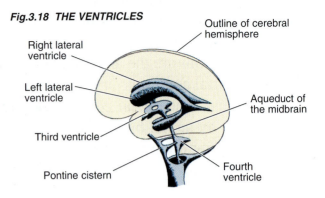

Fig.3.18 THE VENTRICLES

Outline of cerebral hemisphere

Right lateral ventricle

Left lateral ventricle

Third ventricle

Pontine cistern

Aqueduct of the midbrain

Fourth ventricle

meninges become thinner and the pia mater is covered by specialised epithelial cells, the ependyma, that line all the ventricles and the central canal of the spinal cord. If circulation of cerebrospinal fluid is prevented, by a tumour for example, the subsequent increase in intracranial pressure may cause serious damage to the neurones of the brain and spinal cord.

Fig.3.19 THE CIRCULATION OF CEREBROSPINAL FLUID

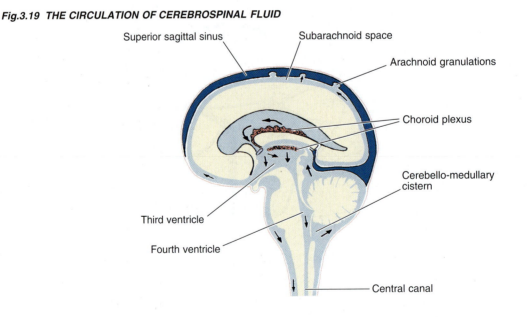

Superior sagittal sinus

Subarachnoid space

Arachnoid granulations

Choroid plexus

Cerebello-medullary cistern

Third ventricle

Fourth ventricle

Central canal

Chapter 4

THE SKULL

The skull is comprised of the cranium (the rigid box-like structure which contains the brain), the facial skeleton, the mandible (the movable lower jaw), and the hyoid bone which is suspended from the temporal bones providing a base for tongue movements.

There are eight cranial bones and fourteen facial bones forming the skull. The eight cranial bones are the paired temporal and parietal bones, and the unpaired frontal, occipital, sphenoid and ethmoid bones. The facial bones are the paired maxilla, zygomatic, nasal, lacrimal, palatine and inferior nasal conchae and the unpaired vomer and mandible.

The bones of the skull are joined at serrated lines (sutures) which are gradually obliterated with age as the bones fuse together. In some cases, as in the orbit, there is incomplete union of two bones, or a space may exist between two processes or wings of a particular bone. Such a gap is called a fissure. The bones of the skull are covered by the connective tissue periosteum which is attached firmly at the sutures.

The bones are penetrated by many canals which transmit blood vessels and nerves between the cavities of the cranium. The opening of such a canal is known as a foramen. A smooth depression or basin which can hold a structure is a fossa and the major fossae of the skull, (the anterior, middle and posterior cranial fossae), can be seen when the skull cap or calva is removed and the interior floor of the skull is viewed from above (see Fig.4.7b).

The views of the skull shown below in Figs.4.1-4.4 are used in the descriptions of the individual bones which follow.

Fig.4.1 LATERAL VIEW OF SKULL

Fig.4.2 FLOOR OF SKULL
(Calva removed)

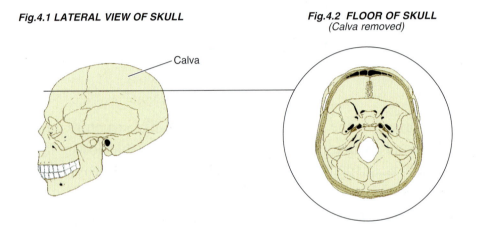

Calva

Fig.4.3 ANTERIOR VIEW OF SKULL

Fig.4.4 MEDIAN SECTION THROUGH SKULL
(Mandible and calva removed)

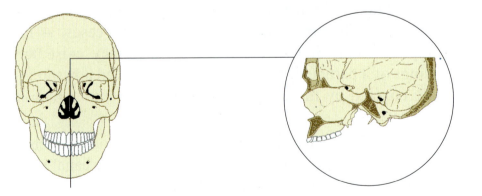

Fig.4.5 ANTERIOR VIEW OF THE SKULL

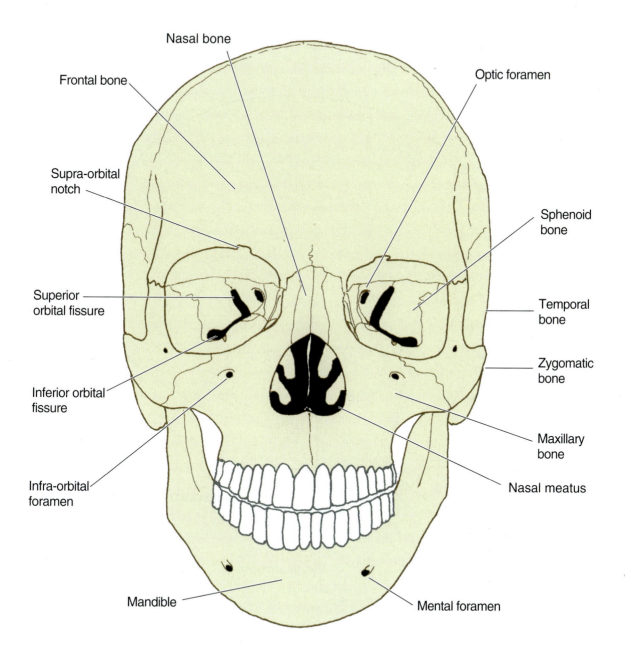

Nasal bone

Frontal bone

Optic foramen

Supra-orbital notch

Sphenoid bone

Superior orbital fissure

Temporal bone

Inferior orbital fissure

Zygomatic bone

Maxillary bone

Infra-orbital foramen

Nasal meatus

Mandible

Mental foramen

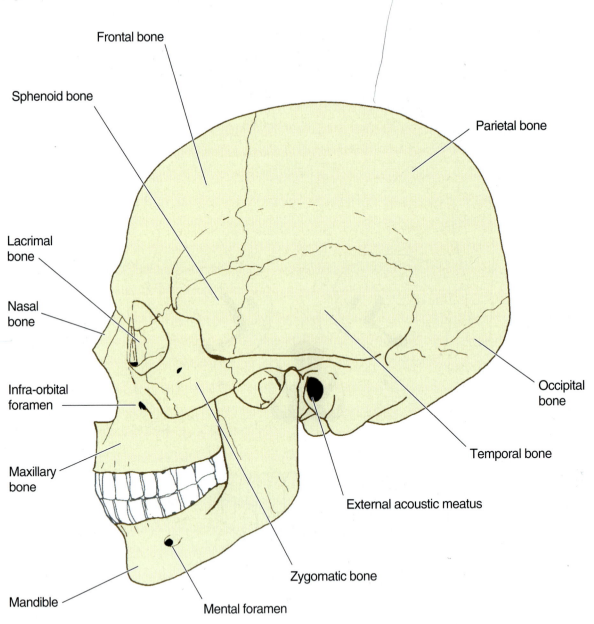

Fig.4.6 LATERAL VIEW OF SKULL

Frontal bone

Sphenoid bone

Parietal bone

Lacrimal bone

Nasal bone

Infra-orbital foramen

Maxillary bone

Occipital bone

Temporal bone

External acoustic meatus

Zygomatic bone

Mandible

Mental foramen

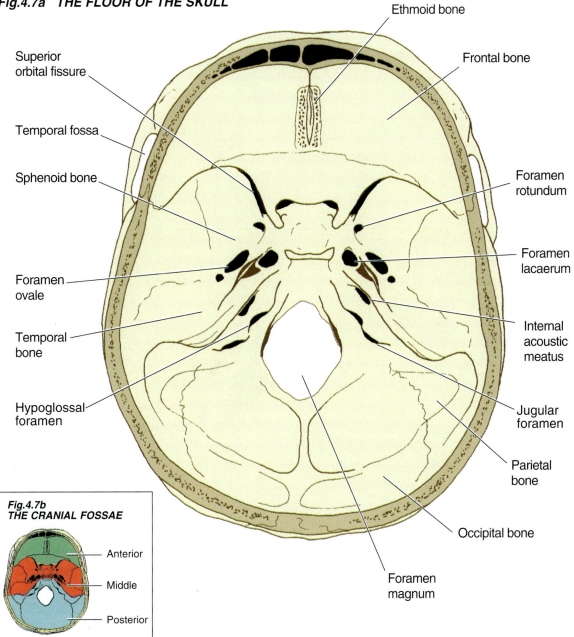

Fig.4.7a THE FLOOR OF THE SKULL

Ethmoid bone

Frontal bone

Superior
orbital fissure

Temporal fossa

Sphenoid bone

Foramen
rotundum

Foramen
lacaerum

Foramen
ovale

Internal
acoustic
meatus

Temporal
bone

Hypoglossal
foramen

Jugular
foramen

Parietal
bone

Occipital bone

Foramen
magnum

Fig.4.7b
THE CRANIAL FOSSAE

Anterior

Middle

Posterior

Fig.4.8 MEDIAN SECTION THROUGH THE SKULL

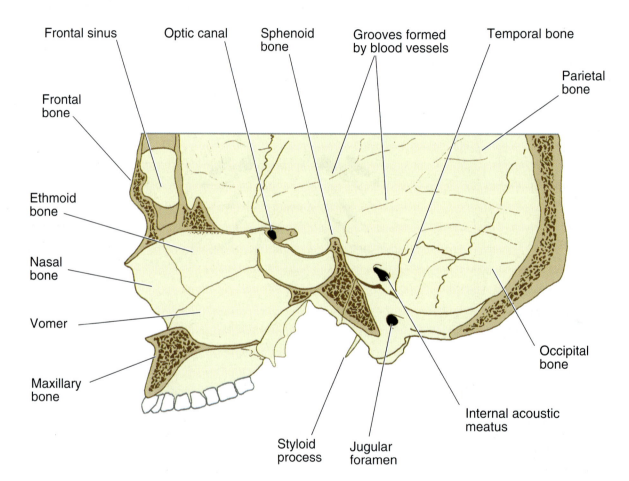

Frontal sinus

Optic canal

Sphenoid bone

Grooves formed by blood vessels

Temporal bone

Parietal bone

Frontal bone

Ethmoid bone

Nasal bone

Vomer

Maxillary bone

Occipital bone

Internal acoustic meatus

Styloid process

Jugular foramen

Temporal bones

These bones form the lower lateral surfaces of the skull and extend inwards to form part of the cranial floor. Each temporal bone has four main areas, petrous, squamous, tympanic and mastoid.

The petrous part appears as a triangular pyramid which points inwards towards the midline of the cranium. The upper ridge of this marks the division between the middle and posterior cranial fossae. The jugular foramen, the foramen lacaerum, the internal acoustic meatus and the carotid canal are all situated in the petrous part of the temporal. Deep within the bone is the inner ear containing the sensory receptors for balance and hearing.

The squamous part of the temporal bone is in contact with the parietal and zygomatic bones and carries a thin extension of bone that shapes the cheeks, the zygomatic process. The mandibular fossa acts as a socket for the upper end of the jaw-bone.

The tympanic region contains the external acoustic meatus through which sounds pass to reach the inner ear. Inferior to the meatus is the styloid process which provides anchorage for a number of muscles and the tendon that attaches the hyoid bone.

Fig.4.9 THE TEMPORAL BONE

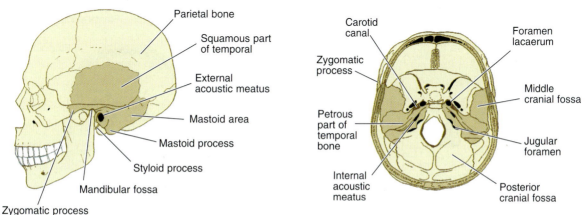

Parietal bone
Squamous part of temporal
External acoustic meatus
Mastoid area
Mastoid process
Styloid process
Mandibular fossa
Zygomatic process

Carotid canal
Foramen lacaerum
Zygomatic process
Middle cranial fossa
Petrous part of temporal bone
Jugular foramen
Internal acoustic meatus
Posterior cranial fossa

The mastoid area of the temporal bone has the mastoid process as its most obvious feature which can be felt in vivo as a solid lump just behind the ear. Between the mastoid and styloid processes is the stylomastoid foramen through which the facial nerve passes.

Frontal bone

This forms the forehead, the floor of the anterior cranial fossa and the roof of the orbits. Posteriorly the coronal suture forms the junction of the frontal bone with the parietal bones.

Just above the orbital margins the bone thickens to form the supraciliary arches between which lies the smooth glabella. Behind the glabella the frontal bone is notched to take the cribriform plate of the ethmoid bone. The supra-orbital artery and nerve pass from the orbit via the supra-orbital notch or foramen.

The frontal bone is composed of two sheets of compact bone separated by a layer of spongy cancellous bone. This makes the bone light in weight but strong. Further reduction in weight is produced by the presence of spaces within the bone known as the frontal sinuses.

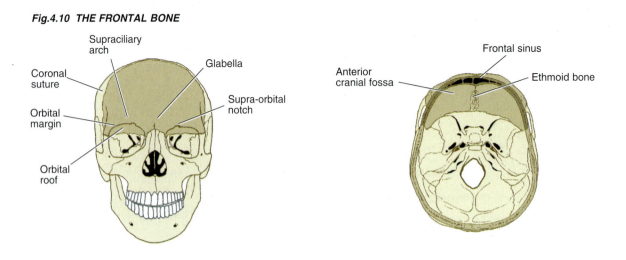

Fig.4.10 THE FRONTAL BONE

Supraciliary arch

Glabella

Coronal suture

Supra-orbital notch

Orbital margin

Orbital roof

Anterior cranial fossa

Frontal sinus

Ethmoid bone

Occipital bone

The occipital bone forms part of the posterior wall of the skull and the bulk of the floor of the posterior cranial fossa. Anteriorly the lambdoid sutures form a link with the parietal bones and the occipito-mastoid sutures link the bone to the mastoid parts of the temporal bones. At the anterior border of the posterior cranial fossa the occipital joins the sphenoid.

The large opening in the occipital bone is the foramen magnum through which the lower end of the brainstem passes. Just beyond the anterolateral edge of the foramen magnum lie the canals for the hypoglossal nerves. A notch in the anterior border of the occipital forms the wall of the jugular foramen where it meets the temporal bone. On the underside of the bone two projections, the occipital condyles, form rockers which articulate with the atlas vertebra at the top of the spinal column.

Fig.4.11 THE OCCIPITAL BONE

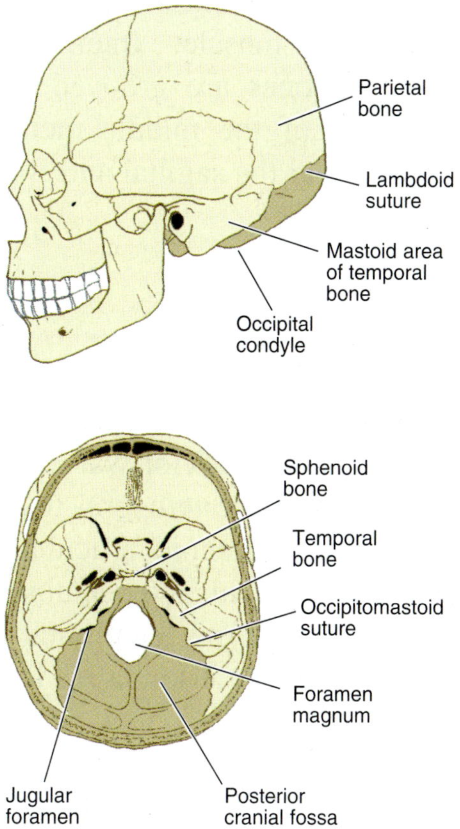

Parietal bone

Lambdoid suture

Mastoid area of temporal bone

Occipital condyle

Sphenoid bone

Temporal bone

Occipitomastoid suture

Foramen magnum

Jugular foramen

Posterior cranial fossa

Parietal bones

These form most of the top and upper sides of the skull. The parietal bones contribute to the four main cranial sutures. The coronal suture forms the junction with the frontal bone, the squamous sutures are the junction with the temporal bones and the lambdoid suture is the join to the occipital bone. The two parietal bones themselves are joined at the sagittal suture.

The external surface is generally smooth but carries an arcuate ridge marking the attachment of the temporalis muscle. Internally the parietal bones are grooved by the branches of the middle meningeal arteries and the sagittal and sigmoid sinuses.

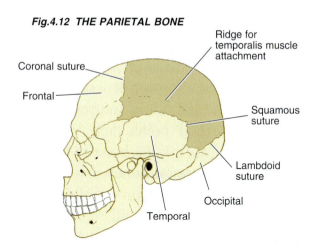

Fig.4.12 THE PARIETAL BONE

Ridge for temporalis muscle attachment

Coronal suture

Frontal

Squamous suture

Lambdoid suture

Occipital

Temporal

Sphenoid bone

The sphenoid extends across the cranial cavity forming the greater part of the floor and the anterior wall of the middle cranial fossa. Its wing-like extensions are found in the temporal fossae and within the orbits. The central region, the body of the sphenoid, articulates posteriorly with the occipital bone and anteriorly with the ethmoid, and contains large air sinuses. In the upper surface of the body a depression forms the pituitary (or hypophyseal) fossa. The transverse processes anterior and posterior to this fossa form a saddle shape known as the sella turcica.

Fig.4.13 THE SUPEROPOSTERIOR ASPECT OF THE ISOLATED SPHENOID BONE

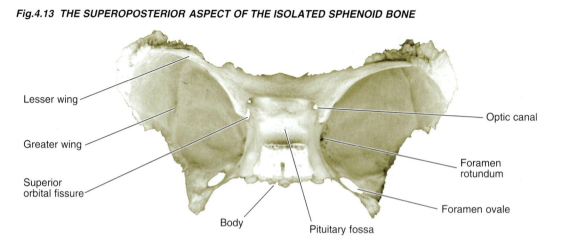

Lesser wing

Greater wing

Superior orbital fissure

Optic canal

Foramen rotundum

Foramen ovale

Body

Pituitary fossa

Extending from each side of the body are the greater wings. Openings in these communicate between the middle cranial fossa and the base of the skull. The foramen rotundum carries the maxillary nerve from the inferior orbital fissure, while the foramen ovale transfers the mandibular nerve from the mandible to the middle cranial fossa. At its junction with the temporal bone the sphenoid forms the anterior border of the foramen lacaerum.

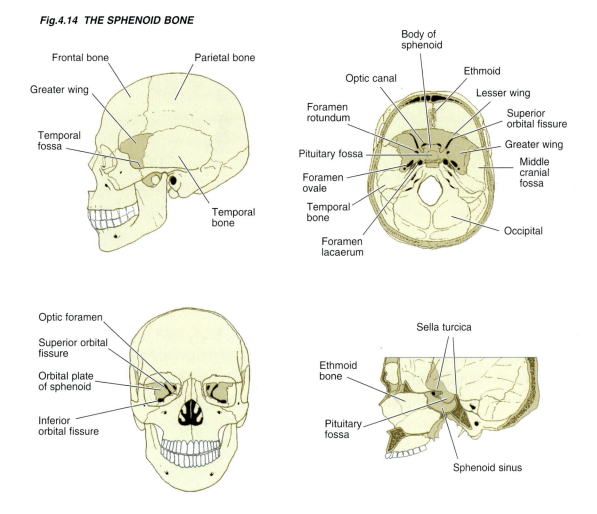

Fig.4.14 THE SPHENOID BONE

Fig.4.15 ANTERIOR ASPECT OF THE ISOLATED SPHENOID BONE

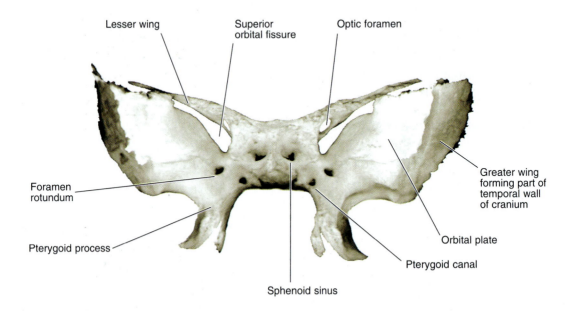

Lesser wing

Superior orbital fissure

Optic foramen

Greater wing forming part of temporal wall of cranium

Foramen rotundum

Pterygoid process

Orbital plate

Pterygoid canal

Sphenoid sinus

The lesser wings project laterally from the upper anterior surface of the body. They form part of the anterior cranial fossa and the roof of the orbits. The optic canal passes through the lesser wing carrying the optic nerve and the ophthalmic artery. The superior orbital fissure lies between the lesser and greater wings.

Descending from the inferior junction between the body and the greater wings are the pterygoid processes. The process forms a wall to the rear of the inferior orbital fissure and, with the palatine bone, partly encloses the pterygopalatine fossa into which the vidian nerve passes via the pterygoid canal.

Ethmoid bone

The ethmoid is a very delicate box-like bone, containing many sinuses, the ethmoidal air cells. It lies behind the nasal bones and its lateral surfaces form the thin medial walls of the orbits.

It projects upwards into the anterior cranial fossa where its triangular plate, the crista galli, separates the two olfactory bulbs whose sensory fibres pass through the cribriform plate of the ethmoid en route from the nasal meatus.

Within the nasal cavity the perpendicular plate of the ethmoid articulates with the vomer and the septal cartilage of the nose dividing the nasal meatus into right and left halves. Lateral to this plate lie the curved superior and middle nasal conchae.

Fig.4.16 THE ETHMOID BONE

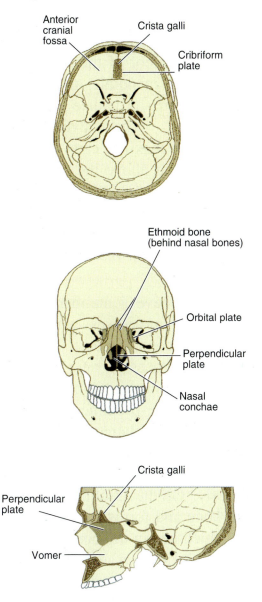

Anterior cranial fossa

Crista galli

Cribriform plate

Ethmoid bone (behind nasal bones)

Orbital plate

Perpendicular plate

Nasal conchae

Crista galli

Perpendicular plate

Vomer

Maxillary bones

The maxillary bones (or maxillae) are fused to form the upper jaw, lateral wall and floor of the nasal cavity and the floor of the orbit. Apart from the mandible, all the other facial bones articulate with the maxillae. The alveolar margins of the maxillae carry the upper teeth, and above the teeth and below the orbital floor lies the maxillary sinus. This large cavity transmits nerves and blood vessels to and from the teeth of the upper jaw.

The maxillae have a number of extensions or processes which link to adjacent bones. The zygomatic process on the temporal side joins the zygomatic bone to form the prominence of the cheek. The palatine process forms the roof of the mouth and articulates with the palatine bone posteriorly. On the nasal margin of the orbit the frontal process rises to meet the frontal bone and forms the anterior wall of the lacrimal fossa. The infra-orbital canal, which lies in the bone between the orbit and the maxillary sinus emerges onto the facial surface as the infra-orbital foramen (see Fig.5.9).

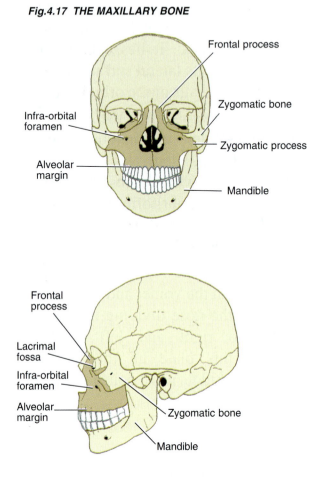

Fig.4.17 THE MAXILLARY BONE

Zygomatic bones

The zygomatic bone forms the prominence of the cheeks (with the maxilla) and provides part of the floor and temporal wall of the orbit. Medially there is articulation with the maxilla and superiorly with the frontal bone. Posteriolaterally the temporal process of the zygomatic bone articulates with the zygomatic process of the temporal bone to form the zygomatic arch. The posterior surface of the zygomatic forms the anterior wall of the temporal fossa. In this surface is the zygomaticotemporal foramen which, with the zygomatico-facial foramen, links the outer surface of the bone with the orbit via the zygomatic foramen (see Fig.5.13).

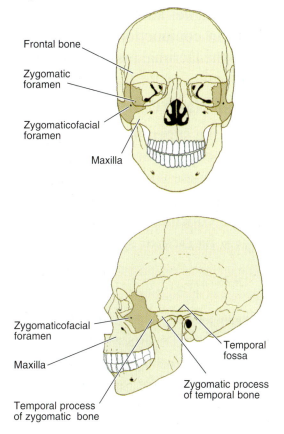

Fig.4.18 THE ZYGOMATIC BONE

Frontal bone

Zygomatic foramen

Zygomaticofacial foramen

Maxilla

Zygomaticofacial foramen

Maxilla

Temporal fossa

Zygomatic process of temporal bone

Temporal process of zygomatic bone

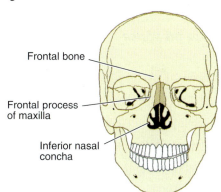

Fig.4.19 THE NASAL BONES

Frontal bone

Frontal process of maxilla

Inferior nasal concha

Nasal bones

These thin rectangular bones form the bridge of the nose. Laterally they articulate with the frontal process of the maxillae, posteriorly with the ethmoid and above with the frontal bone.

87

Lacrimal bones

These fragile, almost rectangular bones lie at the anterior nasal border of each orbit. In conjunction with the frontal process of the maxilla, the lacrimal bone forms the lacrimal fossa which houses the lacrimal sac.

Inferior Nasal Conchae

Unlike the superior and middle conchae which are part of the ethmoid bone, the inferior conchae are separate bones. They form projections into the nasal meatus and articulate with the maxillary, lacrimal and palatine bones. The nasolacrimal canal opens into the inferior nasal meatus, the space between the maxilla and the inferior concha.

Fig.4.20 THE LACRIMAL BONE

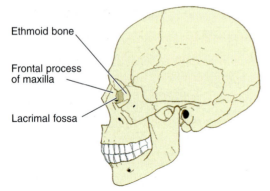

Ethmoid bone

Frontal process of maxilla

Lacrimal fossa

Fig.4.21 THE INFERIOR NASAL CONCHA

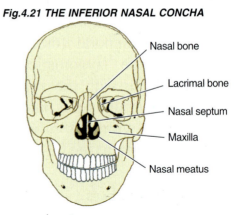

Nasal bone

Lacrimal bone

Nasal septum

Maxilla

Nasal meatus

Vomer

The nasal cavity is formed by the ethmoid, palatine and maxillary bones. Dividing this cavity into two is the nasal septum, the posterior part of which is the vomer. (The rest of the septum is formed by the perpendicular plate of the ethmoid and the septal cartilage.

Fig.4.22 THE VOMER

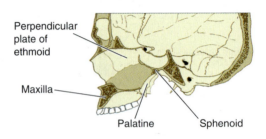

Perpendicular plate of ethmoid

Maxilla

Palatine

Sphenoid

88

Palatine bones

These L-shaped bones are difficult to illustrate in situ as they lie at the back of the nasal cavity. The limbs of the L are formed by the perpendicular and horizontal plates. Sandwiched between the sphenoid and maxillary bones, they form part of the orbital floor and the palate (roof of the mouth). The perpendicular plate contributes to the walls of the inferior orbital fissure and the pterygopalatine fossa (see Fig.5.12).

Mandible

This strong bone forms the lower jaw and articulates via its ascending rami with the mandibular fossa of the temporal bone. The upright mandibular ramus has two processes separated by the mandibular incisure, or notch. The anterior of these, the coronoid process, anchors the temporalis muscle which raises the jaw by making it pivot about the head of the posterior condylar process. The U-shaped mandibular body carries the lower teeth on its alveolar margin.

Two sets of foramina transmit nerves and blood vessels through the jaw via the mandibular canal. The superficial branches of the mandibular nerve pass into the mandibular canal via the anteriorly placed mental foramina and then emerge from the mandibular canal via the mandibular foramina in the medial surface of the rami. (This is the location for anaesthetic injections during dental treatment on the lower molar teeth.)

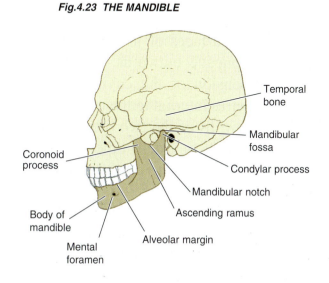

Fig.4.23 THE MANDIBLE

Temporal bone

Mandibular fossa

Condylar process

Mandibular notch

Ascending ramus

Alveolar margin

Coronoid process

Body of mandible

Mental foramen

Chapter 5

THE ORBIT

The anterior entrance to the orbit is an opening about 40mm wide and 35mm high. The orbital margin is in the form of a rounded quadrilateral with its long axis sloping nasally upwards at about 12° (see Fig.5.3). The margin of the orbit loses definition in the inferior nasal corner where it divides to form the lacrimal fossa, and a supra-orbital notch can often be found breaking the regular contours of the nasal half of the upper margin.

The internal surfaces of the orbit are generally concave outwards and the widest dimension of the cavity is a few millimetres internal to the margin. The medial walls of the two orbits lie almost parallel to each other and parallel to the median plane of the skull. The apex of the orbit lies about 40mm behind the orbital margin and here the lateral and medial walls meet at an angle of 45°.

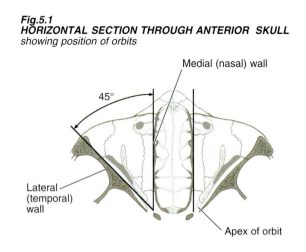

Fig.5.1
HORIZONTAL SECTION THROUGH ANTERIOR SKULL
showing position of orbits

Medial (nasal) wall

45°

Lateral (temporal) wall

Apex of orbit

Fig.5.2 ANTERIOR VIEW OF RIGHT ORBIT

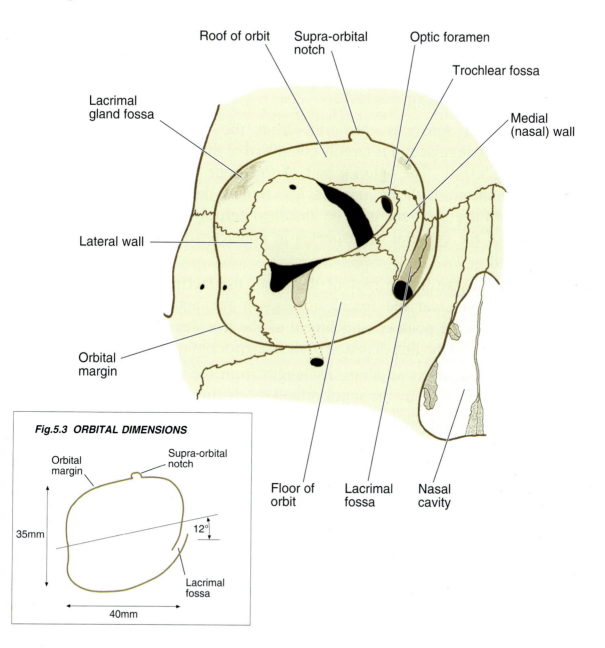

Roof of orbit

Supra-orbital notch

Optic foramen

Trochlear fossa

Lacrimal gland fossa

Medial (nasal) wall

Lateral wall

Orbital margin

Floor of orbit

Lacrimal fossa

Nasal cavity

Fig.5.3 ORBITAL DIMENSIONS

Orbital margin

Supra-orbital notch

35mm

12°

40mm

Lacrimal fossa

Seven bones take part in making up the walls of the orbit. These are the ethmoid, lacrimal, maxillary, palatine, frontal, sphenoid and zygomatic bones. The organisation of the orbit will be described first, followed by an account of the individual bones.

The roof or superior wall

The roof, which separates the orbit from the anterior cranial fossa, is approximately triangular and is largely composed of the orbital plate of the frontal bone (see Fig.5.10a). The anterior part of this bone contains the frontal sinus which communicates with the nasal cavity. Behind the frontal sinus the roof is thin and in old age the bone may be absorbed entirely, leaving the dura of the frontal lobe of the cerebral hemispheres in contact with the connective tissue lining the orbit.

There are two fossae in the roof of the orbit; the lacrimal gland fossa in the anterolateral angle, and the trochlear fossa at the anteromedial angle. The trochlear fossa is the point of attachment of the trochlea, a small cartilaginous loop used to redirect the line of action of the superior oblique muscle.

About one-third of the way along its length from the nasal wall, the anterior orbital margin is marked by the supra-orbital notch. In some cases this is bridged by bone, thus forming a supra-orbital canal and foramen.

Posteriorly, where the roof of the orbit meets the medial wall, the lesser wing of the sphenoid forms the apex of the orbit and contains the optic foramen. This is the anterior entrance to the optic canal which leads to the middle cranial fossa.

The lateral wall

The lateral wall is also triangular in shape, and separates the orbit from the temporal fossa. The orbital margin here is very thick and strong and curves back, an effect which improves the lateral field of view. Just inside the orbital margin is

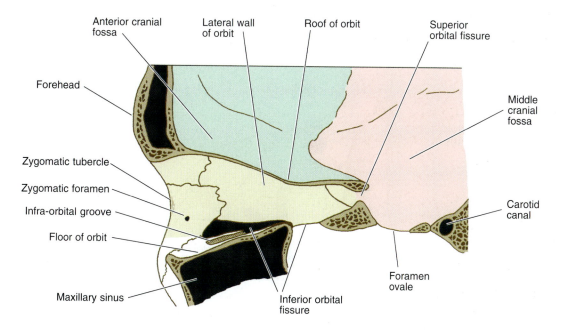

Fig.5.4 LATERAL WALL OF RIGHT ORBIT

Anterior cranial fossa

Lateral wall of orbit

Roof of orbit

Superior orbital fissure

Forehead

Middle cranial fossa

Zygomatic tubercle

Zygomatic foramen

Infra-orbital groove

Floor of orbit

Carotid canal

Maxillary sinus

Foramen ovale

Inferior orbital fissure

the orbital or zygomatic tubercle which forms the point of attachment for the lateral palpebral ligament. Moving back into the orbit the wall becomes thinner as the apex is approached and here the lateral wall terminates at the superior orbital fissure which lies between the two wings of the sphenoid. The greater wing of the sphenoid forms the posterior part of this wall with the zygomatic bone forming the anterior third (see Fig.5.13b). The upper lateral margin of the orbit is closed by the zygomatic process of the frontal bone.

Within the orbit, the zygomatic foramen forms the entrance to the zygomaticofacial and the zygomaticotemporal canals. Close to the anterior end of the superior orbital fissure is the meningeal foramen communicating with the middle cranial fossa behind. Below this, at the junction of the superior and inferior orbital fissures, is the spina recti lateralis to which is attached the common tendon of the four recti muscles (see Fig.11.5).

Fig.5.5 FLOOR OF SKULL AND RIGHT ORBIT

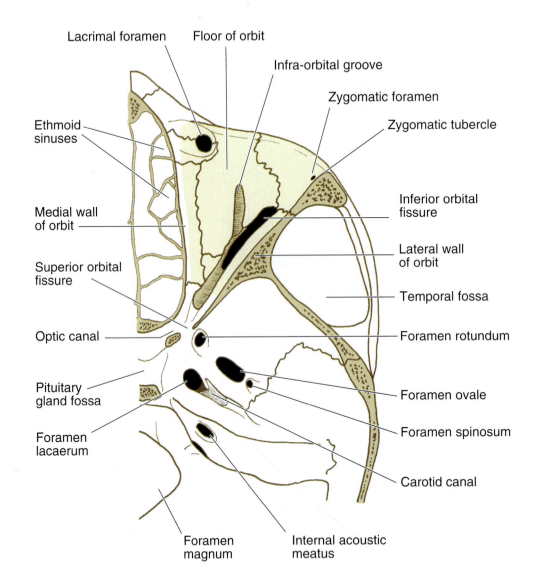

Lacrimal foramen

Floor of orbit

Infra-orbital groove

Zygomatic foramen

Zygomatic tubercle

Ethmoid sinuses

Medial wall of orbit

Superior orbital fissure

Optic canal

Pituitary gland fossa

Foramen lacaerum

Inferior orbital fissure

Lateral wall of orbit

Temporal fossa

Foramen rotundum

Foramen ovale

Foramen spinosum

Carotid canal

Foramen magnum

Internal acoustic meatus

The inferior wall or floor

The triangular floor of the orbit also forms the roof of the maxillary sinus. The major part of the floor is formed by the orbital plate of the maxilla which slopes down anterolaterally to meet the zygomatic bone. This fills the triangle between the orbital margin and the lateral wall and forms half the anterior margin. Another small triangular section, the orbital plate of the palatine bone, completes the posterior part of the floor.

Running parallel to the lateral wall is the inferior orbital fissure which separates the maxilla and palatine bone from the greater wing of the sphenoid. The medial anterior edge of this fissure is divided by the infra-orbital groove which, passing directly forward, becomes the infra-orbital canal and emerges anteriorly as the infra-orbital foramen about 10mm below the orbital margin. These discontinuities in the bone and its general thinness within the orbit make the orbital floor prone to fracture.

The medial wall

The medial wall is more rectangular than the others, and part of it is extremely thin so that the ethmoid air sinuses may be identified through it. The anterior margin is formed by the angular process of the frontal bone and the frontal process of the maxilla. The margin is not continuous but is broken by the lacrimal fossa, a depression approximately 15mm high and 5mm deep. Traced downwards the margin passes behind the lacrimal fossa forming a ridge in the lacrimal bone, the posterior lacrimal crest. The anterior border of the fossa is marked by the anterior lacrimal crest of the maxilla. These crests form the attachment points for the tendon of the inferior oblique muscle and the medial palpebral ligament. The lacrimal fossa extends downwards through the lacrimal foramen to become the nasolacrimal canal.

The bulk of the medial wall of each orbit is composed of the orbital plate of the ethmoid bone. This cuboidal bone contains the ethmoid air sinuses, forming the

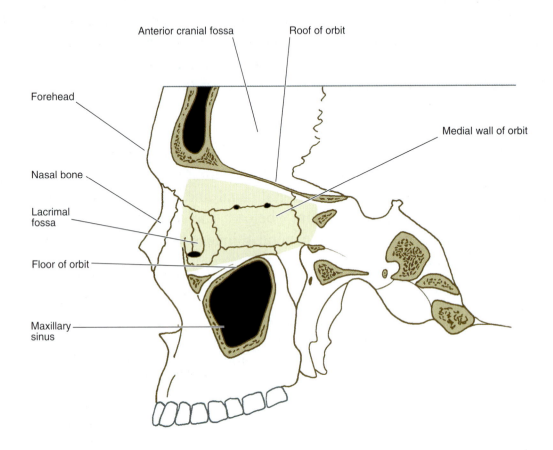

Fig.5.6 SAGITTAL SECTION THROUGH LEFT ORBIT
showing medial wall

Anterior cranial fossa

Roof of orbit

Forehead

Medial wall of orbit

Nasal bone

Lacrimal fossa

Floor of orbit

Maxillary sinus

posterior part of the nasal cavity. Continuing posteriorly, the medial wall of the orbit is formed by part of the lateral surface of the body of the sphenoid bone. The sinuses within this bone are continuous with the sinuses of the ethmoid bone. At the junction of the ethmoid and the frontal bone are the two ethmoidal foramina which transmit nerves and blood vessels from the orbit to the anterior cranial fossa.

Ethmoid bone

The rectangular orbital plates of the ethmoid bone make up much of the medial walls of the orbits. Anteriorly it is attached to the lacrimal bones and posteriorly to the sphenoid bone. On its superior margin where it meets the frontal bone are found the small ethmoidal foramina, two in each orbit. These foramina communicate with the ethmoidal sinuses. The inferior edge of the ethmoid bone joins to the maxillary and palatine bones.

Fig.5.7a ANTERIOR VIEW OF RIGHT ORBIT
Ethmoid bone shown shaded

Fig.5.7b MEDIAL WALL OF LEFT ORBIT
Ethmoid bone shown shaded

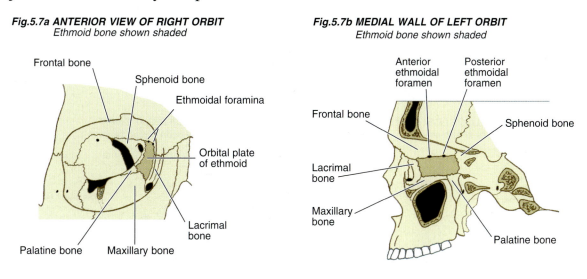

Frontal bone

Sphenoid bone

Ethmoidal foramina

Orbital plate of ethmoid

Lacrimal bone

Palatine bone   Maxillary bone

Anterior ethmoidal foramen

Posterior ethmoidal foramen

Frontal bone

Sphenoid bone

Lacrimal bone

Maxillary bone

Palatine bone

Fig.5.7c FLOOR OF RIGHT ORBIT
Ethmoid bone shown shaded

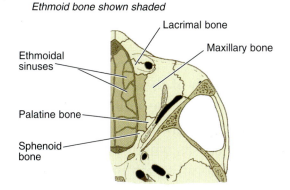

Lacrimal bone

Maxillary bone

Ethmoidal sinuses

Palatine bone

Sphenoid bone

Lacrimal bones

These small fragile bones are found at the anterior of the nasal wall in each orbit. They are attached to the frontal bone above, the ethmoid bone posteriorly and the maxillary bone anteriorly and inferiorly. A vertical ridge of bone, the posterior lacrimal crest, forms the posterior edge of the lacrimal fossa, at the base of which is found the lacrimal foramen.

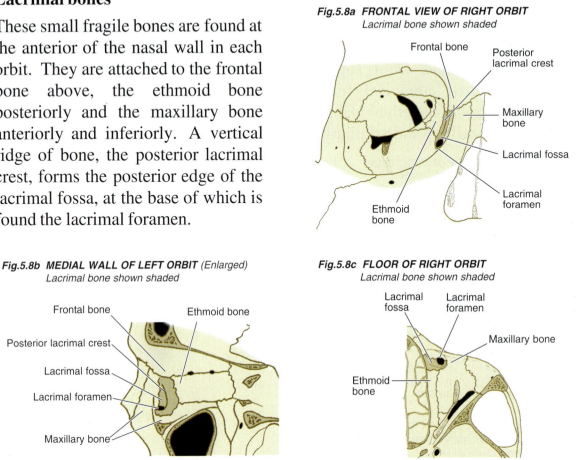

Fig.5.8a FRONTAL VIEW OF RIGHT ORBIT
Lacrimal bone shown shaded

Frontal bone
Posterior lacrimal crest
Maxillary bone
Lacrimal fossa
Lacrimal foramen
Ethmoid bone

Fig.5.8b MEDIAL WALL OF LEFT ORBIT (Enlarged)
Lacrimal bone shown shaded

Frontal bone
Ethmoid bone
Posterior lacrimal crest
Lacrimal fossa
Lacrimal foramen
Maxillary bone

Fig.5.8c FLOOR OF RIGHT ORBIT
Lacrimal bone shown shaded

Lacrimal fossa
Lacrimal foramen
Maxillary bone
Ethmoid bone

Maxillary bones

The orbital plates of the maxillary bones form much of the orbital floors and the inferior orbital margins. Nasally they are attached to the ethmoid and lacrimal bones. The maxillae extend upwards anteriorly to form the anterior lacrimal crests of the lacrimal fossae and the frontal processes which are attached to the frontal bone either side of the nasal bones. Temporally each maxilla is joined to the zygomatic bone at the anterior of the orbital floor and posteriorly an incomplete junction with the sphenoid and palatine bones forms the inferior orbital fissure. The infra-orbital groove extends forwards from the inferior orbital fissure, gradually deepening until it becomes the infra-orbital canal which emerges below the inferior orbital margin as the infra-orbital foramen.

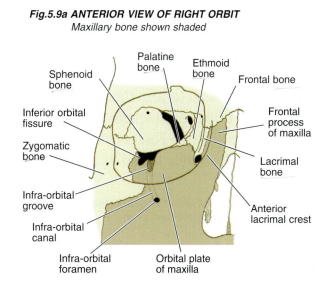

Fig.5.9a ANTERIOR VIEW OF RIGHT ORBIT
Maxillary bone shown shaded

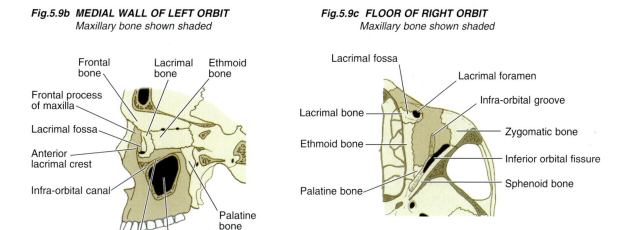

Fig.5.9b MEDIAL WALL OF LEFT ORBIT
Maxillary bone shown shaded

Fig.5.9c FLOOR OF RIGHT ORBIT
Maxillary bone shown shaded

Frontal bone

The orbital plates of the frontal bone make up the roofs of the orbits and their edges form the superior orbital margins. The frontal bone extends downwards into the lateral wall of the orbit to meet the sphenoid and zygomatic bones and into the nasal wall to join the ethmoid and lacrimal bones. At the apex of the orbit the frontal bone is attached to the sphenoid. At the anterior of each orbit the frontal bone has two fossae, the lacrimal gland fossa and the trochlear fossa. The supra-orbital notch is found in the orbital margin.

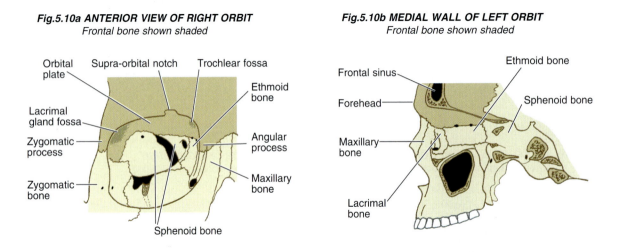

Fig.5.10a ANTERIOR VIEW OF RIGHT ORBIT
Frontal bone shown shaded

Orbital plate · Supra-orbital notch · Trochlear fossa · Ethmoid bone · Lacrimal gland fossa · Zygomatic process · Angular process · Zygomatic bone · Maxillary bone · Sphenoid bone

Fig.5.10b MEDIAL WALL OF LEFT ORBIT
Frontal bone shown shaded

Frontal sinus · Ethmoid bone · Forehead · Sphenoid bone · Maxillary bone · Lacrimal bone

Sphenoid bone (See Figs.4.13 and 4.15)

This bone extends across the cranial cavity forming much of the floor of the middle cranial fossa and the apices of the orbits. With the exception of the lacrimal bones it is attached to all the other orbital bones. It has two pairs of wings, the greater and lesser wings which extend from its cuboidal body. The anterior surface of the greater wing forms the posterior region of the lateral wall of the orbit meeting the frontal bone above and the zygomatic anteriorly. The lower margin of the greater wing forms the posterior border of the inferior orbital fissure and the medial edge forms the lateral side of the superior orbital fissure. The medial side of the superior orbital fissure is made up of the lesser wing which meets the frontal bone to form the posterior region of the roof of the orbit. The optic foramen leading to the optic canal is found at the base of the lesser wing at the apex of the orbit. The anterior part of the lateral surfaces of the body are attached to the ethmoid bone to form the posterior medial wall of the orbit.

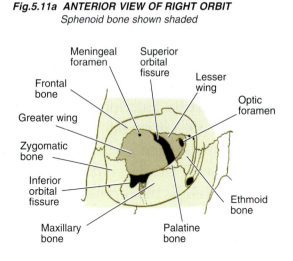

Fig.5.11a ANTERIOR VIEW OF RIGHT ORBIT
Sphenoid bone shown shaded

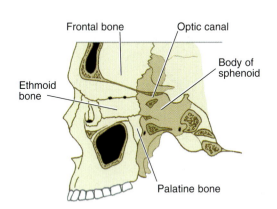

Fig.5.11b MEDIAL WALL OF LEFT ORBIT
Sphenoid bone shown shaded

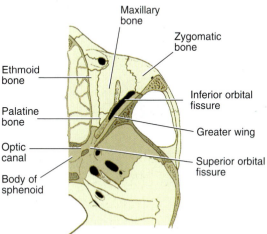
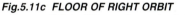

Fig.5.11c FLOOR OF RIGHT ORBIT
Sphenoid bone shown shaded

Palatine bones

The orbital surface of the palatine bone forms a small triangular portion of the posterior floor of the orbit. It is attached to the ethmoid bone nasally and the maxilla anteriorly. The third side of the triangle is directed posterolaterally and contributes to the anterior wall of the inferior orbital fissure. Below the orbital floor the anterior edge of the palatine bone forms part of the medial wall of the pterygopalatine fossa.

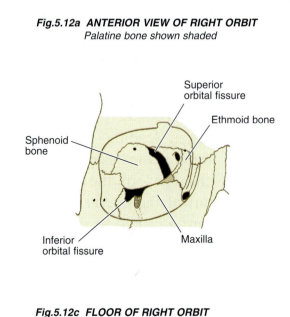

Fig.5.12a ANTERIOR VIEW OF RIGHT ORBIT
Palatine bone shown shaded

Superior orbital fissure

Ethmoid bone

Sphenoid bone

Maxilla

Inferior orbital fissure

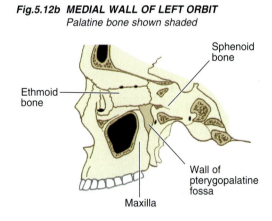

Fig.5.12b MEDIAL WALL OF LEFT ORBIT
Palatine bone shown shaded

Sphenoid bone

Ethmoid bone

Wall of pterygopalatine fossa

Maxilla

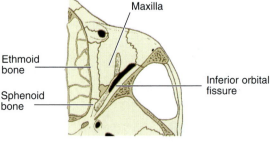

Fig.5.12c FLOOR OF RIGHT ORBIT
Palatine bone shown shaded

Maxilla

Ethmoid bone

Sphenoid bone

Inferior orbital fissure

Zygomatic bones

The orbital plate of the zygomatic bone forms the anterior region of the orbital floor and lateral wall, and the lower temporal quadrant of the orbital margin. On its superior edge it is attached to the frontal bone and medially it meets the maxilla. The posterior margin joins the greater wing of the sphenoid. The zygomatic bone may be pierced by one or more canals carrying nerves and blood vessels between the orbit and the cheeks. The openings of these are known as the zygomatico-temporal, the zygomaticofacial and zygomatic foramina.

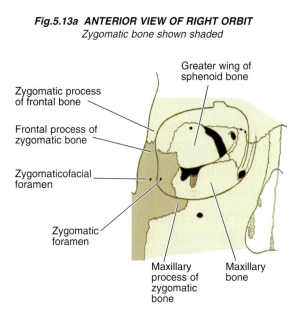

Fig.5.13a ANTERIOR VIEW OF RIGHT ORBIT
Zygomatic bone shown shaded

Greater wing of sphenoid bone

Zygomatic process of frontal bone

Frontal process of zygomatic bone

Zygomaticofacial foramen

Zygomatic foramen

Maxillary process of zygomatic bone

Maxillary bone

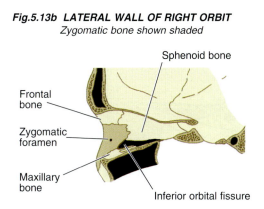

Fig.5.13b LATERAL WALL OF RIGHT ORBIT
Zygomatic bone shown shaded

Sphenoid bone

Frontal bone

Zygomatic foramen

Maxillary bone

Inferior orbital fissure

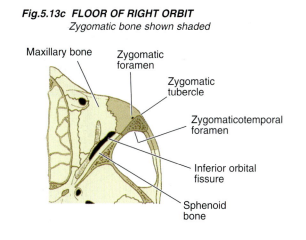

Fig.5.13c FLOOR OF RIGHT ORBIT
Zygomatic bone shown shaded

Maxillary bone

Zygomatic foramen

Zygomatic tubercle

Zygomaticotemporal foramen

Inferior orbital fissure

Sphenoid bone

The orbital fasciae

The periorbita that covers the orbital bones is equivalent to, and continuous with, the periosteum of the rest of the cranium, and is a membraneous vascular structure with a superficial layer of white fibrous tissue and an inner fine elastic layer. The surface apposed to the bone is lined with quiescent osteocytes and becomes less vascular with age. The periorbita is also continuous with the dura mater that lines the optic canal and with other fibrous structures that are anchored to the walls of the orbit. It splits into a double layer at the lacrimal fossa and at the infra-orbital groove, enclosing the structures lying in these depressions.

While the bulk of the orbit is filled by the globe and its associated tissues and muscles, the remaining space is filled with fat, supported by connective tissue sheets. Anteriorly, this fat is contained within the orbit by the orbital septum, a thin sheet of connective tissue which is continuous with the periorbita at the margin of the orbit, with the tarsal plates of the lids and the palpebral ligaments that anchor the lids to the orbital walls. This septum, together with the periorbita and other connective tissue within the orbit form a system of orbital fasciae described further in Chapter 14.

Fig.5.14 SAGITTAL SECTION THROUGH ORBIT

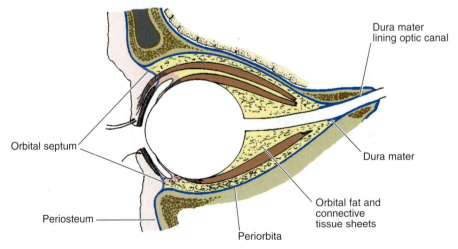

Dura mater lining optic canal

Dura mater

Orbital fat and connective tissue sheets

Orbital septum

Periosteum

Periorbita

Chapter 6

INTRODUCTION TO THE EYE

The eyeball (or globe) fills about a quarter of the volume of the orbit. It is approximately spherical with an average diameter of 25mm.

The globe is seen externally to have two major areas; a transparent anterior part, the cornea, and a larger generally white region, the sclera. The cornea's main constituent is regularly arranged collagen and this is covered by an anterior layer of epithelium and a posterior layer of endothelium. The sclera is essentially dense fibrous collagenous connective tissue.

The cornea and sclera are linked by a transition zone, the limbus or limbal region and here two connective tissue sacs merge with the globe. One, the conjunctiva, is a transparent vascular structure with a surface layer of epithelium. The conjunctiva links the globe to the eyelids. The other connective tissue sac, which is known as Tenon's capsule or the fascia bulbi, forms the fascial sheath of the eyeball and encloses the globe. Tenon's capsule is pierced by nerves, blood vessels and the tendons of the extrinsic ocular muscles and these structures have

Fig.6.1 VERTICAL SECTION THROUGH THE LEFT ORBIT

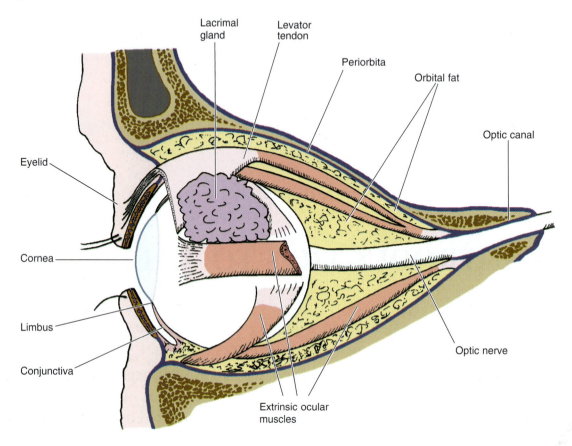

connective tissue sheaths which are continuous with the capsule. The six extrinsic ocular muscles (four rectus muscles, two oblique muscles) are responsible for eye movements.

On the posterior surface of the globe the most prominent feature is the optic nerve which passes from the globe to the apex of the orbit.

The globe is supported by expansions of the muscle sheaths that link it to the orbital walls and by the fat that lies between it and the periosteum lining the orbit. On the upper temporal quadrant of the globe rests the lacrimal gland which produces the bulk of the tears (lacrimal fluid). The lacrimal gland is split into two portions by the tendon of an eyelid muscle, the levator palpebrae. The eyelids lie anterior to the globe and form a protective external barrier. The lid muscles move the lids and so move the tears film across the cornea by the act of blinking. The lids also contain fine canals, the lacrimal canaliculi, which form part of the drainage system for this fluid, transferring it to the lacrimal sac situated in the lacrimal fossa of the bony orbit.

Within the globe, protected by the sclera, is a vascular, pigmented layer, the uvea, comprising the iris, ciliary body and choroid.

The iris is a disc shaped structure with a central aperture, the pupil. The diameter of the pupil is altered by two smooth muscles within the iris, the sphincter pupillae muscle and the dilatator pupillae. Pupil size varies with changes in light levels and is also influenced by emotional factors.

The ciliary body is a ridged triangular structure from which the transparent crystalline lens is suspended by zonular fibres. The ciliary body contains a smooth muscle, the ciliary muscle, which alters the tension on the zonular fibres to change the curvatures of the lens surfaces producing accommodation.

The highly vascular choroid supports and nourishes the innermost layer of the eye, the neural retina, whose receptors and neurone network convert light into coded signals. These signals are passed into the optic nerve by the axons of retinal cells known as ganglion cells. These axons pass through an aperture in the sclera which is bridged by an open meshwork of collagen fibres called the lamina cribrosa. The optic nerve travels to the apex of the orbit within the cone of the four rectus muscles and then enters the middle cranial fossa via the optic canal to reach the optic chiasma.

Fig.6.2 HORIZONTAL SECTION THROUGH THE EYE

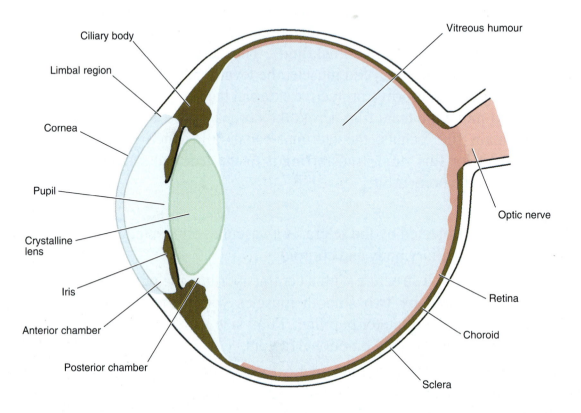

Ciliary body

Limbal region

Cornea

Pupil

Crystalline lens

Iris

Anterior chamber

Posterior chamber

Vitreous humour

Optic nerve

Retina

Choroid

Sclera

Supporting the retina internally is the gel-like vitreous humour which fills the vitreous chamber of the globe. The aqueous (watery) humour fills the chambers which lie anterior and immediately posterior to the iris. The aqueous is produced in the posterior chamber by the ciliary body and enters the anterior chamber via the pupil. It is drained away by a channel situated in the posterior of the limbus, the canal of Schlemm. Aqueous humour provides metabolites to the cornea and lens and its pressure helps to maintain the shape of the globe. The transparent aqueous and vitreous humours, the crystalline lens and the cornea form the optical media of the eye.

Chapter 7

THE OUTER COAT

THE CORNEA

The cornea is the projecting transparent anterior region of the outer protective coat of the globe. Its principal function is to provide the bulk of the refractive power of the eye's dioptric system. This function is served by the smoothness of the anterior surface, the regularity of the connective tissue stroma and the absence of blood vessels or myelinated nerve fibres which might otherwise impair its transparency.

The cornea is covered anteriorly by the tears film and this is in contact with the conjunctiva of the eyelids or the atmosphere. The posterior surface of the cornea is bathed in the aqueous humour circulating in the anterior chamber. At the periphery is the limbus, a region of transition between the tissues of the cornea and those of the conjunctiva, the sclera, the ciliary body, the iris and the fascial tissue of the globe.

Anteriorly the cornea is in the form of a horizontal ellipse and the surface may be toroidal giving rise to corneal astigmatism. The posterior aspect is circular, leading to different degrees of obliquity in the line joining the anterior and posterior edges (Fig.7.1).

The corneal curvature flattens towards the limbus and figures quoted for corneal radii normally refer to the central cap. The cornea is also frequently quoted as forming one-sixth of the globe, this figure refers to its proportion of the circumference, whereas in terms of area the cornea covers about one-thirteenth of the surface of the eyeball.

The dimensions of the cornea are shown in Fig.7.1.

Fig.7.1 THE DIMENSIONS OF THE CORNEA

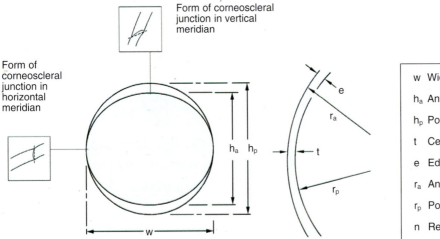

w	Width	11.6mm
h_a	Anterior height	10.6mm
h_p	Posterior height	11.6mm
t	Centre thickness	0.5mm
e	Edge thickness	0.7mm
r_a	Anterior radius	7.8mm
r_p	Posterior radius	6.7mm
n	Refractive index	1.376

STRUCTURE OF THE CORNEA

It is convenient to describe the cornea as having five main layers, although in microscope examination using low powers, the second and fourth layers appear only as modifications of the third layer (see Fig.7.2).

The layers are:
- Epithelium
- Anterior limiting lamina
- Stroma
- Posterior limiting lamina
- Endothelium

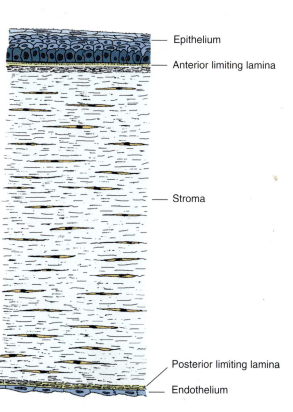

Fig.7.3 TRANSVERSE SECTION OF CORNEA

— Epithelium

— Anterior limiting lamina

— Stroma

— Posterior limiting lamina

— Endothelium

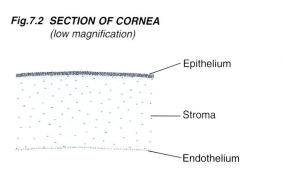

Fig.7.2 SECTION OF CORNEA
(low magnification)

— Epithelium

— Stroma

— Endothelium

The epithelium

The corneal epithelium is non-keratinising stratified squamous epithelium of extreme regularity with a uniform thickness of about 50µm. It consists of five or six layers of cells of three identifiable types.

The basal cells are a single layer of columnar epithelial cells, about 20µm high and 10µm wide. These are linked to their basement membrane by numerous hemidesmosomes and to each other by desmosomes. Each cell has an oval nucleus located in the apex and the surrounding cytoplasm contains few mitochondria and a large number of filaments. Lymphocytes may be found between the cells of this layer, particularly in the periphery of the cornea, and the number of these increases rapidly in corneal inflammation.

Superficial to the columnar cells are 2-3 layers of cells known as wing or umbrella cells. These cells flatten towards the surface and are formed by migration from the basal layer. They have numerous desmosomes and their membranes interdigitate with each other and with those of the basal cells. Their cytoplasm also contains many filaments.

The superficial cells form the final two layers producing a smooth anterior surface. These flat hexagonal cells are up to 4µm thick and may be as much as 45µm across. They have many cytoplasmic vesicles and glycogen granules and their membranes are linked at the corneal surface by zonular occlusions. The exposed surface is covered with microvilli and microplicae (folds) up to 0.5µm high which project into the tears film. The surface cells are eventually lost into the tears, to be replaced by cells moving up from beneath.

The normal turnover time for the epithelial cells is about seven days. If the corneal epithelium is damaged, an initial inhibition of mitosis results and this lasts a few hours. During this time the basal cells spread out to cover the wounded area, then cell growth recommences to heal the wound with normal thickness achieved in a few days. The length of the healing time depends on the nature and

Fig.7.4 THE CORNEAL EPITHELIUM

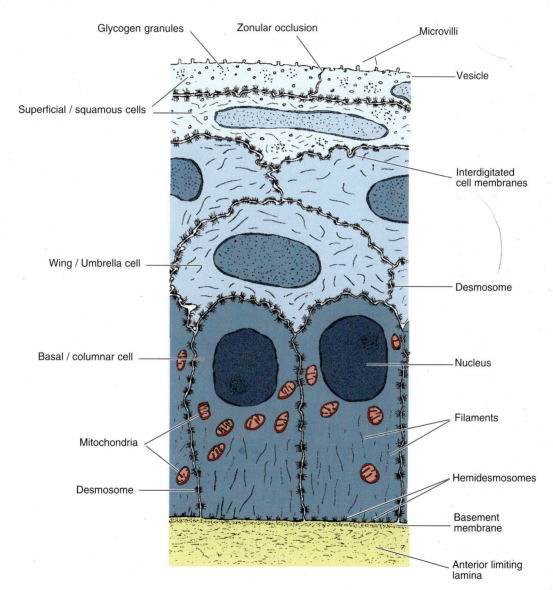

Glycogen granules

Zonular occlusion

Microvilli

Vesicle

Superficial / squamous cells

Interdigitated cell membranes

Wing / Umbrella cell

Desmosome

Basal / columnar cell

Nucleus

Filaments

Mitochondria

Hemidesmosomes

Desmosome

Basement membrane

Anterior limiting lamina

113

extent of the trauma, with thermal lesions recovering more slowly than those caused mechanically. Should the corneal epithelium be completely removed, regrowth is initiated by cells of the limbal conjunctiva.

The fibres of the corneal nerves travel between the epithelial cells and terminate in free endings just below the superficial layers (Fig.7.8).

The epithelium provides a smooth surface to the cornea. The rapid regeneration of its cells and their constant loss into the tears film gives protection against invading organisms and trauma. The extreme sensitivity of this layer produced by its numerous nerve endings gives rise to protective reflex lid closure and lacrimation. The cells form a route for the transport of metabolites and waste products.

The anterior limiting lamina

Below the epithelium, and separated from it by the basement membrane of the basal cells, lies the anterior limiting lamina, or Bowman's membrane. This was originally described by Sir William Bowman (1816-1892) as the 'anterior elastic lamina', although it is now evident that the layer does not contain elastin. It is composed of 25nm diameter collagen fibrils with no obvious arrangement, lying in a mucopolysaccharide matrix. This layer is acellular except for the corneal nerve fibres en route to the limbus and the Schwann cells which accompany the nerve fibres. The anterior limiting lamina, which is about 10μm thick, terminates at the edge of the cornea and is used to mark the anterior corneolimbal junction.

If damaged, the anterior limiting lamina may be invaded by scar tissue, or by ingrowths of basal epithelium.

The fine collagen fibrils of this layer fill the irregularities of the corneal stroma and so creates a smooth surface for the epithelium.

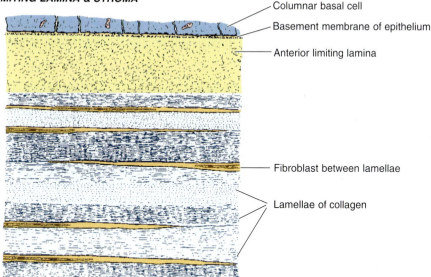

Fig.7.5 ANTERIOR LIMITING LAMINA & STROMA

Columnar basal cell

Basement membrane of epithelium

Anterior limiting lamina

Fibroblast between lamellae

Lamellae of collagen

The stroma

The stroma or substantia propria of the cornea has a thickness of about 500μm, and is formed of layers or lamellae of collagen in a mucopolysaccharide matrix with fibroblasts spread between the layers. The lamellae are poorly defined anteriorly where they blend with the anterior limiting lamina. In the central region of the cornea there are about two hundred lamellae forming approximately 450μm of the total thickness.

The lamellae are 2μm thick bands which vary in width from 10-250μm and extend from limbus to limbus. These bands consist of evenly spaced and uniformly orientated collagen fibrils lying in the mucopolysaccharide. Although the fibrils are parallel to each other within a given lamella, the individual lamellae cross each other obliquely, while remaining parallel to the surface of the cornea (see Fig.7.7). Towards the limbus additional lamellae are present, progressively increasing the corneal thickness to 0.7mm. The fibroblasts (called corneal corpuscles by Virchow, 1908) are stellate cells flattened between the lamellae and are frequently less than 1µm thick. Their processes sometimes enter the lamellae but are principally interlamellar and can be seen to contact the processes of other cells lying at the same level in the cornea. These cells appear to have phagocytic abilities as well as the ability to produce collagen when the cornea is damaged.

The overlapping bands of collagen give the cornea strength and mechanical stability, providing protection to the internal structures of the globe. The increased thickness of the stroma in the periphery of the cornea provides greater resistance to the intraocular pressure than the central region. This results in the cornea being more steeply curved in the centre than at the periphery, thus reducing spherical aberration. The role of the stroma in corneal transparency is described on page 118.

The posterior limiting lamina

The posterior limiting lamina (or Descemet's membrane) although ascribed to Descemet, was referred to some thirty years prior to his description of it by an English oculist, Duddell, in 1729. It terminates as a discrete layer at the edge of the cornea and this termination is used to mark the posterior corneolimbal junction. This layer, like the anterior limiting lamina, is composed of fine collagen fibrils but having a layered arrangement and illustrated by Weddell (1971) as forming an interconnecting pattern of triangularly arranged nodes in flat section, although this organisation is lost posteriorly. At birth, this layer is about 4µm thick, but thickens with age to about 10µm. It acts as the basement membrane for the next layer of the cornea, the endothelium. The endothelium produces the basement membrane material and can reform it if the membrane is damaged in minor trauma. The endothelial cells produce excess membrane in the adult forming mounds (Hassall-Henle warts) which project into the anterior chamber. Bowman described this layer as elastic and, although not containing elastin, it shows elastic tendencies and is clearly under tension, as it recoils when cut.

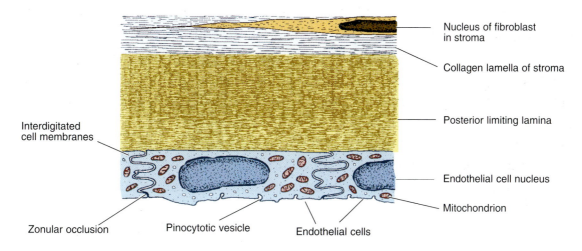

Fig.7.6 THE POSTERIOR LIMITING LAMINA & ENDOTHELIUM

Nucleus of fibroblast in stroma

Collagen lamella of stroma

Posterior limiting lamina

Interdigitated cell membranes

Endothelial cell nucleus

Mitochondrion

Zonular occlusion

Pinocytotic vesicle

Endothelial cells

The endothelium

The cells that cover the posterior limiting lamina are usually described as endothelial, although some authorities prefer to call them mesothelial since they are not lining a vessel and since they exhibit the mesothelial property of membrane secretion in pathological conditions. The cells form a single layer 5μm thick, with individual cells being up to 20μm across. The cells do not divide, but spread to fill gaps caused by cell loss, thus the cell population decreases with age. Cell counts taken by Bourne and Kaufman (1976) indicate a mean of about 3000 cells per mm^2.

The cell membranes show considerable interdigitation with the apical edges sealed by zonular occlusions thus creating a barrier to the passage of fluid between the cells. The cells are packed with mitochondria, implying a high level of activity, and this, together with the movement of pinocytotic vesicles through the cell, indicates that the cells regulate corneal hydration and actively transport metabolites from the anterior chamber to the corneal stroma.

CORNEAL TRANSPARENCY

It has been well established (Poullot 1904, Leber 1873) that the cornea loses its transparency if it is deprived of oxygen or if its cellular layers are extensively damaged, but an explanation of normal corneal transparency has proved difficult to establish. The most widely accepted explanation is that proposed by Maurice (1957) in which the regularly spaced parallel collagen fibrils of the stromal lamellae are considered to behave as a diffraction grating. Since the spacing between the fibrils is less than the wavelength of light, normally incident light is undeviated and for this regular matrix of fibrils in the stroma, grating patterns can be found to explain transmission for different angles of incidence.

If the distance between the fibrils is increased the cornea loses transparency. This may occur as a result of failure of the endothelium to control the amount of fluid in the corneal stroma. The excess fluid is absorbed by the mucopolysaccharide between the fibrils which then swells increasing the fibril separation.

Fig.7.7 TRANSPARENCY OF THE CORNEAL STROMA

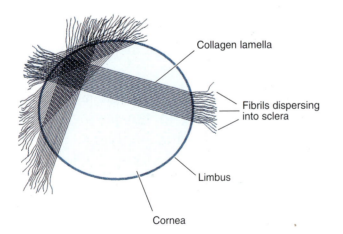

Collagen lamella

Fibrils dispersing into sclera

Limbus

Cornea

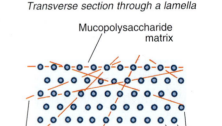

Transverse section through a lamella

Mucopolysaccharide matrix

'Diffraction gratings'

Collagen fibrils

NERVE SUPPLY

Only sensory neurones have been identified in the human cornea, forming seventy or eighty trunks which pass radially through the limbus to join the ciliary nerves which in turn pass to the nasociliary branch of the ophthalmic division of the trigeminal nerve. The afferent nerve fibre endings are found in a dense plexus just below the squamous superficial epithelial layers and, although surrounded by epithelial cells, are referred to as 'free' nerve endings. This differentiates them from the 'corpuscular' endings found elsewhere in the body which terminate in large receptors and are used to detect specific stimuli such as pressure, temperature etc. Free nerve endings are generally considered to be pain or irritation receptors and these are the principal sensations reported for the cornea. Each corneal nerve fibre is terminated by a varicosity and similar smaller varicosities are found along much of the intracorneal length of the fibre. At the level of the anterior limiting lamina, the fibres gain a Schwann cell covering but generally do not become myelinated until 0.5mm from the limbus. However, myelinated nerve fibres may occasionally be found traversing the cornea.

Fig.7.8 NERVE FIBRES IN THE CORNEAL EPITHELIUM

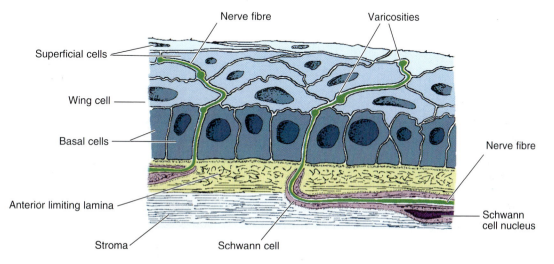

Fibres forming the corneal nerves are collected from wide sectors of the cornea, a factor which reduces localisation of stimuli, but which ensures that sensibility remains even after a pericorneal incision. Sensitivity is greatest in the centre of the cornea, and, like other sensory functions generally, this sensitivity is reduced with age. Permanent damage to the corneal innervation produces corneal anaesthesia and loss of the protective lacrimation and lid closure reflexes. This may result in keratitis (corneal inflammation) and to subsequent corneal degeneration.

CORNEAL METABOLISM

Since blood vessels would reduce its transparency, the cornea is avascular, and it receives its metabolites from the vessels of the limbus, and via the tears and aqueous humour. These routes had been identified by the turn of the century by observation of the changes that occurred in the cornea when the normal function of these pathways was interrupted experimentally.

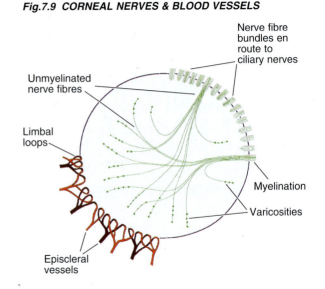

Fig.7.9 CORNEAL NERVES & BLOOD VESSELS

Nerve fibre bundles en route to ciliary nerves

Unmyelinated nerve fibres

Limbal loops

Myelination

Varicosities

Episcleral vessels

The chief source of glucose for the cornea is the aqueous of the anterior chamber, the pericorneal vessels playing only a minor role in its supply. The tears appear to be an important source for amino acids, and like the aqueous, are vital for the supply of oxygen to the cornea. When the eyelids are closed and atmospheric oxygen is not directly available, oxygen is obtained by the corneal epithelium from the vascular palpebral conjunctiva.

THE LIMBUS

The limbus or limbal region is a 1-1.5mm zone of transition between the cornea and sclera. Most authors agree that the corneolimbal junction lies along a line joining the edge of the anterior limiting lamina to the edge of the posterior limiting lamina, but there is less agreement about the limboscleral junction. A line perpendicular to the scleral surface and passing to the root of the iris will be adopted here since it would include between it and the corneo-limbal line the main features of this region.

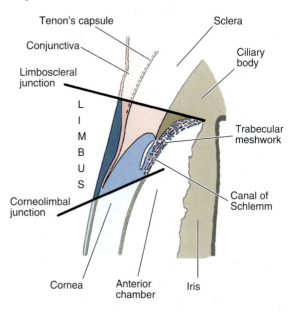

Fig.7.10 THE POSITION & EXTENT OF THE LIMBUS

Tenon's capsule

Conjunctiva

Limboscleral junction

L
I
M
B
U
S

Corneolimbal junction

Cornea

Anterior chamber

Iris

Sclera

Ciliary body

Trabecular meshwork

Canal of Schlemm

At the limbus the steeply curved cornea meets the much flatter sclera and forms the external scleral sulcus. Here the smooth regular layer of epithelium on the anterior surface of the cornea gives way to the conjunctival epithelium, with ten to twelve layers of cells filling the external scleral sulcus. Beyond the limboscleral junction, the epithelial layer is 2-3 cells thick and follows the folds in the surface of the stroma of the conjunctiva. Amongst the superficial conjunctival epithelial cells are found mucin secreting goblet cells.

The vascular conjunctival stroma, the bulbar fascia (Tenon's capsule) and the superficial vascular layer of the sclera (the episclera) all commence at the level of the anterior limiting lamina. Limbal capillaries also appear at this level.

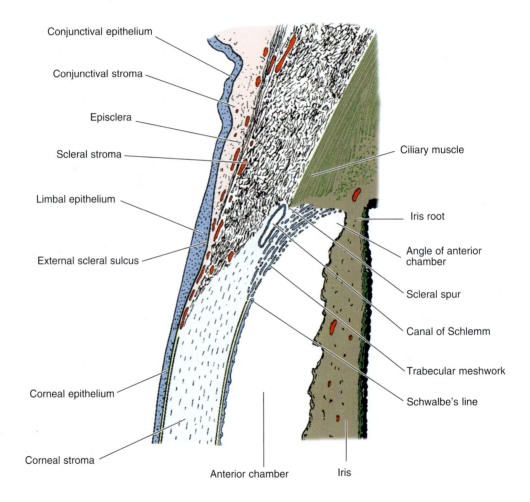

Fig.7.11 THE LIMBAL REGION

Conjunctival epithelium

Conjunctival stroma

Episclera

Scleral stroma

Limbal epithelium

External scleral sulcus

Corneal epithelium

Corneal stroma

Ciliary muscle

Iris root

Angle of anterior chamber

Scleral spur

Canal of Schlemm

Trabecular meshwork

Schwalbe's line

Anterior chamber

Iris

These blood vessels are terminal loops of the anterior ciliary arteries which pass towards the cornea in the connective tissue outside the scleral stroma. Venous drainage is to the venous plexus formed by the vessels in the scleral stroma which, together with the episcleral vessels, drain into the anterior ciliary veins.

Lymphatic vessels are also present in the conjunctiva and those surrounding the limbus drain to a pericorneal lymphatic trunk (see Chapter 12 and Fig.12.31).

The regular lamellae of the corneal stroma blend into the oblique and circularly orientated lamellae of the sclera, and in the limbus close to the anterior chamber wall is the pericorneal canal of Schlemm. This (often multi-channelled) vessel is located in a fold of sclera consisting of circumferential collagen fibres, known as the scleral spur. The scleral spur (or roll) also acts as an attachment for the longitudinal fibres of the ciliary muscle (see page 140).

The canal of Schlemm is lined with endothelial cells. Aqueous humour passing from the anterior chamber into the canal is transported through these cells. Outflow from the canal is via collector channels which are also lined with endothelium. These channels deliver the aqueous to the episcleral veins. Aqueous pressure is sufficient to displace the blood in some of these veins near the limbus thus forming aqueous veins (see Fig.7.12 and page 186) which have been described in detail by Ascher (1942).

To reach the endothelium of the canal, the aqueous must pass through the trabecular meshwork which fills the internal scleral sulcus. This is the limbal extension of the posterior limiting lamina and corneal endothelium. The trabeculae are composed of cores of collagen overlaid by endothelial cells. Close to the canal the trabeculae are in the form of perforated sheets and this is known as the corneoscleral meshwork. In the angle of the anterior chamber the trabeculae become cord-like and this region is referred to as the uveal meshwork. The raised junction between the trabecular meshwork and the corneal endothelium is called Schwalbe's line (or ring).

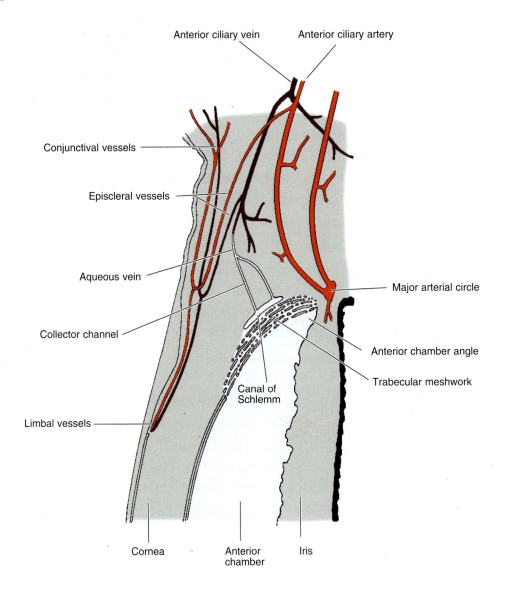

Fig.7.12 THE VASCULAR SYSTEM OF THE LIMBUS

Anterior ciliary vein

Anterior ciliary artery

Conjunctival vessels

Episcleral vessels

Aqueous vein

Major arterial circle

Collector channel

Anterior chamber angle

Trabecular meshwork

Canal of
Schlemm

Limbal vessels

Cornea

Anterior
chamber

Iris

124

THE SCLERA

The sclera is the tough collagenous outer coat of the globe commonly known as the white of the eye. The white appearance is due to the scattering of all wavelengths of light by its dense irregular bundles of collagen. It is protective and provides support and anchorage for structures inside and outside the globe.

Its thickness varies from 0.5mm at the equator to 1mm at the posterior pole. At the limbus the thickness is about 0.7mm and the thinnest point is at the insertion of the rectus muscles where it is only 0.3mm, although the combined thickness of the tendon and the sclera produce a zone that is 0.6mm thick. The radius of curvature also varies and is about 11.5mm posterior to the equator. Anteriorly the radius of curvature is between 12.5mm and 15.0mm.

Although the sclera is generally white, slight increase or marked decrease in its water content causes it to become almost transparent. Thinning of the sclera may cause it to take on a blue tinge and, in old age, fat deposits may give it a yellow appearance. Brown areas of pigmentation may occur.

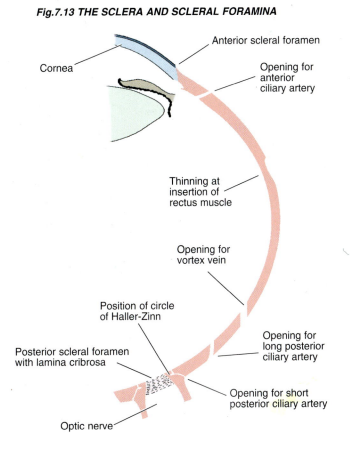

Fig.7.13 THE SCLERA AND SCLERAL FORAMINA

Cornea

Anterior scleral foramen

Opening for anterior ciliary artery

Thinning at insertion of rectus muscle

Opening for vortex vein

Position of circle of Haller-Zinn

Posterior scleral foramen with lamina cribrosa

Opening for long posterior ciliary artery

Opening for short posterior ciliary artery

Optic nerve

The sclera has a number of openings or channels (see Fig.7.13). With the cornea removed there would be a large anterior opening, the anterior scleral foramen, while at the back of the globe the posterior scleral foramen allows the passage of the optic nerve fibres. This latter opening is funnel-shaped with a 3mm external and 1.5-2.0mm internal diameter. Numerous other small canals pass through the sclera carrying nerves and blood vessels.

STRUCTURE OF THE SCLERA

The sclera is generally considered to consist of three layers.
- Episclera
- Stroma
- Lamina fusca

The episclera

The episclera is a vascular connective tissue layer lying between the scleral stroma and the avascular tissue of Tenon's capsule. The collagen fibres that form the bulk of this layer are continuous with Tenon's capsule and the meshwork of the scleral stroma. The episclera becomes less vascular towards the posterior part of the globe.

The stroma

The stroma of the sclera is composed of collagen and elastic fibres, fibroblasts and ground substance and it is relatively avascular. Unlike the cornea, the collagen fibrils are of various thicknesses, have irregular spacing and the bundles lack a regular arrangement. The collagen fibre bundles generally run circumferentially in front of the equator and more longitudinally between the equator and the optic nerve head, where they again form a circumferential pattern. There are few fibroblasts in the sclera, and those that are present are not in close contact with each other.

The lamina fusca

The lamina fusca is the connective tissue inner surface of the sclera. Its dark appearance is due to melanocytes lying between the collagen fibres. These fibres form weak trabeculae which link the scleral stroma to the ciliary body and choroid. Blood vessels and nerve fibres are found in this layer, but they are mainly en route to other regions of the globe.

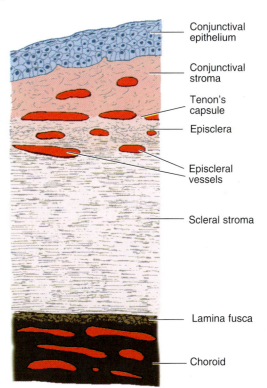

Fig.7.14 SECTION THROUGH THE SCLERA

Conjunctival epithelium

Conjunctival stroma

Tenon's capsule

Episclera

Episcleral vessels

Scleral stroma

Lamina fusca

Choroid

BLOOD SUPPLY

The sclera has few vessels, except anteriorly in the region traversed by the anterior ciliary arteries and veins. Posteriorly, around the optic nerve head, it is supplied by vessels derived from the circle of Haller-Zinn.

NERVE SUPPLY

Few sensory nerve fibres supply the sclera but those that are present join the long or short posterior ciliary nerves which are branches of the ophthalmic division of the trigeminal (fifth cranial) nerve. There appears to be no autonomic innervation to the sclera.

Bundles of the long ciliary nerves loop outwards to form 1-2mm diameter bulges in the surface of the sclera. These are the intrascleral nerve loops of Axenfeld which are found about 5mm from the limbus.

Chapter 8

THE UVEA

The iris, ciliary body and choroid together constitute the uvea, the vascular pigmented middle coat of the globe. The order in which they are described here is merely a descriptive convenience and is not intended to indicate their relative importance.

THE IRIS

The iris is the most anterior part of the uvea and is visible through the cornea. The iris diaphragm forms the division between the anterior and posterior chambers. Its central aperture, the pupil, may change in diameter to vary the amount of light reaching the retina, to reduce aberrations and, to some extent, to communicate the emotional state of the individual.

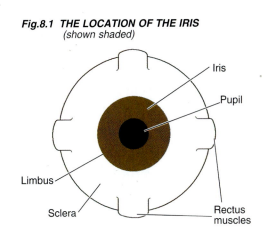

Fig.8.1 THE LOCATION OF THE IRIS
(shown shaded)

Iris

Pupil

Limbus

Sclera

Rectus muscles

The free surface of the iris is bathed in aqueous humour and it is peripherally continuous with the ciliary body at the iris root. Posteriorly the iris rests on the crystalline lens and, because the lens is convex, it pushes the pupil plane anterior to the plane through the root of the iris (Fig.8.2). If the lens is missing or displaced and the lens is unsupported posteriorly, iris tremor (iridodonesis) may be observed.

The iris diameter is about 13mm. Its thickness is about 0.1mm at the root and 0.6mm at the thickest point, the collarette. This lies 1.5mm from the pupil margin and divides the anterior surface of the iris into two zones, the pupillary and ciliary regions.

THE PUPIL

The pupil is not exactly centred in the iris, but is displaced slightly down and in. The pupil diameter can vary from 1mm to 8mm giving a 1:64 variation in the amount of light passing through the pupil into the vitreous chamber. This is not a large variation by comparison with the range of luminances encountered by the eye, or with the adaptation ability of the retina, but does serve to speed adaptation to differing light levels. The term for pupil dilation is mydriasis and the term for pupil constriction is miosis. Due to the organisation of the contractile structures within the iris, it is

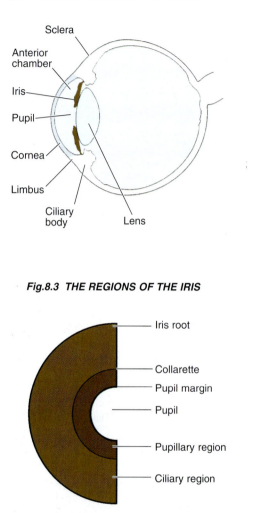

Fig.8.2 SECTION THROUGH THE GLOBE

Sclera
Anterior chamber
Iris
Pupil
Cornea
Limbus
Ciliary body
Lens

Fig.8.3 THE REGIONS OF THE IRIS

Iris root
Collarette
Pupil margin
Pupil
Pupillary region
Ciliary region

the width of the ciliary region that alters the most during mydriasis and miosis, the width of the pupillary zone remaining almost constant.

IRIS COLOUR

The colour of the iris depends principally upon the pigmentation of the anterior surface. The greater the amount of pigmentation the browner the iris appears, and the more the underlying stroma is hidden from view. If there is little or no pigment in the anterior surface the texture of the stroma is visible and any pigment cells in this layer make the iris appear freckled. Scattering of light in the stroma gives a blue appearance. Absence of pigment in all layers of the iris will give a pink coloration, mainly due to reflection from the vascular tissues in the posterior part of the globe. The colour of the iris is inherited, with brown being dominant and blue recessive.

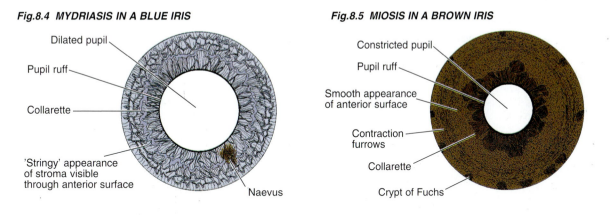

Fig.8.4 MYDRIASIS IN A BLUE IRIS

Dilated pupil
Pupil ruff
Collarette
'Stringy' appearance of stroma visible through anterior surface
Naevus

Fig.8.5 MIOSIS IN A BROWN IRIS

Constricted pupil
Pupil ruff
Smooth appearance of anterior surface
Contraction furrows
Collarette
Crypt of Fuchs

The overall appearance of the iris may also depend upon the distribution of surface depressions (the crypts of Fuchs) and contraction furrows. A dense flat area of pigment may occur forming an iris naevus or freckle. Larger variations of coloration produce heterochromia which may be confined to one iris or cause the irides to differ from each other.

Fig.8.6 TRANSVERSE SECTION THROUGH THE IRIS

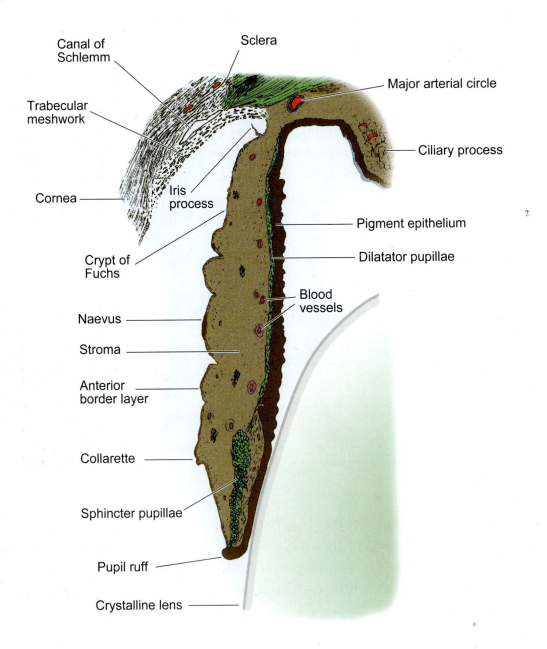

Canal of Schlemm

Sclera

Major arterial circle

Trabecular meshwork

Ciliary process

Cornea

Iris process

Pigment epithelium

Crypt of Fuchs

Dilatator pupillae

Blood vessels

Naevus

Stroma

Anterior border layer

Collarette

Sphincter pupillae

Pupil ruff

Crystalline lens

STRUCTURE OF THE IRIS

The iris may be considered as a three layered structure.

- Anterior border layer
- Stroma
- Epithelium

The anterior border layer

This layer forms the anterior surface of the iris and consists of two types of cell; fibroblasts and melanocytes. Both of these are stellate cells, but the melanocytes contain granules of the pigment melanin. If the proportion of melanocytes is high, the anterior surface takes on the velvety appearance common to brown irides. The pigment cells are absent at the crypts, while projections of cells into the anterior chamber close to its angle form iris processes.

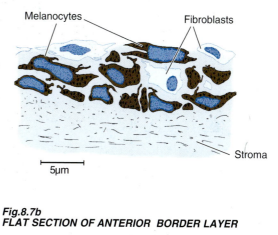

Fig.8.7a
TRANSVERSE SECTION OF ANTERIOR BORDER LAYER

Melanocytes   Fibroblasts

Stroma

5µm

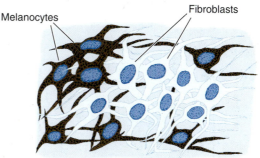

Fig.8.7b
FLAT SECTION OF ANTERIOR BORDER LAYER

Melanocytes   Fibroblasts

The stroma

The iris stroma is composed of collagenous connective tissue containing fibroblasts and pigment cells. The stroma also contains the iris vessels and a ring of smooth muscle fibres at the pupil margin, the iris sphincter pupillae muscle. The bulk of the collagen is radially orientated, forming columns which enclose the blood vessels and nerve fibres. This is best examined in the blue iris where the sinuous, but generally radial course of the vessels can be easily seen. The pigment cells of the stroma are melanocytes, which are found principally around blood vessels, and clump cells, which are more spherical, resembling macrophages that have ingested pigment granules.

The sphincter pupillae muscle is a band of smooth muscle 0.75-1mm wide, 0.1mm thick, running parallel to the pupil margin. The muscle is supported by a dense bed of collagen which separates it from the posterior epithelial layers. The cells forming the sphincter are grouped together with gap junctions uniting them. Since these cells are innervated by axons peripheral to them, the gap junctions are used to spread the depolarization directly between the other cells in the group. The amount of contraction of the sphincter is noteworthy, for the circumference of the whole muscle can be reduced to around 15% of its original length in extreme miosis.

Fig.8.8 SECTION THROUGH PUPILLARY REGION

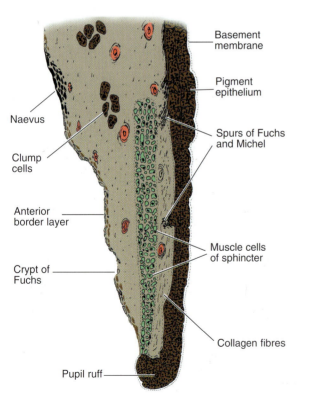

Basement membrane

Pigment epithelium

Spurs of Fuchs and Michel

Naevus

Clump cells

Anterior border layer

Muscle cells of sphincter

Crypt of Fuchs

Collagen fibres

Pupil ruff

Fig.8.9 SECTION THROUGH IRIS
showing sphincter muscle

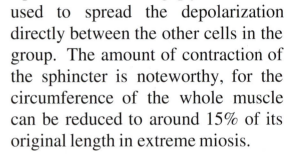

Ciliary body

Trabecular meshwork

Sphincter muscle

Collarette

Iris root

The epithelium

The double layer of epithelium that lies behind the stroma also extends around the pupil margin to appear as the pigmented pupil ruff, visible anteriorly. From the margin of the pupil to the peripheral edge of the iris sphincter, both layers of cells are deeply pigmented, but peripheral to the sphincter, the most anterior of these layers carries contractile processes. These processes are radially directed and form the dilatator pupillae muscle. The processes are up to 70μm long, and are linked by gap junctions in a similar way to the cells of the sphincter muscle. The processes contract to produce mydriasis drawing the collarette outwards towards the iris root. The spurs of Fuchs and Michel (see Fig.8.8) are epithelial projections which link this layer with the periphery of the iris sphincter. The anterior epithelial cells are about 15μm high with the processes basally and with the apical part of the cell containing the nucleus and pigment granules. The posterior epithelial cells which form the posterior pigment epithelium are about 35-50μm high. They are densely packed with melanin and therefore absorb light preventing it from passing through the iris. The cells are linked to each other and to the anterior cells by

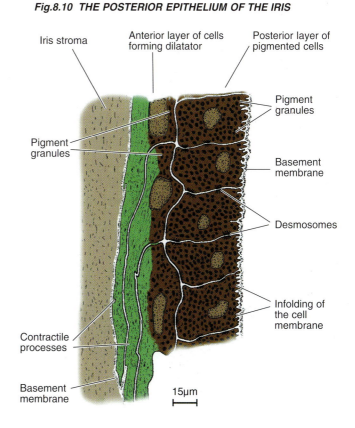

Fig.8.10 THE POSTERIOR EPITHELIUM OF THE IRIS

Iris stroma

Anterior layer of cells forming dilatator

Posterior layer of pigmented cells

Pigment granules

Pigment granules

Basement membrane

Desmosomes

Infolding of the cell membrane

Contractile processes

Basement membrane

15μm

desmosomes, while the free surface shows marked infolding and is covered by a basement membrane.

The whole posterior surface of the iris appears black and is marked by circular furrows and ridged by the radial contraction and structural folds of Schwalbe.

BLOOD SUPPLY

Blood vessels running radially through the iris have a spiral course to enable adequate movement during mydriasis and miosis. The walls of the vessels are surrounded by dense columns of collagen fibrils separated from the endothelium by a looser collagen layer. The arteries have no elastic lamina and only longitudinal muscle cells while the veins have fewer muscle fibres. The arteries are derived from the major arterial circle situated in the ciliary body, and run radially through the iris to anastomose in the minor iridic circle at the level of the collarette. From here capillary loops pass towards the pupil margin. Venous drainage follows approximately the same path back to the ciliary plexus and thence to the anterior ciliary veins or vortex veins. In addition to supplying the tissues of the iris, these blood vessels also serve as a route of exchange for the

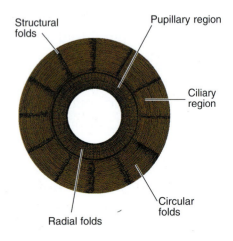

Fig. 8.11 POSTERIOR ASPECT OF THE IRIS

Structural folds
Pupillary region
Ciliary region
Circular folds
Radial folds

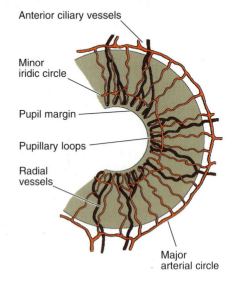

Fig.8.12 BLOOD VESSELS OF THE IRIS

Anterior ciliary vessels
Minor iridic circle
Pupil margin
Pupillary loops
Radial vessels
Major arterial circle

metabolites and waste products of the aqueous humour. In the foetus, a vascular membrane covers the pupil (see page 376 and Fig.18.23), and remnants of this pupillary membrane can sometimes be found in the adult eye.

NERVE SUPPLY

The sensory supply for the iris is formed by nerve fibres that join the long or short ciliary nerves en route to the nasociliary branch of the ophthalmic division of the trigeminal nerve.

The iris receives both sympathetic and parasympathetic autonomic motor nerves. Nerve terminals related to both divisions of the autonomic system have been found close to the muscle cells of both the sphincter and the dilatator. However, the sphincter is considered to have principally parasympathetic innervation and this is derived from the parasympathetic root of the oculomotor (third cranial) nerve whose fibres synapse with cells in the ciliary ganglion. Stimulation of the midbrain parasympathetic system brings about miosis.

The dilatator has mainly sympathetic innervation and this originates in cells situated in the superior cervical ganglion. Stimulation of the sympathetic system causes mydriasis. The nerve pathways for the reflexes involving pupillary changes are described in Chapter 17.

Fig.8.13 PUPIL SIZE
The iris is cut away to show the change in thickness

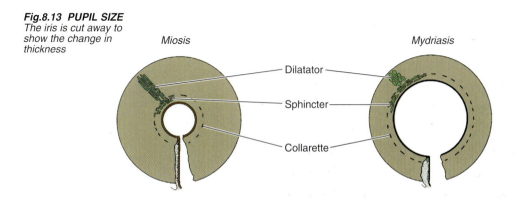

THE CILIARY BODY

The ciliary body is an annular structure that appears triangular or wedge shaped in radial section and extends from the scleral spur to the ora serrata. The scleral spur, which marks the anterior border of the ciliary body, is about 1.5mm from the limbus. The posterior boundary at the ora serrata lies about 7.5mm behind the limbus on the temporal side of the globe, and 6.5mm posterior to the limbus on the nasal side, so that the anterior-posterior length of the ciliary body varies between 5mm and 6mm.

The outer surface of the ciliary body, the supraciliaris, lines the sclera from the scleral spur to the choroid, with which it blends posteriorly. Its inner border fills the angle between the iris and the cornea at the edge of the anterior chamber. Moving back from the iris root, the inner surface of the ciliary body is formed into a number of ridges, the pars plicata which occupies about 2mm of the length of the ciliary body. Beyond the pars

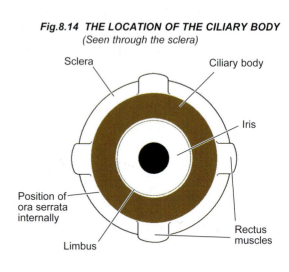

Fig.8.14 THE LOCATION OF THE CILIARY BODY
(Seen through the sclera)

Sclera — Ciliary body — Iris — Position of ora serrata internally — Limbus — Rectus muscles

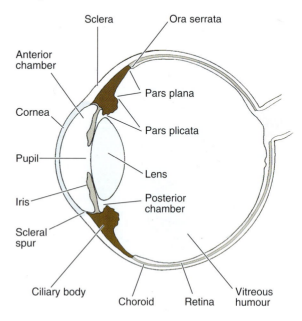

Fig.8.15 SECTION THROUGH GLOBE

Sclera — Ora serrata — Anterior chamber — Pars plana — Cornea — Pars plicata — Pupil — Lens — Iris — Posterior chamber — Scleral spur — Ciliary body — Choroid — Retina — Vitreous humour

plicata is the smoother pars plana which merges with the retina at a scalloped line, the ora serrata (Figs.8.19 and 9.3), 3mm in front of the equator of the globe. The pars plicata and the anterior part of the pars plana are bathed in aqueous humour, while the vitreous is attached to the posterior pars plana at the vitreous base (Fig.10.15).

As with the rest of the uvea, the ciliary body is a highly vascular, pigmented structure, but its special functions are found in its involvement in accommodation, and in the production of aqueous and vitreous constituents. It contributes to the mechanism of accommodation since it contains the ciliary muscle and anchors the lens suspensory fibres. Although aqueous metabolite exchange takes place in the iris vessels, the initial source of aqueous humour is the ciliary body which also produces the acid mucopolysaccharide component of the vitreous humour.

STRUCTURE OF THE CILIARY BODY

The ciliary body may be considered as a three layered structure.

- The supraciliaris
- The stroma
- The epithelium

The supraciliaris

The supraciliaris is the zone of transition from the ciliary stroma to the sclera and is the ciliary body's equivalent of the scleral lamina fusca. It consists of strands of collagen interlaced with fibroblasts and melanocytes.

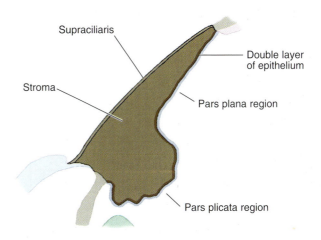

Fig.8.16 LAYERS AND REGIONS OF THE CILIARY BODY

Supraciliaris

Double layer of epithelium

Stroma

Pars plana region

Pars plicata region

Fig.8.17 THE STRUCTURE OF THE CILIARY BODY

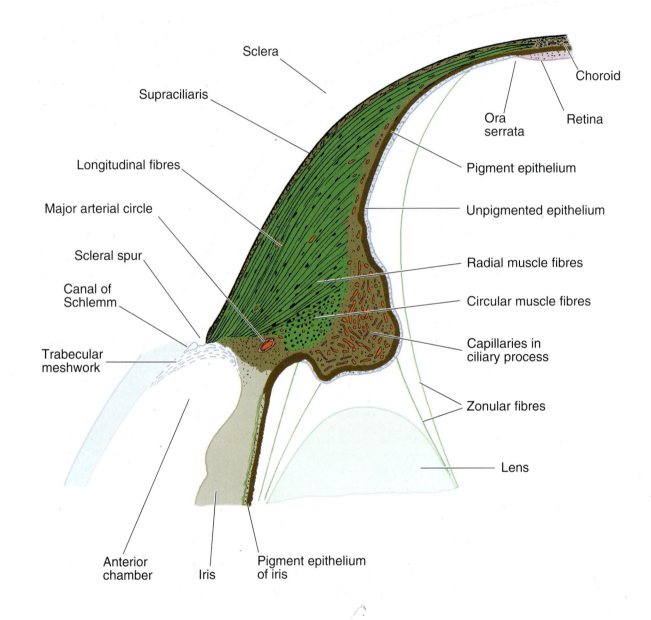

Sclera

Supraciliaris

Longitudinal fibres

Major arterial circle

Scleral spur

Canal of Schlemm

Trabecular meshwork

Choroid

Ora serrata

Retina

Pigment epithelium

Unpigmented epithelium

Radial muscle fibres

Circular muscle fibres

Capillaries in ciliary process

Zonular fibres

Lens

Anterior chamber

Iris

Pigment epithelium of iris

The stroma

The bulk of the stroma of the ciliary body is filled by the ciliary muscle that extends from the scleral spur to the choroid. The muscle is anchored to the scleral spur anteriorly and its fibres disperse posteriorly into the stroma of the choroid. The smooth muscle fibres of the ciliary muscle are considered to be divided into three groups. The longitudinal fibres (usually named after Brücke 1846) extend from the scleral spur to the choroid and run parallel to the inner surface of the sclera. The radial fibres (described by Bowman 1847 and van Reeken 1855) are also called oblique fibres. The circular fibres (claimed to have been identified by Müller 1855) have a sphincter-like orientation close to the iris root. The suggestion has been made by various histologists, and detailed by Rohen (1952) and Calasans (1953), that the ciliary muscle fibres are not in separate groups, but that the cell processes form a lattice work of V-shaped formations with the base of the V being inserted into the choroid and the limbs of the Vs being drawn out to form a T-shape in the region of the circular fibres. The net effect of contraction of this muscle is to reduce tension on the suspensory fibres of the crystalline lens and hence produce accommodation (Fig.8.18).

The metabolic requirements of the ciliary muscle are met by many thick walled blood vessels found between the bundles of muscle fibres. Light-absorbing melanocytes are found within the connective tissue surrounding these vessels.

A layer of vascular connective tissue lines the inner surface of the muscle. In addition to collagen this layer also contains some elastin remnants from the basal lamina of the choroid. This connective tissue is separated from the epithelium by a basement membrane.

The pars plicata is folded into seventy to eighty processes which greatly increases the surface area of the ciliary body. These processes are about 1mm high and 0.5mm thick and their crests lie about 0.5mm from the periphery of the crystalline lens. The stroma within the processes is packed with fenestrated capillaries, which supply constituents for the production of aqueous humour.

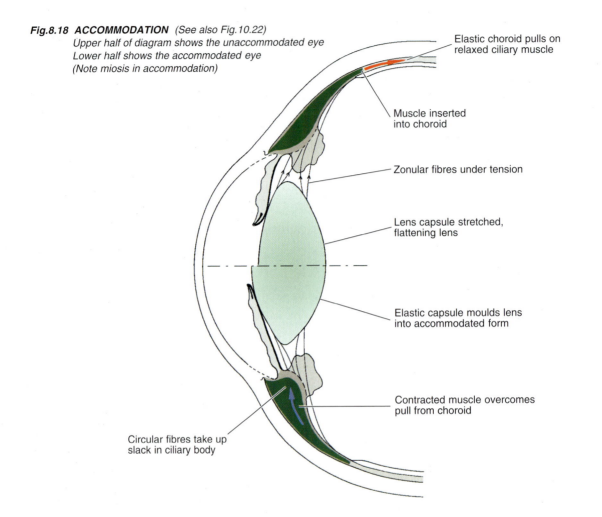

Fig.8.18 ACCOMMODATION *(See also Fig.10.22)*
Upper half of diagram shows the unaccommodated eye
Lower half shows the accommodated eye
(Note miosis in accommodation)

Elastic choroid pulls on
relaxed ciliary muscle

Muscle inserted
into choroid

Zonular fibres under tension

Lens capsule stretched,
flattening lens

Elastic capsule moulds lens
into accommodated form

Contracted muscle overcomes
pull from choroid

Circular fibres take up
slack in ciliary body

The epithelium

The epithelium of the ciliary body is a double layer of cells extending from the iris root to the retina. The deep layer consists of cuboidal pigment epithelial cells which are 15μm wide and 10μm high. The cells are firmly linked to each other and to the unpigmented cells in the superficial layer by desmosomes. The superficial cells are cuboidal in the pars plicata but become columnar in the pars plana, where they are 10μm wide and 30μm high.

The cells in the pigmented layer that lie along the crests of the processes contain fewer pigment granules which produces the radially striated appearance of the pars plicata. The overall effect of the epithelial layers is to give the ciliary body a grey appearance internally. However, pigmentation of these cells may increase with age causing the region to take on a darker coloration. The pigmented cells of the ciliary body prevent light which has passed through the sclera from reaching the retina.

The unpigmented epithelial cells modify metabolites which diffuse from the capillaries of the ciliary processes and secrete the product as aqueous into the posterior chamber. The cytoplasm of the unpigmented cells in the pars plicata therefore contains many mitochondria and stacked rough endoplasmic reticulum and the cells along the ridges of the ciliary processes contain large amounts of glycogen. The

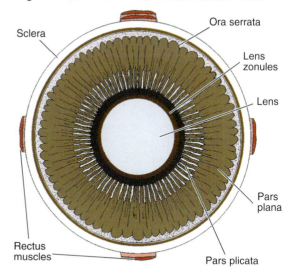

Fig.8.19 POSTERIOR VIEW OF THE CILIARY BODY

Sclera
Ora serrata
Lens zonules
Lens
Pars plana
Pars plicata
Rectus muscles

Fig.8.20
CORONAL SECTION THROUGH CILIARY PROCESSES

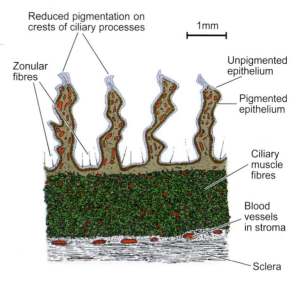

Reduced pigmentation on crests of ciliary processes
1mm
Zonular fibres
Unpigmented epithelium
Pigmented epithelium
Ciliary muscle fibres
Blood vessels in stroma
Sclera

Fig.8.21 THE EPITHELIUM OF THE CILIARY BODY

EPITHELIUM FROM PARS PLICATA

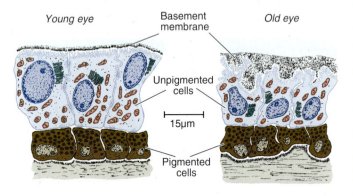

EPITHELIUM FROM PARS PLANA NEAR ORA SERRATA

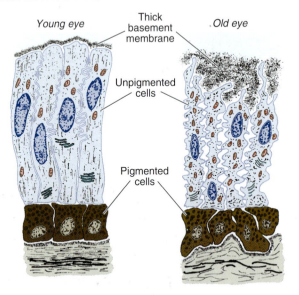

unpigmented cells of the pars plana contain large quantities of endoplasmic reticulum but fewer mitochondria. Between the apical edges of adjacent unpigmented cells, zonular occlusions appear to prevent materials passing from the surroundings into the gaps between the cells. In the pars plicata the cell membranes at the basal (free) surface of the cells shows marked infolding (see Fig.8.21).

Between the cell membranes and the aqueous anteriorly or the vitreous posteriorly lies the internal basement membrane of the ciliary body. This basement membrane thickens with age and fills the infoldings which develop in the cells.

The suspensory zonules of the crystalline lens extend from the basement membrane in the region of the pars plana and pass between the ciliary processes of the pars plicata.

BLOOD SUPPLY

The ciliary body contains the major arterial circle near its attachment to the root of the iris. This annular vessel is formed by the anastomosis of the two long posterior ciliary arteries and the four to six anterior ciliary arteries. Recurrent vessels pass from the major arterial circle to the choroid and branches supply the ciliary muscle and the extensive capillary bed in the ciliary processes. Venous drainage from the ciliary body is via the vortex veins posteriorly and, to a lesser extent, the anterior ciliary veins.

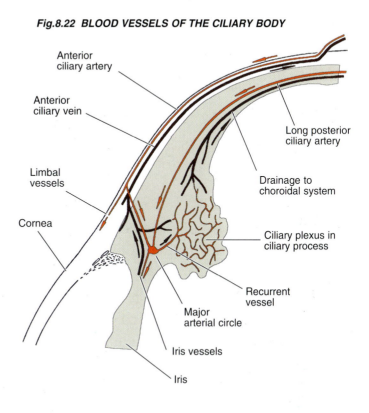

Fig.8.22 BLOOD VESSELS OF THE CILIARY BODY

Anterior ciliary artery

Anterior ciliary vein

Limbal vessels

Cornea

Long posterior ciliary artery

Drainage to choroidal system

Ciliary plexus in ciliary process

Recurrent vessel

Major arterial circle

Iris vessels

Iris

NERVE SUPPLY

In the supraciliaris and stroma are sensory neurones passing back from the anterior regions of the eye, including the ciliary body, to join the ciliary nerves. Autonomic parasympathetic nerve fibres are also found. Some of these are en route to the iris to produce miosis while others pass to the ciliary muscle to produce accommodation (see page 329). The parasympathetic fibres are postganglionic, derived from cells in the ciliary ganglion which have received preganglionic axons from the motor root of the oculomotor nerve (Fig.17.4).

Ganglion cells are frequently found in the supraciliaris of the pars plana and it is likely that these are misplaced (or ectopic) from the ciliary ganglion.

Sympathetic neurones are also present, some travelling to the iris to produce mydriasis. For those that terminate in the ciliary body, vasoconstriction may be the main role.

THE CHOROID

The choroid is a vascular pigmented layer some 0.2mm thick that lines the sclera from the ora serrata up to the edge of the optic disc.

The choroid provides a route for vessels to the anterior of the eye as well as supplying metabolites to and removing waste products from the retinal receptors. The high blood flow through the choroidal vessels may serve to regulate temperature. Pigment in the choroid absorbs light that has passed through the retina and any that might enter the eye through the sclera. The innermost layer of the choroid provides a smooth surface for the retina.

STRUCTURE OF THE CHOROID

The choroid may be considered as a structure consisting of four layers.

- Suprachoroid
- Stroma
- Choriocapillaris
- Basal lamina

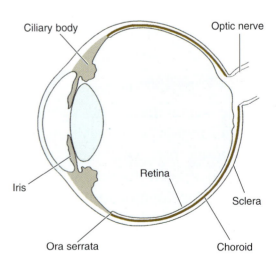

Fig.8.23 *SECTION THROUGH THE GLOBE*

Ciliary body

Optic nerve

Iris

Retina

Sclera

Ora serrata

Choroid

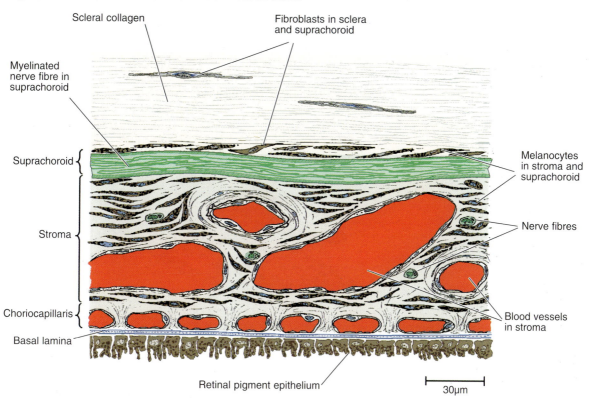

Fig.8.24 TRANSVERSE SECTION THROUGH THE CHOROID

Scleral collagen

Fibroblasts in sclera and suprachoroid

Myelinated nerve fibre in suprachoroid

Suprachoroid

Melanocytes in stroma and suprachoroid

Stroma

Nerve fibres

Choriocapillaris

Basal lamina

Blood vessels in stroma

Retinal pigment epithelium

30μm

The suprachoroid

The outer layer, the suprachoroid, is a transition zone between the choroid and sclera and is about 30μm thick. It is the choroidal equivalent of the lamina fusca of the sclera. It consists of collagen fibres continuous with those of the sclera accompanied by melanocytes and fibroblasts. Because of the loose attachment between sclera and choroid this region has been referred to as the suprachoroidal space. It is, however, only a potential space, carrying nerves and blood vessels to and from the anterior uvea. Smooth muscle cells in this layer, close to the ora serrata, form groups described as muscle stars.

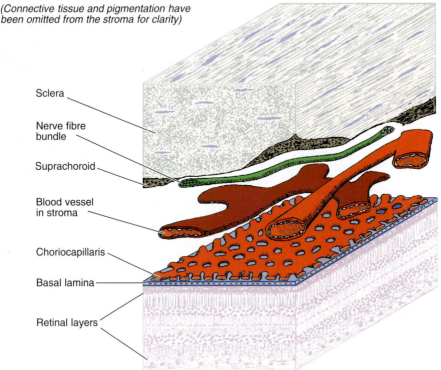

Fig.8.25 THE STRUCTURE OF THE CHOROID
(Connective tissue and pigmentation have been omitted from the stroma for clarity)

Sclera

Nerve fibre bundle

Suprachoroid

Blood vessel in stroma

Choriocapillaris

Basal lamina

Retinal layers

The stroma

The stroma is a pigmented layer which consists principally of blood vessels. Between the vessels are melanocytes and fibroblasts, with collagen and ground substance occupying the remaining space. Since the tissue is so vascular, macrophages and lymphocytes are also found. The macrophages are often filled with pigment and they have a similar appearance to the clump cells of the iris. The blood vessels in this layer are sometimes divided into an external layer of large vessels (Haller's layer) and an internal layer of smaller vessels (Sattler's layer), but such a division is difficult to justify, although the large veins of the vortex system do lie externally.

The choriocapillaris

The choriocapillaris is a single layer of short wide bore capillaries lying in a plane against the basal lamina. This arrangement is unusual as capillaries normally have a three-dimensional distribution throughout the thickness of a tissue. The capillaries have an average diameter of about 30μm which is significantly larger than those found elsewhere in the body.

Along the inner wall (i.e. the wall nearest the retina) the capillaries have regular fenestrations of about 80nm diameter. These are areas where the cell membrane on the inside surface of the capillary fuses with the membrane on the outside surface producing a barrier which, from electron micrographs, appears to be only 10nm thick. Pericytes are found along the outer wall of some capillaries, but the role of these remains uncertain.

Fine collagen fibres are present between the capillaries together with fibroblasts and unmyelinated nerve fibres, but the choriocapillaris is free of pigment.

Since there is a general reduction in the preretinal vessels in the macular/foveal region, various researchers have suggested that the choriocapillaris thickens to

Fig.8.26 THE CHORIOCAPILLARIS AND BASAL LAMINA

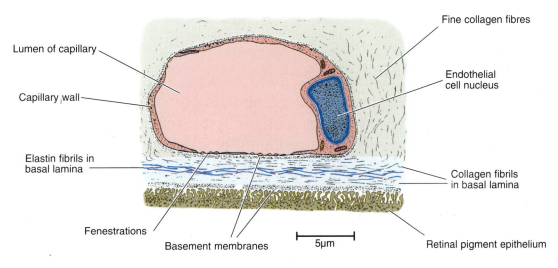

Fine collagen fibres

Lumen of capillary

Capillary wall

Endothelial cell nucleus

Elastin fibrils in basal lamina

Collagen fibrils in basal lamina

Fenestrations

Basement membranes

5μm

Retinal pigment epithelium

give an increased postretinal blood supply. However, although the meshes between the capillaries are generally narrower posteriorly, there is no increase in the diameter of the capillaries in the submacular region.

The basal lamina

The 2-4µm thick basal lamina provides a smooth surface for the pigment epithelial cells of the retina. It is a five layered structure.

- Basement membrane of the choriocapillaris
- Collagen
- Elastin
- Collagen
- Basement membrane of the retinal pigment epithelium.

The basal lamina is attached to the choroidal stroma by collagen fibres that pass between the capillaries of the choriocapillaris.

With ageing, the basal lamina may become thickened, forming mounds called drusen. These contain granular material, possibly secreted by the retinal pigment epithelial cells.

BLOOD SUPPLY

The choroid receives arterial blood from branches of the circle of Haller-Zinn which is formed by the anastomosis of the short posterior ciliary arteries and via recurrent arteries from the major arterial circle. These branches pass into the choroid and there is a sudden transition to the capillary layer without the usual graduation of vessel size. The capillaries return blood to the venous system, again with a rapid change in size. The veins converge in the posterior half of the globe to form the four vortex (or vorticose) veins. These pass obliquely through the sclera along 4-5mm canals and emerge about 7mm behind the equator, one vein appearing in each posterior quadrant of the globe. The vortex veins finally drain into the superior and inferior ophthalmic veins.

The rate of blood flow through the choroid is very high and venous pressure is likely to be above 20mmHg to prevent compression of the veins by the intraocular pressure.

Fig.8.27 THE VASCULAR SYSTEM OF THE CHOROID
Upper half of diagram shows the arterial supply and the lower half shows the venous drainage

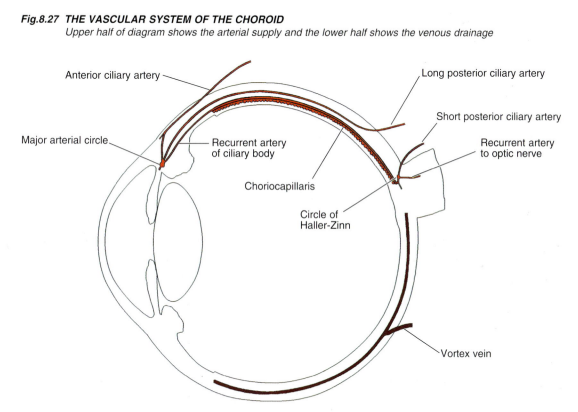

NERVE SUPPLY

Nerve fibres passing to and from the anterior of the eye are found in the suprachoroid. The nerves that terminate in the choroid are generally derived from the short posterior ciliary nerves. Stimulation of the sympathetic supply produces marked vasoconstriction with a consequent reduction in choroidal blood flow.

Chapter 9

THE RETINA

The function of the retina is to convert the information contained in the retinal image into neural signals, and to process these signals for transmission in the visual pathway. The retina is a delicate complex structure which contains the light sensitive receptors of the eye. It lines the choroid, extending from the ora serrata to the optic nerve head, and is supported internally by the vitreous humour.

The cells of the retina are derived from the same embryological source as the two layers of epithelium lining the ciliary body and the posterior layers of the iris (Figs. 9.2, 18.19 and 18.20). At the ora serrata, the common origin of these cells is shown by the continuity of the outermost layer of the retina, the retinal pigment epithelium, with the pigmented epithelial layer of the ciliary body. Posterior to the ora serrata, the inner, superficial layer of unpigmented cells has differentiated to form the multilayered transparent neural retina.

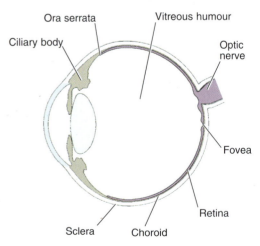

Fig.9.1 SECTION THROUGH THE GLOBE

152

Externally the pigment epithelium is attached to the basal lamina of the choroid. The neural retina is firmly attached at the ora serrata and at the optic nerve head, but elsewhere the neural layers are only held in contact with the retinal pigment epithelium by the vitreous humour.

The retina has distinct regional variations, and can be divided into a central area consisting of the macula, fovea and foveola, surrounded by the peripheral area which also contains the optic nerve head and which terminates in a 2mm wide band, the ora serrata.

The total area of the retina is approximately 1300mm². Its average thickness is about 200μm, but it thickens at the edge of the optic nerve head and within the macula, and thins at the ora serrata and the fovea. The retina is highly vascular and, when viewed in the living eye with the ophthalmoscope, the blood in its vessels gives it its characteristic orange-red appearance.

The description of the retinal histology that follows applies to the peripheral or general retina. This therefore excludes

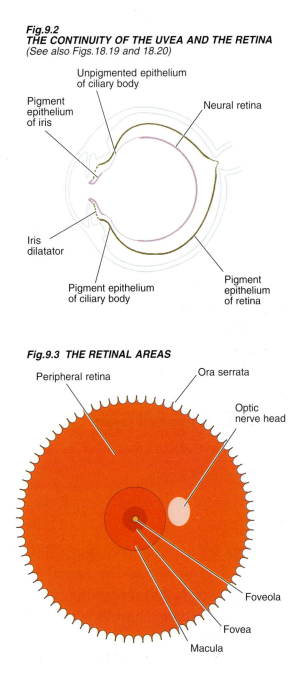

Fig.9.2
THE CONTINUITY OF THE UVEA AND THE RETINA
(See also Figs.18.19 and 18.20)

Unpigmented epithelium of ciliary body

Pigment epithelium of iris

Neural retina

Iris dilatator

Pigment epithelium of ciliary body

Pigment epithelium of retina

Fig.9.3 THE RETINAL AREAS

Peripheral retina

Ora serrata

Optic nerve head

Foveola

Fovea

Macula

the modified central areas and the regions of transition (the ora serrata and optic nerve head) which will be described separately.

STRUCTURE OF THE RETINA

Light micrographs of retinal sections show alternating layers of cell nuclei and their processes, and the alternating pattern of retinal layers is indicated by the dark and light typeface below.

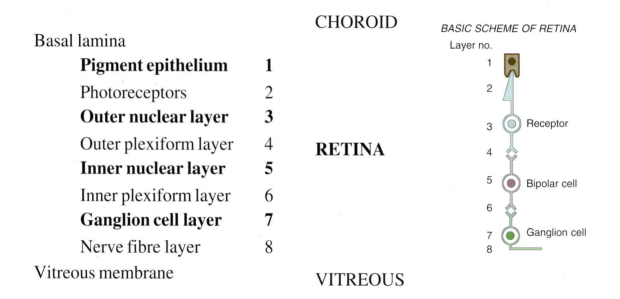

CHOROID

Basal lamina	
Pigment epithelium	**1**
Photoreceptors	2
Outer nuclear layer	**3**
Outer plexiform layer	4
Inner nuclear layer	**5**
Inner plexiform layer	6
Ganglion cell layer	**7**
Nerve fibre layer	8
Vitreous membrane	

RETINA

VITREOUS

BASIC SCHEME OF RETINA
Layer no.

1
2
3 — Receptor
4
5 — Bipolar cell
6
7 — Ganglion cell
8

Cell nuclei are found in those layers whose names are printed in **dark** type. Layers 2-8 constitute the neural retina and within these layers are also found neuroglial cells and retinal blood vessels. The basal lamina marks the junction of the retina with the choroid, while the vitreous membrane marks the junction of the retina with the vitreous.

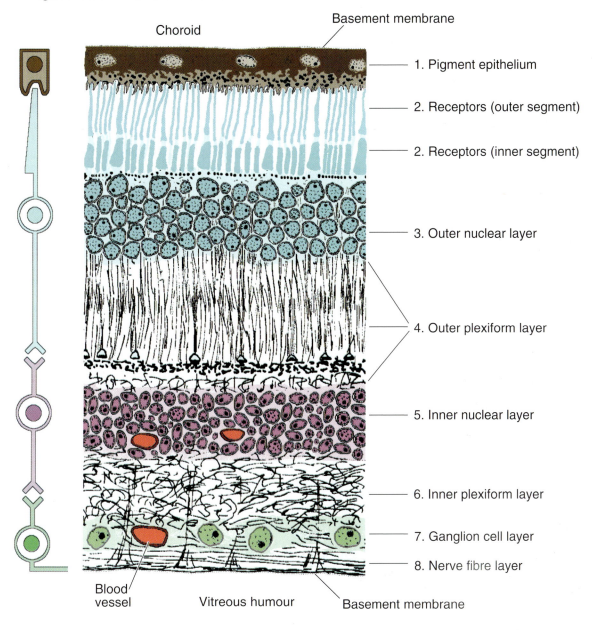

Fig.9.4 THE LAYERS OF THE RETINA

Choroid

Basement membrane

1. Pigment epithelium

2. Receptors (outer segment)

2. Receptors (inner segment)

3. Outer nuclear layer

4. Outer plexiform layer

5. Inner nuclear layer

6. Inner plexiform layer

7. Ganglion cell layer

8. Nerve fibre layer

Blood vessel

Vitreous humour

Basement membrane

155

1. Pigment epithelium

This is a single layer of cells extending from the ora serrata to the optic nerve head. The approximately cuboidal cells are 15μm high and 15μm wide. They are densely packed and appear hexagonal in flat section. The cells have an irregular basal surface covered by a basement membrane through which they are firmly attached to the basal lamina of the choroid. The cells are also firmly linked to each other, having zonular occlusions and adhesions near their apices. Gap or communication junctions are also present in these regions (see Fig.9.5).

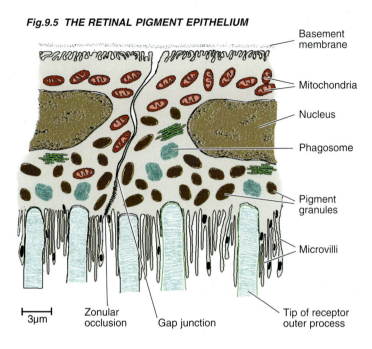

Fig.9.5 THE RETINAL PIGMENT EPITHELIUM

Basement membrane

Mitochondria

Nucleus

Phagosome

Pigment granules

Microvilli

Tip of receptor outer process

3μm

Zonular occlusion

Gap junction

The apical surface of the cell is formed into microvilli, about 7μm long, which surround the tips of the receptor outer processes. The cell body contains large amounts of endoplasmic reticulum and mitochondria, and is packed with melanin granules. Membrane-bound inclusions called phagosomes, containing debris from the receptors, are found and the pigment lipofuscin is present. Lipofuscin is also found in ageing neurones but in the retinal pigment epithelium is assumed to come from the receptor processes.

The functions of the pigment epithelium cells are to absorb stray light, to provide a pathway for metabolites to the receptors from the choriocapillaris, and to remove exhausted material shed from the receptors. The cells also give mechanical stability to the tips of the rods and cones.

2. The photoreceptor (rod and cone, bacillary) layer

The photoreceptor layer contains the photosensitive part of the rods and cones. The cell bodies and inner processes of the rods and cones are found in the outer nuclear and outer plexiform layers.

The outer segment of the cell is joined by a cilium to an inner segment which in turn is linked to the cell body by the cell's outer fibre. The cell body has a second process or inner fibre which terminates in the outer plexiform layer (see Figs.9.15 and 9.17).

In both types of receptor the outer segments are cylindrical. However, the inner segment of a cone is about three times the diameter of that of a rod and tapers to meet the outer segment. It is the outer segment that carries the visual photopigment in both types of receptor.

Fig.9.6 THE PHOTORECEPTORS

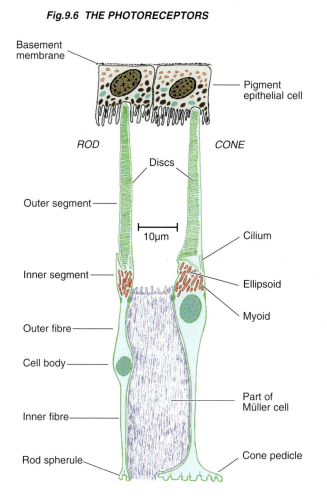

Basement membrane

Pigment epithelial cell

ROD

CONE

Discs

Outer segment

10μm

Cilium

Inner segment

Ellipsoid

Myoid

Outer fibre

Cell body

Part of Müller cell

Inner fibre

Rod spherule

Cone pedicle

Fig.9.7 PART OF A ROD OUTER SEGMENT
(cut away to show discs)

157

2.1 Outer segments and visual photopigments

Electron microscopy shows the outer segments to contain approximately 1000 disc-like sacs. In rods, these discs lie freely stacked within the outer segment (Fig.9.7). However, in cones they appear to be formed by the infolding of the cell membrane of the outer segment. Radio-active tracer studies have shown that renewal of the discs occurs at a steady rate at the basal end of the outer segment of the rods. The discs are shed into the pigment epithelium in groups of between eight and thirty (Young 1971) and here they are absorbed by the phagosomes.

The disc membranes incorporate the visual photopigments which react in light to produce depolarization of the receptor membrane. The receptor photopigments have been extensively studied since Müller (1851) noted that the outer segments in the frog retina had a reddish colour and the observation by Boll (1876) that the colour faded in light. Because of the loss of colour by the photopigments, they are said to bleach in the presence of light. Kuhne (1878), also using frog retina, isolated a pigment which he called sehpurpur or rhodopsin.

Vitamin A (retinol) was found to be present in rhodopsin by Wald (1933) following work by Tansley (1931). Wald also isolated a breakdown product of the visual pigment which is now known as retinal. Retinal has two isomers which means that it has two forms with identical chemical components, but which have different arrangements of their molecules (Fig.9.8). Rhodopsin consists of the protein opsin locked to the 11-cis form of retinal. Breakdown of rhodopsin is initiated by photon absorption which converts the 11-cis retinal to the all-trans form, freeing it from the opsin molecule (Fig.9.9). In darkness, the all-trans retinal is converted by enzyme action to 11-cis retinal which is recombined with opsin to form rhodopsin. Some all-trans retinal is broken down to retinol and this is held in the pigment epithelium. This is converted to 11-cis retinal during dark adaptation and then returned to the receptors. Kuhne found that contact between the receptors and the pigment epithelium was required for the regeneration of the visual pigment.

Fig.9.8 THE CHEMICAL STRUCTURE OF RETINAL

All-trans Retinal

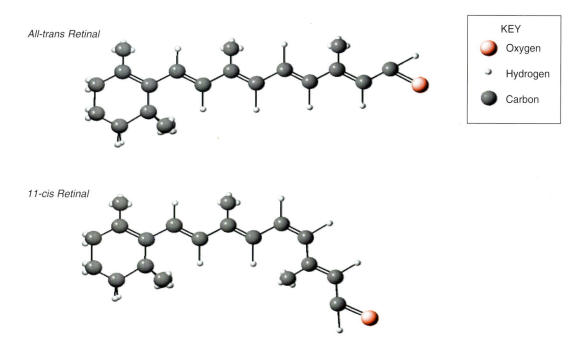

KEY
- Oxygen
- Hydrogen
- Carbon

11-cis Retinal

Fig.9.9 THE RHODOPSIN RETINAL CYCLE

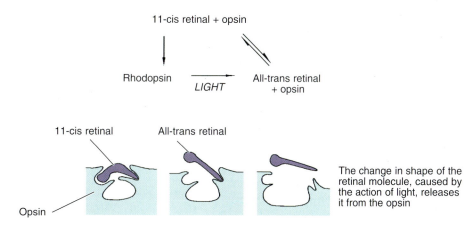

11-cis retinal + opsin

Rhodopsin → All-trans retinal + opsin
LIGHT

11-cis retinal   All-trans retinal

Opsin

The change in shape of the retinal molecule, caused by the action of light, releases it from the opsin

159

The close correlation between the absorption spectrum of rhodopsin and the absorption spectra found for isolated human rods supports the view that rhodopsin is the visual pigment contained in human rods (Fig.9.10). Both have a maximum at about 500nm and the involvement of rods in scotopic (dark adapted) vision is evidenced by the scotopic sensitivity curve also having its maximum located at this wavelength (Fig.9.32).

Cones not only have a different shape from rods but also differ in their photo-pigment. They are classified according to the wavelength at which they show maximum response and there appear to be three main groups. Those with maximum sensitivity in the range 560-570nm are red cones, those with a maximum sensitivity at 530-540nm are green and those with a maximum between 420nm and 440nm are blue cones.

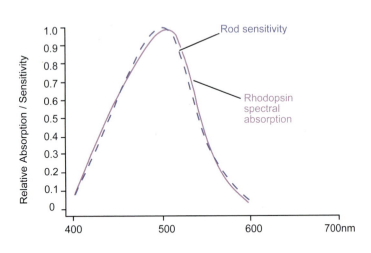

Fig.9.10 COMPARISON OF ROD SENSITIVITY WITH RHODOPSIN SPECTRAL ABSORPTION

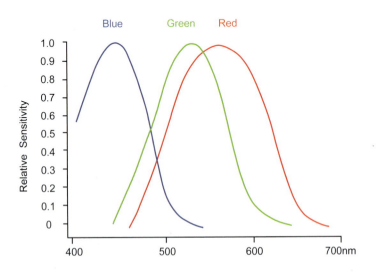

Fig.9.11
ABSORPTION SPECTRA FOR THE THREE CLASSES OF CONES

Since these cones all have the same microscopic appearance, the difference in response may lie in the nature of the cone photopigments, or in the way the pigment is bound to the disc membrane.

2.2 Inner segments

Fig.9.12 FLAT SECTION THROUGH THE RECEPTOR INNER SEGMENTS

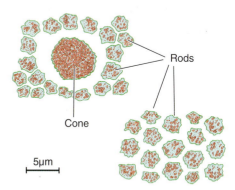

The inner segments are composed of an outer ellipsoid and an inner myoid (Fig.9.6). The receptors are derived from primitive ciliated ependymal cells and the outer segment is joined to the inner segment at the ellipsoid by a cilium. The cilium has nine pairs of tubules, but lacks the usual central elements of mobile cilia. The ellipsoid contains mitochondria and, by comparison with those of rods, the ellipsoids of peripheral cones are vastly distended, containing a greater number of mitochondria. The myoid, which in some species is contractile, contains endoplasmic reticulum, Golgi apparatus and free ribosomes.

Close to the ellipsoid, the outer segments of rods and cones have a diameter of 1.5μm, while the inner segments are about 2μm in diameter in rods and about 5μm in cones. The total length of the outer and inner segments of both rods and cones is approximately 60μm but, towards the periphery of the retina, the segments become progressively shorter.

There are approximately 110-125 million rods and 6.3-6.8 million cones in the retina (Østerberg 1935). Their relative distribution across the retina is shown in Fig.9.13.

In addition to the support provided by the apices of the pigment epithelial cells, the receptor processes are supported by the mucopolysaccharide ground substance that fills all the extracellular space in the photoreceptor layer.

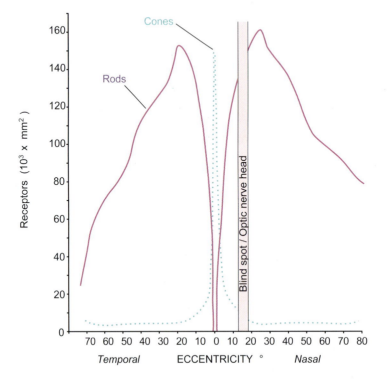

Fig.9.13 DISTRIBUTION OF RODS AND CONES ACROSS THE RETINA

Receptors (10³ × mm²)

Cones

Rods

Blind spot / Optic nerve head

70 60 50 40 30 20 10 0 10 20 30 40 50 60 70 80

Temporal　　ECCENTRICITY °　　*Nasal*

3. Outer nuclear layer

The outer nuclear layer is readily identified microscopically by the several rows of cell nuclei that it contains. In the periphery it is about 30μm thick and consists of three or four layers of rod nuclei together with a single layer of cone nuclei. Since the cones have virtually no outer fibre their nuclei lie close to their inner segment and are found in the outer part of this layer. The long outer fibres of the rods pass between the cell bodies of the cones to reach rod nuclei which are generally located closer to the outer plexiform layer.

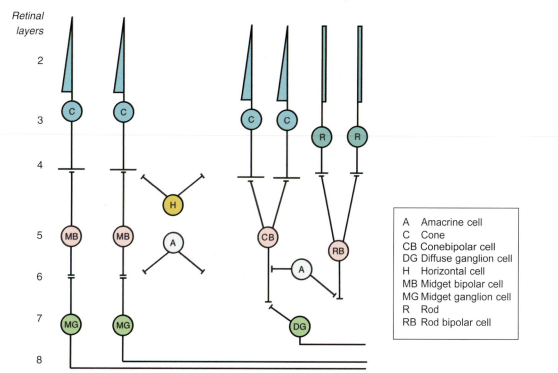

Fig.9.14   GENERAL SCHEME OF NEURONES IN THE RETINA *(See also Figs. 9.15, 9.17, 9.18)*
Horizontal and amacrine cell synapses have been omitted for clarity

Retinal layers

A   Amacrine cell
C   Cone
CB Conebipolar cell
DG Diffuse ganglion cell
H   Horizontal cell
MB Midget bipolar cell
MG Midget ganglion cell
R   Rod
RB Rod bipolar cell

4. Outer plexiform layer

This layer of processes and synapses lies between the nuclei of the receptors and the nuclei of the cells of the inner nuclear layer. It can be subdivided into an outer zone containing the inner fibres of the rods and cones, a middle zone in which the synapses occur and an inner zone which has a plexiform or network appearance produced by the branching processes of horizontal cells and the various types of bipolar cells of the next (inner nuclear) layer.

This layer has a thickness of about 40μm just outside the macula and thins rapidly towards the periphery.

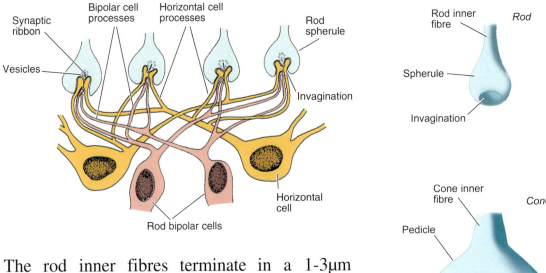

Fig.9.15 ROD CONNECTIONS IN OUTER PLEXIFORM LAYER

Synaptic ribbon

Bipolar cell processes

Horizontal cell processes

Rod spherule

Vesicles

Invagination

Horizontal cell

Rod bipolar cells

Fig.9.16 RECEPTOR TERMINATIONS

Rod inner fibre

Rod

Spherule

Invagination

Cone inner fibre

Cone

Pedicle

Invaginations

The rod inner fibres terminate in a 1-3μm diameter spherule with an invagination (pocket) formed by the infolding of the cell membrane. Into this fit the processes of the rod bipolar cells which connect the rods to the ganglion cells. Also present are the axon processes of the horizontal cells which form connections across the retina with other rod spherules. Within the spherule, opposite the junction of incoming pairs of horizontal cell processes, is found a dense structure surrounded by vesicles called a synaptic ribbon.

The terminations of the cones, called pedicles, are flattened hemispheres about 5-8μm wide having up to twenty-five invaginations in the base. Only three processes enter these forming a triad. A dendrite of an invaginating midget bipolar cell forms the central process of the triad. The outer pair of processes of each triad are derived from horizontal cell dendrites and, as in the rod spherule, synaptic ribbon complexes are found at the junction of these processes. In the fovea the cones have fewer invaginations and the central process in these is

164

derived from a single invaginating midget bipolar cell. The surface of the pedicle receives dendrites from flat midget and flat diffuse bipolars. The midget bipolars contact a single pedicle while the diffuse type may contact the surface of six or more pedicles. Cone pedicles sometimes receive processes from adjacent cones and sometimes send processes to contact the surface of a rod spherule.

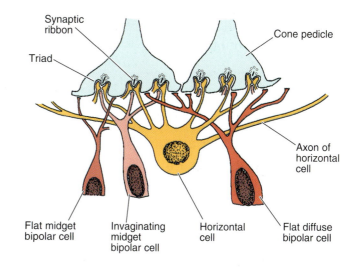

Fig.9.17 CONE CONNECTIONS IN THE OUTER PLEXIFORM LAYER

Synaptic ribbon

Triad

Cone pedicle

Axon of horizontal cell

Flat midget bipolar cell

Invaginating midget bipolar cell

Horizontal cell

Flat diffuse bipolar cell

The horizontal cells have clusters of short dendrites, forming the outer processes of the cone triads, and an axon that synapses in the rod invaginations. Rodieck (1973) has suggested that each rod is probably in contact with up to five rod bipolar cells and two horizontal cells, while each cone is in contact with one invaginating midget bipolar, one flat midget bipolar, three flat diffuse bipolars and about four horizontal cells. However, the spread of interconnections across the retina increases away from the fovea with a corresponding decrease in visual acuity.

5. Inner nuclear layer

This layer contains the nuclei of the horizontal cells, the various types of bipolar cells, the amacrine cells and also the neuroglial Müller cells. It is about half the thickness of the outer nuclear layer and thins slightly towards the periphery of the retina. As described above, the horizontal cells communicate across the retina between cone and rod terminations, and the bipolar cells communicate through the retina between the receptor terminations and the ganglion cells. The amacrine cells also communicate across the retina but at the level of the ganglion cell and inner plexiform layers.

6. Inner plexiform layer

This layer is formed by the processes and synapses of the bipolar, amacrine and ganglion cells, and appears plexiform throughout its thickness (unlike the outer plexiform layer, see Fig.9.4). The amacrine cells form horizontal connections between bipolar, ganglion cells and other amacrines. There are two main groups of amacrine cells; diffuse which cover an area up to 30μm across, and stratified which may extend for up to 1mm and which potentially contact thousands of other cells.

Dowling and Boycott (1966) found that the axon terminal of bipolar cells contained a synaptic ribbon, thus enabling it to be identified from the multiplicity of other processes found in this layer. The axons of bipolar cells terminate either on amacrine or ganglion cell processes but not on other bipolar cells. These synapses are found throughout this layer, with the rod bipolars and invaginating midget bipolars terminating closer to the ganglion cell layer than the flat midget or flat diffuse bipolar cells whose terminations are found nearer to the inner nuclear layer.

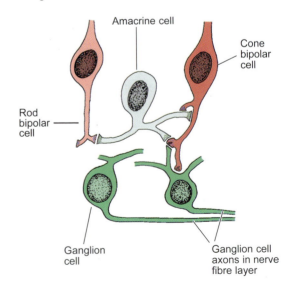

Fig.9.18 *THE INNER PLEXIFORM LAYER*

Amacrine cell

Cone bipolar cell

Rod bipolar cell

Ganglion cell

Ganglion cell axons in nerve fibre layer

7. The ganglion cell layer

The nuclei of the ganglion cells lie in a single layer throughout the peripheral retina, a feature which serves to distinguish the peripheral from the central retina where they form a layer of up to 10 cell nuclei in thickness. There are approximately one million ganglion cells in the human retina and Boycott and Dowling (1969) classified these as follows. Midget ganglion cells have processes that pass into the inner plexiform layer to synapse with individual midget or flat midget bipolar cells at the different levels previously mentioned. Diffuse ganglion cells have dendrites that spread up to 60µm both vertically and horizontally, while stratified ganglion cells may be the unistratified type with a spread of 200µm or the more bushy diffuse stratified type with a spread of 70µm.

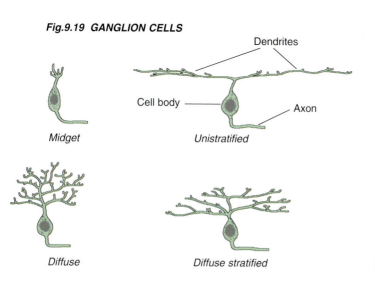

Fig.9.19 *GANGLION CELLS*

Dendrites

Cell body

Axon

Midget

Unistratified

Diffuse

Diffuse stratified

8. The nerve fibre layer

This layer consists of the axons of the ganglion cells which run across the inner surface of the retina towards the optic nerve head. Those which originate on the temporal side of the retina form arcs as they pass around the central retinal area. The axons are formed into bundles and these are surrounded by the retinal neuroglial cells, although within the bundles the individual axons may not be isolated from one another by glial tissue. The path of the various bundles of axons in the nerve fibre layer is shown in Fig.9.20.

The temporal retinal raphé is the division between those ganglion cells whose axons reach the optic nerve head by passing above the central retinal area, and those whose axons pass inferiorly. The papillomacular bundle consists of axons passing to the optic nerve head from the central retinal area. At the optic nerve head, the axons pass through the lamina cribrosa of the sclera and acquire a myelin sheath.

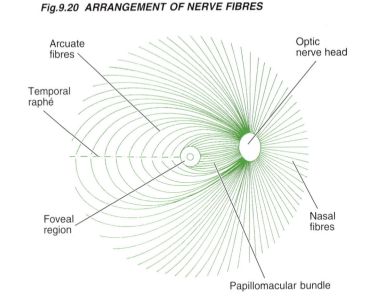

Fig.9.20 ARRANGEMENT OF NERVE FIBRES

Arcuate fibres

Temporal raphé

Foveal region

Optic nerve head

Nasal fibres

Papillomacular bundle

NEUROGLIAL CELLS

Reference has been made to the Müller cells and these are the only neuroglial cells in the outer half of the neural retina. In the inner half are found two additional types; astrocytes and microglia.

The astrocytes of the retina are similar to those found elsewhere in the central nervous system and are either of the fibrous or protoplasmic type. In the inner plexiform layer, they are the stellate protoplasmic type of cell having a foot-like process that makes contact with the retinal

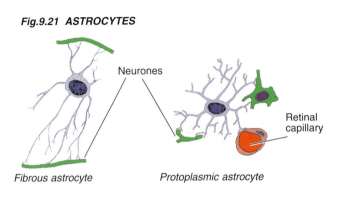

Fig.9.21 ASTROCYTES

Neurones

Retinal capillary

Fibrous astrocyte

Protoplasmic astrocyte

capillaries, while fibrous astrocytes are found in the nerve fibre layer. Some glial cells surround blood vessels and are referred to as perivascular glia. These and the footplates of the astrocytes isolate the capillaries from the neural cells. A few phagocytic microglial cells are usually identifiable by material that they have ingested, but they are not numerous in healthy tissue.

Müller cells form the bulk of the supportive space-occupying tissue of the retina. They are rich in glycogen and are therefore assumed to be nutritive as well as supportive. They fill virtually all the space between the neural elements and extend from the vitreous radially through the neural layers to terminate between the inner segments of the receptors. Here the Müller cell membrane is formed into villi which project 4-5μm into the mucopolysaccharide. The Müller cell

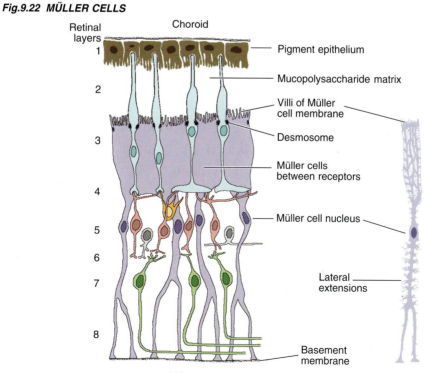

Fig.9.22 MÜLLER CELLS

Retinal layers
Choroid

1 — Pigment epithelium

2 — Mucopolysaccharide matrix

Villi of Müller cell membrane

Desmosome

3 — Müller cells between receptors

4

5 — Müller cell nucleus

6

7 — Lateral extensions

8

Basement membrane

Vitreous

membranes and the cell membrane of the receptors are linked by desmosome-like attachments at the junction of the inner segment and the outer fibre. The line of these thickened membranes, which is visible with the light microscope, has been called the 'outer limiting membrane' of the retina.

In the inner retina, lateral extensions of the Müller cells fill the spaces between the neural cells and the blood vessels. The extensions between the ganglion cell axons have their vitreal surface covered by a thick basement membrane which merges with vitreous fibrils and is generally referred to as the inner limiting membrane of the retina. The thickness of this is 0.5-2.0µm and it is continuous anteriorly with the thin basement membrane of the unpigmented epithelium of the ciliary body. In the optic nerve head it is continuous with the basement membrane of the astrocytes that line the central cup but thins to less than 0.1µm.

A ten-layered structure for the retina was suggested by Cajal (1888 et seq.) in which he described the horizontal, bipolar and amacrine cell layers separately. He did not consider the outer and inner limiting membranes as independent layers since they were actually part of the Müller cells. Later workers tried to equate the structure of the retina with that of the cerebral cortex, with the result that Cajal's original ten neural layers were reduced in number, and the membranes were elevated to 'layer' status. This was reinforced by Wolff who saw the 'outer limiting membrane' as a discrete 'wire netting' layer. In spite of the explanation given by electron microscopists of the true nature of this 'membrane', the term and the significance attached to it, has become firmly established in many texts.

Additional layers have also been proposed. Fortin (1925) described the synapses in the outer plexiform layer as a 'new' structure and Fine and Zimmerman (1962) have described a 'middle limiting membrane' in this same region.

RETINAL SPECIAL AREAS

The special areas of the retina are the regions where the basic peripheral structure, described above, undergoes modification. Modification occurs in three areas.

- In the region surrounding the visual axis, the central retina, where the retina is organised to provide the highest acuity
- At the ora serrata where there is a transition from the peripheral retina to the ciliary epithelium
- At the optic nerve head where the axons of the nerve fibre layer pass through the outer layers of the retina to reach the optic nerve

THE CENTRAL RETINA

The central retina is a region of concentric zones (Fig.9.23), commencing at the edge of the histological macula which coincides with the outer edge of the region also referred to as the perifovea. The histological macula (or area centralis, Müller 1852) is the region within which the ganglion cell layer increases to more than the one cell thickness that it has in the peripheral retina.

Within the histological macula, the neural retina thickens and then thins to form a pit or fovea, and in the centre of this, some of the retinal layers are displaced forming a further small pit, the foveola.

Moving inwards from the edge of the macula across the perifovea, the number of layers of the nuclei in the ganglion cell layer increases from one to four. The 2.5mm diameter zone in which the number of layers is at the maximum is the parafovea, and, at 1.5mm diameter, the thickness of the layers starts to decrease, forming the clivus or sloping inner wall of the foveal pit. This flattens to give a floor some 0.4mm wide and within this lies the 0.35mm wide foveola. In this there is a complete absence of rods while the cones become longer and more cylindrical. The diameter of the cone inner segment decreases to about 1.5μm and

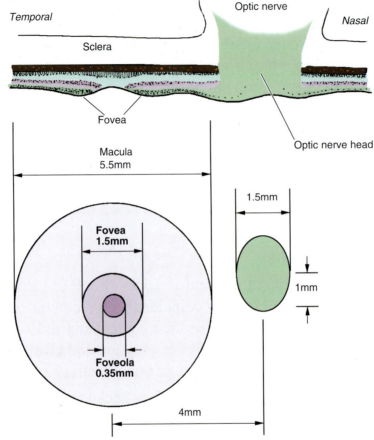

Fig.9.23 THE CENTRAL RETINA

Temporal

Optic nerve

Nasal

Sclera

Fovea

Optic nerve head

Macula
5.5mm

Fovea
1.5mm

1.5mm

1mm

Foveola
0.35mm

4mm

that of the outer segment to 1µm, while the combined segment length increases to 80µm. This increase in length produces an anterior bow to the outer nuclear layer and hence also to the 'outer limiting membrane'.

In the parafoveal region, the retina increases in thickness due to the centrifugal displacement of the inner layers. This displacement of the cell bodies provides a central region of receptors to which light has more direct access, with only the receptor nuclei and their inner fibres between the vitreous and the bacillary layer. The inner fibres bend acutely after leaving the cone nuclei and run parallel to the

172

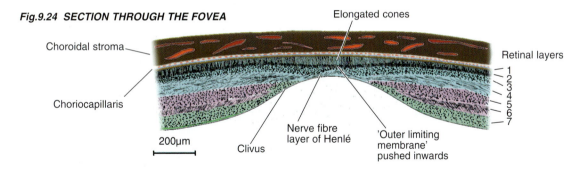

Fig.9.24 SECTION THROUGH THE FOVEA

Choroidal stroma

Elongated cones

Retinal layers
1
2
3
4
5
6
7

Choriocapillaris

200µm

Clivus

Nerve fibre
layer of Henlé

'Outer limiting
membrane'
pushed inwards

vitreous surface before turning anteriorly to synapse with the bipolars of the inner nuclear layer. These oblique fibres form the nerve fibre layer of Henlé and gradually become orientated perpendicular to the surface of the retina as the edge of the central area is approached. In view of the high acuity achieved by the foveolar region, it is assumed that there is a one-to-one ratio between cones, midget bipolar cells and midget ganglion cells in this region. Müller cells are found throughout this area but capillaries are not found closer than 0.25mm to the foveola, making this region of the neural retina avascular. In the centre of the visual field there is a blue scotoma subtending 20', resulting from a region in the centre of the foveola about 100µm wide that lacks blue sensitive cones.

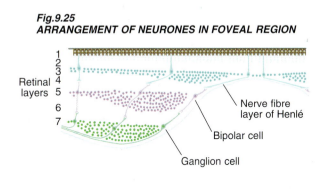

Fig.9.25
ARRANGEMENT OF NEURONES IN FOVEAL REGION

Retinal
layers
1
2
3
4
5
6
7

Nerve fibre
layer of Henlé

Bipolar cell

Ganglion cell

In red-free illumination, the region in and around the fovea has a yellow appearance, and was described by Buzzi (1782) as the macula lutea. This area contains the pigment lutein which absorbs short wavelength blue light and is also dichroic, producing the Haidinger brush phenomenon in which a propeller-shaped pattern, centred on the fixation point, is seen if a uniform blue field is observed through a rotating polarising filter.

Fig.9.26 SECTION THROUGH THE ORA SERRATA

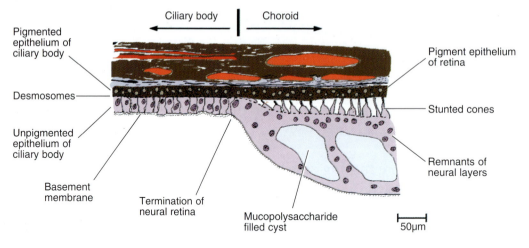

Ciliary body — Choroid

Pigmented epithelium of ciliary body

Pigment epithelium of retina

Desmosomes

Stunted cones

Unpigmented epithelium of ciliary body

Remnants of neural layers

Basement membrane

Termination of neural retina

Mucopolysaccharide filled cyst

50µm

THE ORA SERRATA

Outside the central retina, the cone population decreases while the ratio of rods to cones increases. The ganglion cell population is also reduced producing gaps between neighbouring cells. Close to the ora serrata, the rods terminate and are replaced with short cones which become progressively more stunted, eventually losing all vestiges of an outer segment and with the inner segment reduced to a 2-3µm stump.

The ora serrata takes its name from the serrated appearance of the junction between the retina and the ciliary body when seen with the naked eye (see Fig.9.3). The retina projects forward as a series of several hundred spikes (teeth or dentate processes) into the pars plana area with curved bays between the spikes. This serrated zone is up to 2mm wide with the greatest width being on the temporal side of the globe. It lies about 7mm from the limbus on the nasal side and about 8mm from the temporal side. There is a rapid reduction in the number of neural layers until, at the anterior edge of the sensory retina, they are transformed into the single layer of unpigmented epithelium of the ciliary body.

174

The pigmented and unpigmented epithelial cells of the ciliary body are united by desmosomes and this union effectively forms an anterior closure to the potential space between these layers of cells. The appearance of these dense regions in the apical cell membranes gave rise to the belief of an anterior continuation of the imaginary 'outer limiting membrane' of the retina into the ciliary epithelium.

Degeneration of the retinal layers at the ora serrata increases with age and large numbers of mucopolysaccharide filled cysts may be found in this region.

THE OPTIC NERVE HEAD

The optic nerve head is an obvious landmark in ophthalmoscopy and its appearance has lead it to be called the optic disc. In the seventeenth century, physicians referred to it as the optic papilla and this term has remained in use for some pathological conditions such as papillitis and papilloedema. Because of the absence of receptors, the optic nerve head and its projection into the visual field is known as the blind spot.

The centre of the disc lies about 4mm nasally and about 1mm above the foveola (see Fig.9.23). Its horizontal width is about 1.5mm and it is slightly larger vertically. The physiological cup forms a central concavity through which pass the central retinal artery and vein. The cup may be filled with

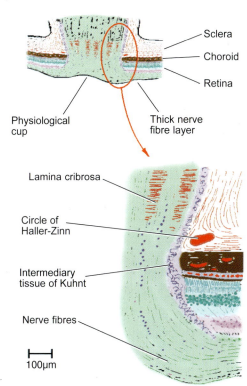

Fig.9.27 SECTION THROUGH OPTIC NERVE HEAD

Sclera

Choroid

Retina

Physiological cup

Thick nerve fibre layer

Lamina cribrosa

Circle of Haller-Zinn

Intermediary tissue of Kuhnt

Nerve fibres

100µm

astrocytes forming a connective tissue meniscus (Kuhnt 1879) surrounding the vessels, and foetal tissue remnants known as Bergmeister's papilla (1877) may be found (see page 375 and Fig.18.20).

Astrocytes support the nerve fibres at the edge of the disc and form the intermediary tissue of Kuhnt. Fibrous astrocytes also divide the axons into bundles within the disc and form the border between the fibres and the choroid. The nerve fibre bundles then pass between the collagen septa of the lamina cribrosa, whose grid-like pattern can be seen in the centre of the optic disc with the ophthalmoscope. Beyond the lamina cribrosa the axons become myelinated thus doubling the diameter of the optic nerve as it reaches the scleral foramen in the outer surface of the globe. Blood vessels derived from the scleral circle of Haller-Zinn (Haller 1754, Zinn 1755) supply this region (Fig.15.8).

The edge of the disc may be marked by various rings due to the retinal and choroidal layers terminating at different points. A scleral crescent is seen if the retina and choroid terminate away from the scleral foramen, a retinal pigment crescent if the pigment epithelium extends close to the edge of the disc, or a choroidal crescent if the retinal pigment epithelium stops short of the margin.

Fig.9.28 OPHTHALMOSCOPIC APPEARANCES OF THE OPTIC DISC

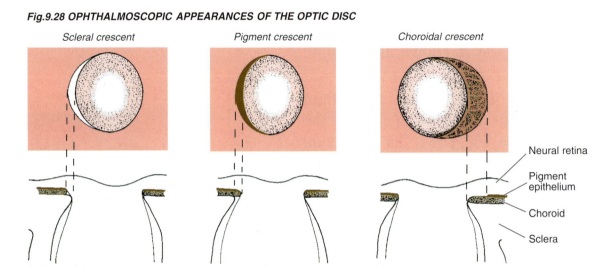

Scleral crescent   Pigment crescent   Choroidal crescent

Neural retina

Pigment epithelium

Choroid

Sclera

A SUMMARY OF THE RETINAL ORGANISATION

Layer	Periphery	Macula	Fovea	Foveola	Ora Serrata
1.Pigment epithelium	Pigment epithelial cells	Present	Present	Present	Present Cells flatter
2.Receptors	Rods & cones	Present	More cones than rods	Elongated cones only	Stunted cones only
3.Outer nuclear	4 layers of rod & cone nuclei	4 layers of rod & cone nuclei	5-6 layers mainly cone nuclei	Virtually no nuclei	Cone nuclei very sparse
4.Outer plexiform	Receptor inner fibres, bipolar & horizontal cell processes and synapses	Present	Processes form nerve fibre layer of Henlé	Cone inner fibres only	Layer very sparse
5.Inner nuclear	Bipolar, horizontal, amacrine & Müller cell nuclei	5-6 layers of cell nuclei	Up to 10 layers. Bipolar cells midget type	Absent	Layer very sparse
6.Inner plexiform	Bipolar, amacrine & ganglion cell processes and synapses	Present	Present	Absent	Layer very sparse
7.Ganglion cell	Single layer of nuclei only	2-10 layers of nuclei	Up to 10 layers of nuclei	Absent	Layer very sparse
8.Nerve fibre	Axons of ganglion cells	Axons of ganglion cells	Axons arc round foveola	Absent	Layer very sparse
9.Inner limiting membrane	Fusion of Müller cell & vitreous membranes	Present	Present	Present but thin	Present

RETINAL BLOOD SUPPLY

The retina has two sources of metabolites; the postretinal choriocapillaris and the preretinal vessels of the central retinal system. The pigment epithelial layer is in close proximity to the choriocapillaris and receives its metabolites from and returns waste products to that system.

The central retinal artery and vein have superior and inferior retinal branches which subdivide into nasal and temporal vessels (Fig.9.30). There is a further rapid subdivision to form arterioles and venules. These major vessels lie close to the surface of the retina, in or just below the internal limiting membrane with the arteries most frequently seen anterior to the veins. The oxygenated blood of the arteries gives them a bright orange appearance by comparison with the darker and flatter veins. The diameter of the veins is generally about one and a half times that of the arteries.

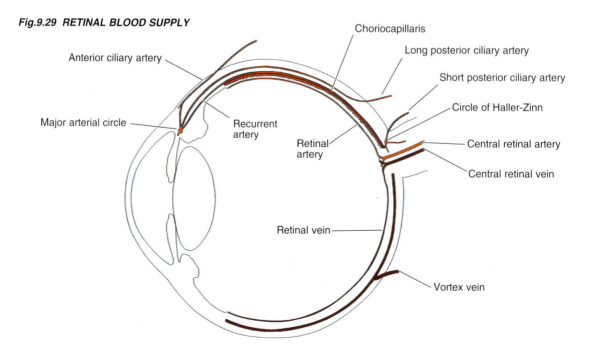

Fig.9.29 RETINAL BLOOD SUPPLY

Fig.9.30 PRERETINAL BLOOD VESSELS

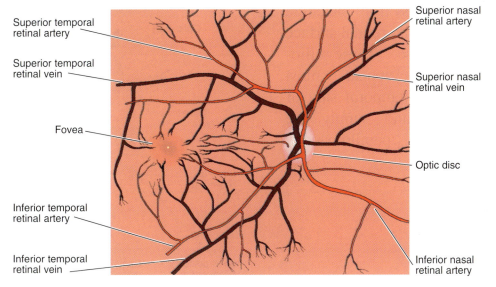

Superior temporal retinal artery

Superior temporal retinal vein

Fovea

Inferior temporal retinal artery

Inferior temporal retinal vein

Superior nasal retinal artery

Superior nasal retinal vein

Optic disc

Inferior nasal retinal artery

Capillaries are derived from arterioles which branch perpendicularly from the larger arteries leaving a zone which is relatively free of capillaries on each side of these vessels. A diffuse three-dimensional network is formed by the capillaries which penetrate the retina as far as the outer border of the inner nuclear layer. Flattened endothelial cells form the capillary walls and attached externally to these are the pericytes or cells termed mural cells. Both types of cell are surrounded by a basement membrane.

The temporal preretinal vessels arc around the fovea and leave a capillary-free zone about 0.5mm in diameter, centred on the foveola. About 1mm from the ora serrata, the preretinal vessels terminate in arcades and here the arterioles appear to communicate directly with the venules via bridging vessels.

There are no connections through the retina between the choroidal and central retinal vascular systems but vessels do occasionally pass from the circle of Haller-Zinn to the retinal surface via the optic disc. These cilio-retinal arteries appear most frequently at the temporal side of the optic disc and supply the macula and the papillomacular bundle.

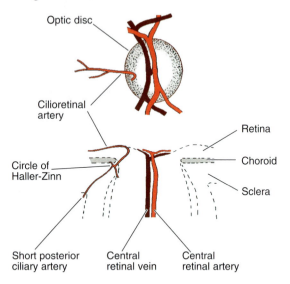

Fig.9.31 CILIORETINAL ARTERY

Optic disc

Cilioretinal artery

Retina

Choroid

Circle of Haller-Zinn

Sclera

Short posterior ciliary artery

Central retinal vein

Central retinal artery

DUPLICITY THEORY OF VISION

Because of the complexity of the visual function it has been found helpful to consider it as a combination of subsystems. Many aspects of visual structure and function can be divided into two parts suggesting an underlying duplex system.

Histologically there are two receptor groups, rods and cones. These have observable structural differences, they have different patterns of distribution and there are differences in the way in which they are linked to the rest of the visual system.

Physiologically the rods and cones respond differently to the wavelength and varying levels of the incident light.

Perceptually there is a distinction between scotopic and photopic vision, achromatic and trichromatic vision and the variation in acuity between central and peripheral vision.

Information on the histology of the receptors can be found earlier in this chapter. In the peripheral retina cones are shorter and thicker than rods. There are approximately 123×10^6 rods but only 7×10^6 cones, so rods outnumber cones 18 to 1.

The greatest density of cones is in the central retina while rods have a maximum density at the edge of the macula (Fig.9.13).

Rod and cone photopigments differ. There is a single rod photopigment but three cone photopigments.

Rods do respond differently to different wavelengths, but as far as the system is concerned the change of wavelength results only in an apparent change in luminance making the system achromatic.

With three different cone pigments the cone system can respond to wavelength as well as luminance changes. The normal cone system provides trichromatic colour vision. However, the cone system can only function if the luminance level is high enough, so that colour vision is only effective in photopic vision. There is a progressive loss of colour vision as luminance levels are reduced. Sensitivity to red is lost before blue (the Purkinje shift) a phenomenon that adds to the effect known as night myopia.

As a system, cones have a maximum sensitivity at 555nm while together the rods are maximally sensitive at 505nm (Fig.9.32). (Note that the individual photopigments have different maxima, shown in Fig.9.11.)

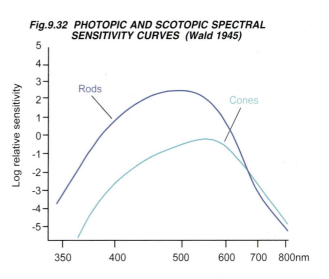

Fig.9.32 **PHOTOPIC AND SCOTOPIC SPECTRAL SENSITIVITY CURVES** (Wald 1945)

The retinal receptors do not exhibit the all-or-none response found in other neurones. The response is graded, the higher the luminance the more negative the cell becomes. However, rods are significantly more sensitive than cones, so they will produce a higher output in very low luminance levels.

A single peripheral ganglion cell may receive input from several hundred rods, whereas in the central retina a midget ganglion cell will be linked via a midget bipolar to a single cone. Ganglion cells will only respond if they receive sufficient stimulation which means that either several photons need to have reached a single cone or that several rods each need to have received a single photon. Since a given ganglion cell will be connected to many rods covering a large area of the peripheral retina, the probability that the rod/bipolar/ganglion cell system will be stimulated in low luminance levels is much higher than that for the cone system. In scotopic conditions there just too few photons to activate a cone/bipolar/ganglion cell pathway.

The differences in interconnections between the cells also affects the performance of the two systems in terms of resolution. In the central retina there are about 100,000 cones which have direct midget bipolar/midget ganglion cell links and hence provide high acuity. This leaves only 1×10^6 ganglion cell axons to carry signals gathered by about 130×10^6 receptors in the peripheral retina which results in a reduction of acuity outside the central area.

As the majority of the peripheral cells belong to the rod system, colour vision is also minimal peripherally. Clinical evidence for this loss of colour vision in the periphery is given by plotting the extent of the visual field for similar sized blue, red, green and white targets. For a 1mm white Traquair target at 1m the field is about 25°, whereas the colour fields are approximately 7°, 3° and 2° for blue, red and green targets with the same angular subtense.

Although not a routine test, a plot of the dark adaptation function can be used to demonstrate the transfer of vision from the cone to rod system with change in luminance. As the luminance of the test target drops the cone system continues to function until, after about 10 minutes in the dark, the efficiency of the rod system causes it to take over from the now poorly functioning cones. This transfer from cone to rod system can be seen from the discontinuity in the curve in Fig.9.33.

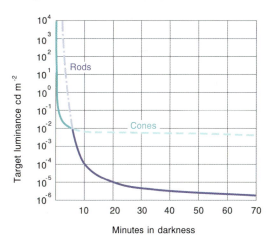

Fig.9.33 THE DARK ADAPTATION FUNCTION

Chapter 10

THE INTERNAL TRANSPARENT MEDIA

The internal transparent refractive media are the aqueous humour, the vitreous humour and the crystalline lens. The aqueous and vitreous are both 99% water and contain secretions derived from the epithelium of the ciliary body. However, unlike the crystalline lens, both the aqueous and vitreous are generally non-cellular in nature.

THE AQUEOUS HUMOUR

The total volume of aqueous is about 340µl, of which about 270µl is contained in the anterior chamber and 70µl in the posterior chamber. In the healthy eye it is a transparent fluid having a refractive index of between 1.3337 and 1.3370, and a viscosity of 1.030 (the viscosity of water is 1.000). It is produced by the ciliary body and contains fluid and metabolites that have diffused from the capillaries of the ciliary processes.

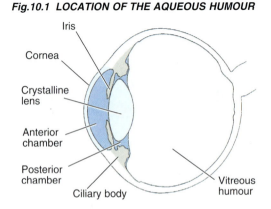

Fig.10.1 LOCATION OF THE AQUEOUS HUMOUR

Iris

Cornea

Crystalline lens

Anterior chamber

Posterior chamber

Ciliary body

Vitreous humour

These constituents have been selectively transported to the posterior chamber by the ciliary epithelium together with secretions elaborated by the unpigmented cells. The fluid thus formed passes from the posterior chamber through the pupil into the anterior chamber, where every minute, about 1% of its volume is removed from the eye via the canal of Schlemm.

The function of the aqueous is to carry metabolites to the avascular lens and cornea, and to remove waste products from these. The aqueous humour also provides positive pressure to give shape to the globe and to maintain the contact between the neural layers of the retina and the pigment epithelium.

MOVEMENT OF AQUEOUS HUMOUR

The flow of aqueous has been demonstrated experimentally by observation of movement into the anterior chamber of substances injected into the posterior chamber. The clinical observation of the bulging forward of the iris (iris bombé), which occurs following complete adhesion between the iris and the lens, provides confirmation that the aqueous is produced posterior to the iris.

The movement of aqueous from the

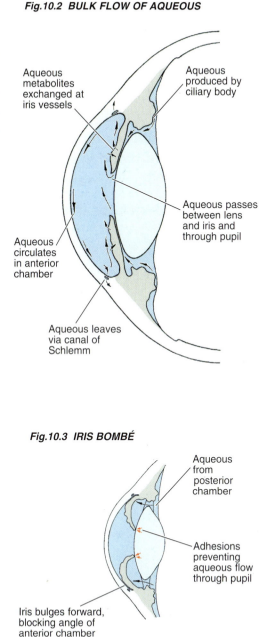

Fig.10.2 BULK FLOW OF AQUEOUS

Aqueous metabolites exchanged at iris vessels

Aqueous produced by ciliary body

Aqueous passes between lens and iris and through pupil

Aqueous circulates in anterior chamber

Aqueous leaves via canal of Schlemm

Fig.10.3 IRIS BOMBÉ

Aqueous from posterior chamber

Adhesions preventing aqueous flow through pupil

Iris bulges forward, blocking angle of anterior chamber

185

posterior chamber to the canal of Schlemm is termed its bulk flow (Fig.10.2) and this provides the major outflow route, although some uveo-scleral outflow has been demonstrated by Francois (1967). The aqueous passes between the trabeculae in the angle of the anterior chamber to reach the canal. It is transported into the canal through the endothelial cell lining by macrovacuoles which form transcellular channels through these cells. From the canal of Schlemm, the aqueous is taken to the episcleral veins by outlet (or collector) channels. The displacement of blood in the veins close to the limbus produces the aqueous veins (of Ascher). The removal of aqueous is at a rate of about 2-3µl per minute.

Fig.10.4 DETAIL OF ANGLE OF ANTERIOR CHAMBER *showing aqueous drainage*

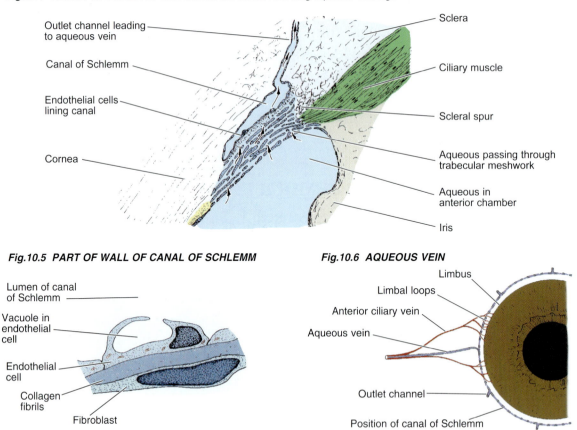

Outlet channel leading to aqueous vein

Canal of Schlemm

Endothelial cells lining canal

Cornea

Sclera

Ciliary muscle

Scleral spur

Aqueous passing through trabecular meshwork

Aqueous in anterior chamber

Iris

Fig.10.5 PART OF WALL OF CANAL OF SCHLEMM

Lumen of canal of Schlemm

Vacuole in endothelial cell

Endothelial cell

Collagen fibrils

Fibroblast

Fig.10.6 AQUEOUS VEIN

Limbus

Limbal loops

Anterior ciliary vein

Aqueous vein

Outlet channel

Position of canal of Schlemm

186

Convection currents within the aqueous in the anterior chamber are caused by the exposed cornea being 3°C cooler than the iris and crystalline lens. This thermal circulation serves to distribute aqueous around the anterior chamber. The effect of thermal circulation may be seen clinically by the deposits of leucocytes from an inflamed iris on the endothelium of the lower part of the cornea. These deposits are known as keratitic precipitates.

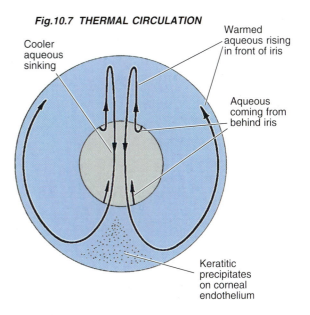

Fig.10.7 THERMAL CIRCULATION

Cooler aqueous sinking

Warmed aqueous rising in front of iris

Aqueous coming from behind iris

Keratitic precipitates on corneal endothelium

PRODUCTION OF AQUEOUS HUMOUR

Diffusion, dialysis, ultrafiltration and secretion have each been proposed as the mechanism for the production of aqueous from the blood vessels of the ciliary processes.

Since the cellular barriers separating the aqueous from its surrounding tissues are not completely impermeable, diffusion will take place, providing that there is a concentration gradient. Substances such as oxygen, carbon dioxide, amino acids, glucose and vitamins may be transferred across the cell membrane by this means.

The capillary walls are normally only slightly permeable to large protein molecules, so that only small particles would pass through them to achieve an equilibrium. This process is known as dialysis. However, in a mixture of salts and proteins (such as the blood plasma) there will be an unequal distribution of the salt ions at the equilibrium state since the positive ions become bound to the negatively charged protein molecules. The balance across the membrane that results is the Gibbs-Donnan equilibrium (Donnan 1911).

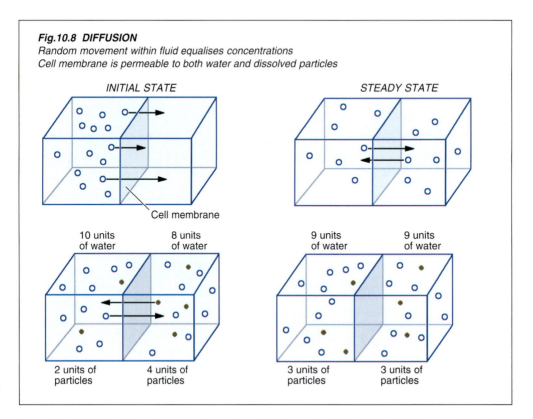

Fig.10.8 DIFFUSION
Random movement within fluid equalises concentrations
Cell membrane is permeable to both water and dissolved particles

INITIAL STATE   STEADY STATE

Cell membrane

| 10 units of water | 8 units of water | | 9 units of water | 9 units of water |

| 2 units of particles | 4 units of particles | | 3 units of particles | 3 units of particles |

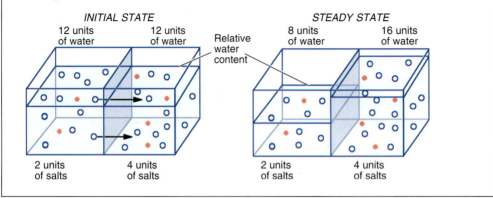

Fig.10.9 OSMOSIS
Higher initial concentration of dissolved salts on right hand side produces osmotic pressure resulting in a movement of water to balance concentrations

INITIAL STATE   STEADY STATE

| 12 units of water | 12 units of water | Relative water content | 8 units of water | 16 units of water |

| 2 units of salts | 4 units of salts | | 2 units of salts | 4 units of salts |

188

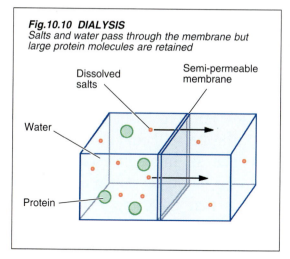

Fig.10.10 DIALYSIS
Salts and water pass through the membrane but large protein molecules are retained

Dissolved salts

Semi-permeable membrane

Water

Protein

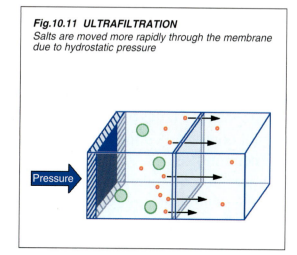

Fig.10.11 ULTRAFILTRATION
Salts are moved more rapidly through the membrane due to hydrostatic pressure

Pressure

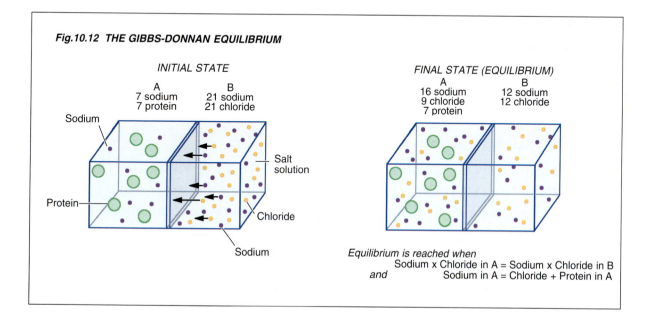

Fig.10.12 THE GIBBS-DONNAN EQUILIBRIUM

INITIAL STATE

A
7 sodium
7 protein

B
21 sodium
21 chloride

Sodium

Protein

Salt solution

Chloride

Sodium

FINAL STATE (EQUILIBRIUM)

A
16 sodium
9 chloride
7 protein

B
12 sodium
12 chloride

Equilibrium is reached when
Sodium x Chloride in A = Sodium x Chloride in B
and
Sodium in A = Chloride + Protein in A

With the large protein molecules trapped in the blood vessels, the salts should be distributed so that the chloride ion concentration is higher in the aqueous than in the blood, and the sodium concentration is lower.

However, when these concentrations are measured, this is not found to be the case. The situation is further complicated by the hydrostatic pressure in the blood vessels which tends to drive fluid through the vessel wall (Fig.10.11). As the wall is not completely impermeable, this fluid, the ultrafiltrate, will contain some large protein molecules. The presence of these produce an imbalance causing an osmotic force which tries to drive water back into the blood vessels in opposition to the hydrostatic pressure. The overall result is that the simple balance of hydrostatic and osmotic pressures and diffusion do not account for the concentrations of substances found in the aqueous humour. The anomalies have to be accounted for by secretion which is the extra factor of the active, selective transport system.

Although researchers have found significant variations between species, the high ratios of sodium, chloride and the extremely high ratio of ascorbate in aqueous when compared with blood plasma, have confirmed the existence of active transport systems which are located in the epithelium of the ciliary body.

INTRAOCULAR PRESSURE

When measured by applanation tonometry, the pressure within the eye has an average value of 15-16mm Hg. This pressure is produced by the combined effects of the pressure in the capillaries and the secretory mechanism of the ciliary epithelium. Although secretion is responsible for more of the aqueous contents than diffusion (Duke Elder 1968), the changes in pressure in the arterial system of the ciliary body produce changes in aqueous pressure. Thus the cardiovascular pulse produces an average 2mm Hg change in the applanation reading accompanied by slight changes due to the respiratory cycle.

Diurnal changes account for a 3mm Hg variation, with the highest reading obtained in the early morning and the minimum about twelve hours later (Fig.10.13). Eye movements produce small alterations in pressure and forcible lid closure can cause the pressure to rise to 70mm Hg. Maintained accommodation produces a reduction in pressure of about 4-5mm Hg.

The aqueous humour is normally transparent, but during iritis (inflammation of the iris), protein is released by the iris vessels and this produces scattering of a light beam shone into the anterior chamber (known as Tyndall's phenomenon or aqueous flare). This protein is sticky and may block the trabecular meshwork or cause adhesions between the crystalline lens and the iris, either of which will tend to produce an increase in intraocular pressure.

Fig.10.13 DIURNAL VARIATIONS IN INTRAOCULAR PRESSURE

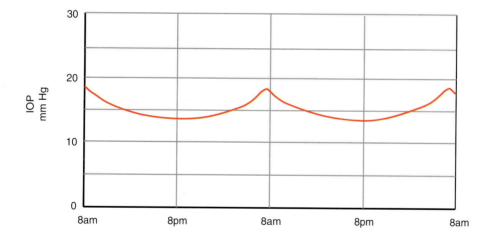

THE VITREOUS HUMOUR

The vitreous humour (or vitreous body) is a transparent gel occupying the vitreous chamber of the globe. It consists of a network of collagen filaments in a semifluid matrix. It has a volume of 4ml and a refractive index of 1.334 (Richards and Hague 1963).

The vitreous is bounded anteriorly by the basement membrane of the ciliary body and by the crystalline lens, which rests in the patellar fossa of the vitreous. Posteriorly it is enclosed by the inner limiting membrane of the retina. The vitreous collagen filaments

Fig.10.14
THE LOCATION OF THE VITREOUS HUMOUR

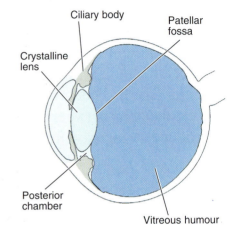

form a diffuse network which becomes denser to form a surface layer about 100μm thick. This layer is the cortical vitreous which has regions of attachment to the surrounding structures at the vitreous base and the area Martegiani (Fig.10.15)

The vitreous base extends forward from the equator to a point about midway along the pars plana. Firm attachment is achieved by the interweaving of the vitreous filaments with the ciliary and retinal inner basement membrane. The filaments in the vitreous base are generally orientated perpendicular to the surface of the membrane (Hogan 1971) and extend for a considerable distance into the vitreous.

Running axially through the vitreous is a zone of primary (foetal) vitreous surrounded by the (adult) secondary vitreous. Development of the primary vitreous commences at the end of the third week of embryonic life and the secondary vitreous starts to develop during the sixth week (see page 378 and

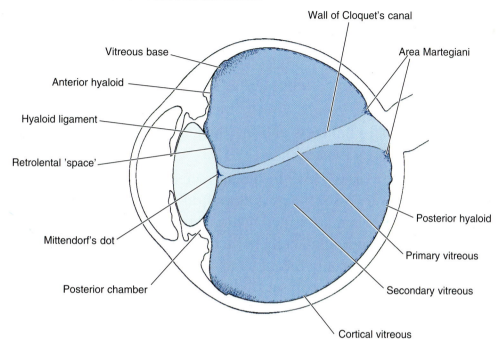

Fig.10.15 HORIZONTAL SECTION THROUGH THE GLOBE

Wall of Cloquet's canal

Vitreous base

Anterior hyaloid

Hyaloid ligament

Retrolental 'space'

Mittendorf's dot

Posterior chamber

Area Martegiani

Posterior hyaloid

Primary vitreous

Secondary vitreous

Cortical vitreous

Fig.18.20). The primary vitreous forms Cloquet's canal and the adult vitreous thickens to form the wall of the canal. Small differences in refractive index of the primary and secondary vitreous may allow the path of the canal to be seen. The posterior end of the canal is firmly attached to the retinal inner limiting membrane around the optic disc in a zone known as the area Martegiani. Mittendorf's dot, a remnant of the embryonic hyaloid vascular system supplying the anterior part of the eye with blood (page 373), may be seen at the anterior end of Cloquet's canal. The cortical vitreous is attached to the capsule of the crystalline lens via the hyaloid (capsular, Wieger's) ligament. This forms a 7-8mm diameter ring within which the lens/vitreous attachment is less firm, producing the potential retrolental space of Berger.

193

The cortex is somewhat thicker anteriorly and the zone in front of the vitreous base is called the anterior hyaloid. It is this which forms a boundary between the vitreous and posterior chambers. This anterior hyaloid has continuity with the zonular suspensory fibres of the crystalline lens emanating from the pars plana and from the sides of the ciliary processes. The zonular fibres of the crystalline lens are seen in the secondary vitreous during the third month of embryonic life.

Posteriorly, the vitreous cortex fibrils are continuous with the basement membrane of the retinal glial cells and the thickened layer of filaments near the surface forms the posterior hyaloid.

Cells are found in the cortex close to the surface of the retina and in particular close to the retinal blood vessels. The majority (about 90%) of these appear to be mononuclear phagocytes and are called hyalocytes (Balazs 1968). The remaining 10% are fibrocytes and neuroglial cells. The fluid matrix of the vitreous gel has a composition which is essentially the same as that of the aqueous humour, except for the presence of the mucopolysaccharide hyaluronic acid produced by the hyalocytes.

The solid component of vitreous consists of a network of collagen filaments 15-20nm diameter with a 22nm banding. (The larger collagen fibrils found in the cornea have 64nm banding). Vitreous collagen fibrils and the collagen of the basement membrane are most likely to be produced by the unpigmented epithelium of the ciliary body and the retinal Müller cells.

Maurice (1957) has suggested that there is diffusion throughout the vitreous and that exchange of metabolites occurs between the vitreous and the aqueous humour, thus leading to difficulty in identifying components that are specific to either the aqueous or the vitreous.

THE CRYSTALLINE LENS

The crystalline lens is a transparent, biconvex structure composed of 65% water and 35% protein. It consists of layers of cells, enclosed in a thick basement membrane or capsule, lying between the vitreous and the iris in the posterior chamber. The anterior surface is ellipsoid in section and the posterior paraboloid, the two surfaces meeting at the rounded periphery or equator of the lens.

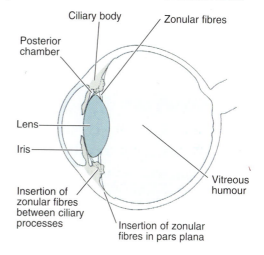

Fig.10.16 *LOCATION OF THE CRYSTALLINE LENS*

Ciliary body
Zonular fibres
Posterior chamber
Lens
Iris
Vitreous humour
Insertion of zonular fibres between ciliary processes
Insertion of zonular fibres in pars plana

The lens is supported by the zonules or suspensory ligaments and its equator is separated from the ciliary processes by the 0.5mm circumlental space. The zonules pass from the valleys between the ciliary processes and from the pars plana of the ciliary body to insert into the lens capsule on either side of the equator in a zone about 2.5mm wide (Fig.10.21).

The lens increases in diameter from about 6mm at birth to 9.5mm in the adult. The axial thickness also increases with age and measurements made on extracted lenses show a thickness of 3.5mm at birth which increases slowly throughout life to 5.0mm by the age of 80.

Measurements of the radii of curvature show considerable variation between individuals and age groups but Gullstrand's (1911) figures of 10mm for the anterior radius and 6mm for the posterior are widely quoted. The refractive index increases progressively towards the lens nucleus but 1.413 can be taken as a mean value. The weight of the lens increases from 65mg at birth to 240mg at age 80.

STRUCTURE OF THE LENS

The lens consists of:

- The capsule
- Cuboidal epithelium
- Lens fibres

The lens capsule

The lens capsule is the body's thickest basement membrane and it is transparent and elastic. The thickness varies from the poles to the equator (see figures shown in Fig.10.17), but is generally thickest where the zonules are inserted. These thickened regions appear to compress the lens when contraction of the ciliary muscle relaxes the tension in the zonules and this causes the lens to bulge at the poles where the capsule is thin. This produces the change in lens power known as accommodation (see Fig.10.22). Normally the traction on the zonular fibres causes the equator of the lens to wrinkle, an effect that is lost when the lens is removed from the eye. Electron microscope observation of the capsule shows it to have a layered filament structure which is presumably collagen in a mucopolysaccharide matrix.

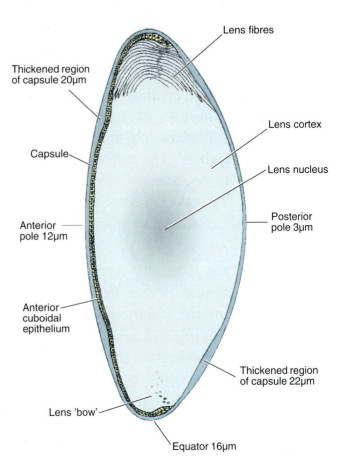

Fig.10.17 SECTION THROUGH CRYSTALLINE LENS
(showing the thickness of the capsule)

Lens fibres

Thickened region of capsule 20μm

Lens cortex

Capsule

Lens nucleus

Anterior pole 12μm

Posterior pole 3μm

Anterior cuboidal epithelium

Thickened region of capsule 22μm

Lens 'bow'

Equator 16μm

The epithelium

At the anterior of the lens below the capsule lies a single layer of cuboidal epithelial cells for which the capsule forms the basement membrane (Fig.10.18). The cells are about 15μm wide and 6μm high in the central region but become progressively columnar and more pyramidal towards the equator where cell division takes place. The cell membranes show interdigitation and, apically, lateral zonular occlusions are found. The cells contain only a small number of organelles and there are no unusual features apart from an increased microtubule population in the equatorial cells.

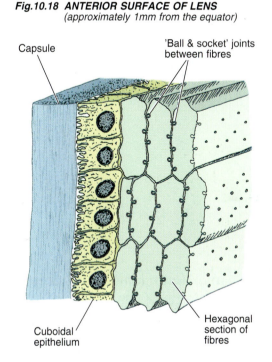

Fig.10.18 ANTERIOR SURFACE OF LENS
(approximately 1mm from the equator)

Capsule

'Ball & socket' joints between fibres

Cuboidal epithelium

Hexagonal section of fibres

The lens fibres

The cells undergo mitotic division at the equator. The new cells produce two processes, one directed anteriorly and the other posteriorly (Fig.10.19). The anterior process passes between the anterior epithelium and the previous layer of processes, while the posteriorly directed process passes along the inner surface of the posterior capsule. The cell division results in the older cells being forced inwards towards the centre or nucleus of the lens, with the newer cells forming the lens cortex. The pattern of displaced cell nuclei in the cortex near the equator is called the lens bow or vortex (Becker 1883). As the cells move inwards they lose their nucleus and other identifiable organelles.

The cell processes are frequently referred to as lens fibres and they all have about

Fig.10.19 DEVELOPMENT OF LENS FIBRES

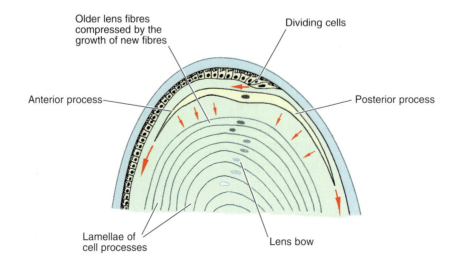

Older lens fibres compressed by the growth of new fibres

Dividing cells

Anterior process

Posterior process

Lamellae of cell processes

Lens bow

the same 10mm length. Adjacent processes interdigitate with each other via small pegs or ball and socket joints (Fig.10.18). As they are compressed by the newly growing cells, the processes develop a flattened hexagonal section 9µm wide by 5µm thick. Compression of the processes increases the density of the inner zones of the lens and it is noted clinically that the nuclear region yellows with age. An anteroposterior section of the adult lens shows the layers of processes forming an onion-skin lamellar arrangement, with some two thousand lamellae making up the total thickness.

The combined length of the anterior and posterior processes is less than the distance between the poles (via the equator). Anterior or posterior displacement of the whole cell relative to the equator results in the processes meeting along a line or suture. In the centre of the lens is the foetal nucleus where these sutures form the shape of a letter **Y** erect anteriorly and inverted posteriorly. These can be observed with the slit lamp in the foetal nuclear region of the adult lens. The simple foetal pattern of sutures develops into a more complex stellate arrangement with many branches in the adult lens.

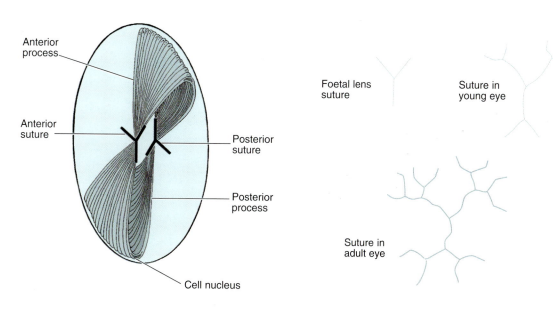

THE ZONULAR FIBRES

The suspensory zonular fibres have been mentioned previously in the discussions of the vitreous humour and the ciliary body. They were described by Zinn (1753) and are referred to as the lens zonules or zonule of Zinn. In the foetal eye the vitreous fibre network develops into zonular fibres and this process has been called the 'condensation of the tertiary vitreous'. The fibres pass from the basement membrane of the unpigmented ciliary epithelial cells to the lens capsule running between the ciliary processes to reach the lens. In the foetal eye the primitive unpigmented cells are in contact with the lens capsule and as the eye grows and the lens moves forwards, the fibres form two main groups or sheets. The zonules insert into the capsule about 1.5mm from the equator anteriorly and about 1mm posteriorly.

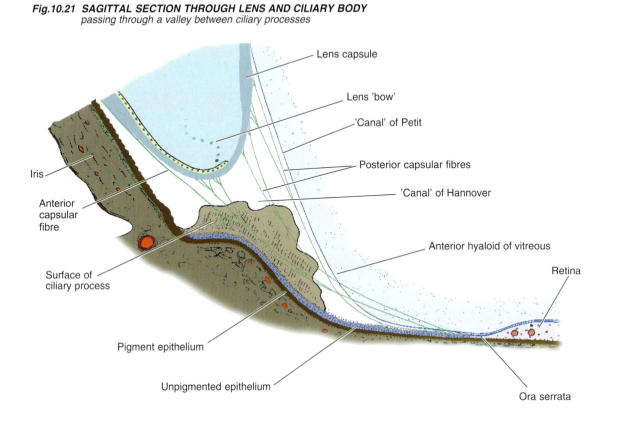

Fig.10.21 SAGITTAL SECTION THROUGH LENS AND CILIARY BODY
passing through a valley between ciliary processes

Lens capsule

Lens 'bow'

'Canal' of Petit

Posterior capsular fibres

'Canal' of Hannover

Anterior hyaloid of vitreous

Retina

Iris

Anterior
capsular
fibre

Surface of
ciliary process

Pigment epithelium

Unpigmented epithelium

Ora serrata

The lens zonules are 5-60µm thick bundles of 1µm diameter fibres which are composed of 10nm diameter filaments or fibrils. Equatorial spaces between the fibres were referred to as canals by Petit (1723) who injected air which was trapped by surface tension between the vitreous face and the posterior fibres. Hannover (1845) repeated the experiment but found air trapped between the anterior and posterior groups of fibres.

METABOLISM OF THE LENS

The metabolic requirements of the lens are fairly low and its cells receive metabolites that have diffused through the capsule from the aqueous humour. Waste products are removed by the same route.

ACCOMMODATION

Stimulation of the cells in the visceral nucleus of the third cranial (oculomotor) nerve brings about contraction of the ciliary muscle thus producing accommodation. (Accommodation is accompanied by miosis since both the ciliary muscle and the iris sphincter pupillae muscle have a common nerve

Fig.10.22 ACCOMMODATION *(See also Fig.8.18)*
The dotted outline shows the lens in the unaccommodated state

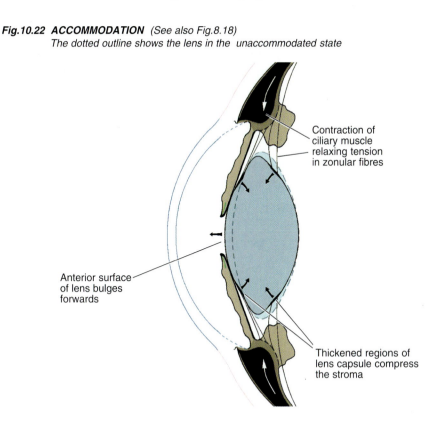

Contraction of ciliary muscle relaxing tension in zonular fibres

Anterior surface of lens bulges forwards

Thickened regions of lens capsule compress the stroma

supply.) Reduction in the diameter of the ciliary sphincter releases the zonular traction on the lens capsule and the elasticity of the lens structures causes the lens to take up its accommodated form with the greatest change in radius of curvature taking place at the anterior surface (Fig.10.22).

Contraction of the ciliary muscle also draws the ora serrata and the choroid forward (see also Fig.8.18). Relaxation of the ciliary muscle allows the elastic choroid to draw the ciliary body backwards pulling on the zonules and flattening the lens into its unaccommodated form (Moses 1970).

PRESBYOPIA

As the lens ages and its cell population increases the cells become more tightly packed within the lens capsule. They are thus less able to move following contraction and relaxation of the ciliary muscle. It becomes progressively more difficult to accommodate and to restore the lens to its unaccommodated state. This is noted by older subjects in having more difficulty to read small print and in their noticing blurred vision when looking up from closework. This loss of accommodation is presbyopia or "old eye".

There may be a reduction in blood supply to the ciliary muscle and reduced elasticity of the lens structure contributing to the loss of accommodation with age, but it is likely that the increased density of the lens is a major factor.

Chapter 11

THE EXTRINSIC OCULAR MUSCLES

The orbit contains a number of striated and smooth muscles concerned with eye rotation and eyelid movement, together with some smooth muscle whose function in man is uncertain. Only the oculorotary muscles are considered in this chapter, descriptions of the other muscles may be found in the chapters on the eyelids and the orbital fasciae.

The globe rotates within the orbit supported by the orbital fat and fasciae. Rotation is brought about by the actions of six muscles (four rectus and two oblique muscles). Each muscle has a proximal tendon and a distal tendon. The proximal tendon is anchored to the connective tissue (periorbita) covering the orbital walls and forms the origin of the muscle. The distal tendon is continuous with the sclera and this junction is referred to as the insertion of the muscle. A line joining the insertion to the origin of the muscle is the muscle's line of action (although this definition does not apply to the superior oblique muscle, see page 218).

Because of the compressible nature of the orbital fat, the globe does not rotate about a fixed centre and slight translational movements occur. However, for the purpose of description of the actions of the extrinsic ocular muscles, a fixed centre

Fig.11.1 *PLANES AND AXES OF ROTATION*

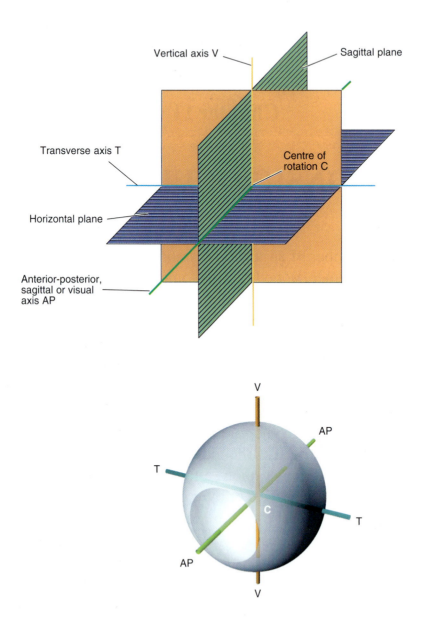

Vertical axis V

Sagittal plane

Transverse axis T

Centre of rotation C

Horizontal plane

Anterior-posterior, sagittal or visual axis AP

V

AP

T

C

T

AP

V

of rotation may be taken to lie 13.5-14.0mm behind the apex of the cornea and 1.65mm to the nasal side of the geometric centre of the globe. When considering the action of the individual muscles it is important to bear in mind the relationship between the line of action of the muscle and the centre of rotation of the eye.

Movements of one eye about its centre of rotation are ductions and each duction is prefixed according to the direction of movement of the anterior pole of the globe.

Movement	Duction	Axis of rotation
Upward	Supraduction	Transverse
Downward	Infraduction	Transverse
Inward (nasally)	Adduction	Vertical
Outward (temporally)	Abduction	Vertical

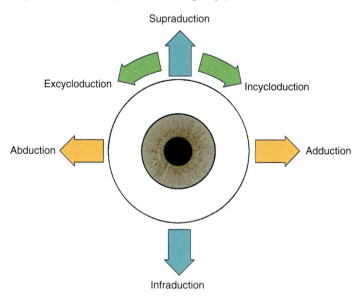

Fig.11.2 DUCTIONS (referred to the right eye)

If the globe rotates about its anterior-posterior axis a cycloduction is produced. When the top of the cornea rotates nasally about this axis the movement is incycloduction, and when the top of the cornea rotates temporally, the effect is excycloduction.

In considering the effect of each muscle the eye is initially assumed to be in the primary position with the visual axis coincident with the sagittal axis. However, the effect produced by a particular muscle will change as the eye rotates away from the primary position, and these changes will be considered as each muscle is described.

The effectiveness of a particular action may be assessed by examining the turning moment produced by the muscle. This is found by considering the globe as a disc perpendicular to a particular axis which forms an axle about which the disc can rotate. If the line of action of the muscle is then resolved into the plane of the disc, the effectiveness of the muscle in rotating the eye can be estimated (see Fig.11.3).

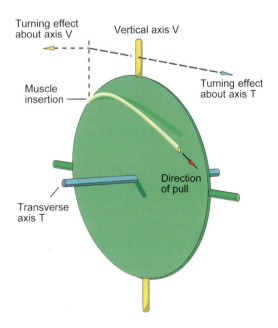

Fig.11.3a **TURNING MOMENTS**

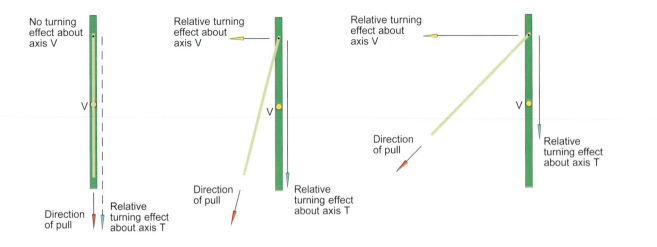

Fig.11.3b **DISC SEEN FROM ABOVE**
As the direction of pull moves away from the disc, the turning effect about axis V increases while the turning effect about axis T decreases

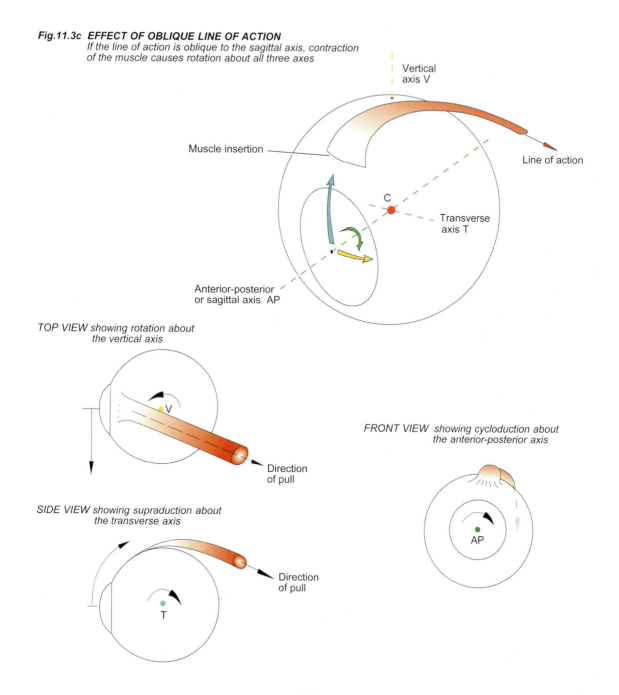

Fig.11.3c EFFECT OF OBLIQUE LINE OF ACTION
If the line of action is oblique to the sagittal axis, contraction of the muscle causes rotation about all three axes

Vertical axis V

Muscle insertion

Line of action

C

Transverse axis T

Anterior-posterior or sagittal axis AP

TOP VIEW showing rotation about the vertical axis

V

Direction of pull

FRONT VIEW showing cycloduction about the anterior-posterior axis

AP

SIDE VIEW showing supraduction about the transverse axis

T

Direction of pull

207

THE RECTUS MUSCLES

The four rectus (straight) muscles have their origin in a common ring of tendon anchored to the periorbita at the apex of the orbit. This ring, known as the annulus of Zinn or common annular tendon, encloses the optic foramen, passing around its superior and medial aspects and extending laterally to enclose the lower part of the superior orbital fissure. This lateral extension is attached to a tubercle, the spina recti lateralis, on the edge of the greater wing of the sphenoid. From this common tendon the muscles pass forward in the orbit forming a cone of muscle around the optic nerve.

Anteriorly, the distal tendons pass through the bulbar fascia to insert into the sclera some 6mm in front of the equator of the globe. The insertions of the four recti are not equidistant from the limbus and correspond approximately to the location of the ora serrata internally. The medial rectus is

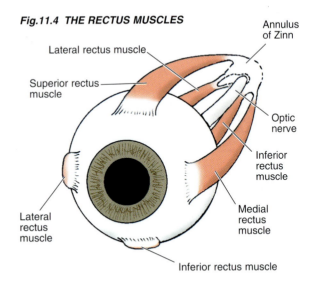

Fig.11.4 THE RECTUS MUSCLES

Lateral rectus muscle

Superior rectus muscle

Annulus of Zinn

Optic nerve

Inferior rectus muscle

Lateral rectus muscle

Medial rectus muscle

Inferior rectus muscle

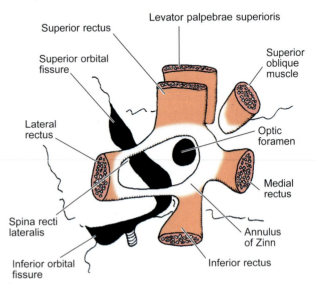

Fig.11.5 THE ANNULUS OF ZINN

Superior rectus

Levator palpebrae superioris

Superior orbital fissure

Superior oblique muscle

Lateral rectus

Optic foramen

Medial rectus

Spina recti lateralis

Annulus of Zinn

Inferior orbital fissure

Inferior rectus

inserted closest to the limbus with the insertions of the inferior, the lateral and the superior recti progressively farther away. This arrangement, shown in Fig.11.6, is known as the spiral of Tillaux. From origin to insertion, each rectus muscle is about 40mm long, and each is enclosed in a connective tissue sheath, having fascial expansions into the surrounding fat and connective tissue.

Blood to the muscles is supplied by one of the muscular branches of the ophthalmic artery and venous drainage is to either the superior or inferior ophthalmic vein. Branches of the arteries pass forward within the connective tissue sheath of the muscles and these continue into the sclera to form the anterior ciliary arteries. The veins parallel the path of the muscular arteries and pass to either the superior or inferior ophthalmic vein.

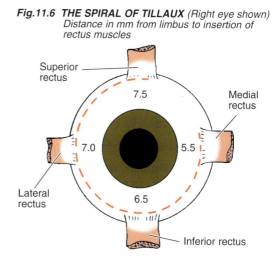

Fig.11.6 **THE SPIRAL OF TILLAUX** (Right eye shown)
Distance in mm from limbus to insertion of rectus muscles

Superior rectus

Medial rectus

7.5

7.0

5.5

Lateral rectus

6.5

Inferior rectus

Fig.11.7 **BLOOD SUPPLY TO MUSCLES**

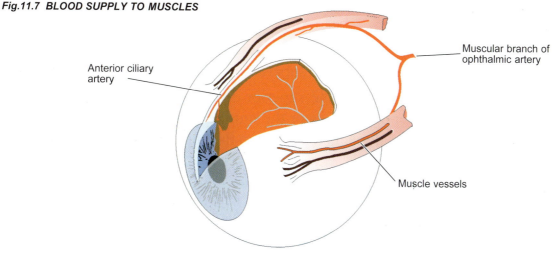

Anterior ciliary artery

Muscular branch of ophthalmic artery

Muscle vessels

THE SUPERIOR RECTUS

This arises from the upper part of the common annular tendon where its sheath is continuous with the dura mater of the optic nerve. It runs forward, up and out making an angle of 23° to the sagittal plane of the orbit. Above it lies the levator palpebrae superioris with which its sheath merges. As it passes over the globe the lateral surface of the tendon of the superior rectus is in contact with the lacrimal gland. The muscle is about 42mm in length and its insertion into the sclera is by a 6mm long tendon, along an 11mm line, whose centre is 7.5mm from the limbus.

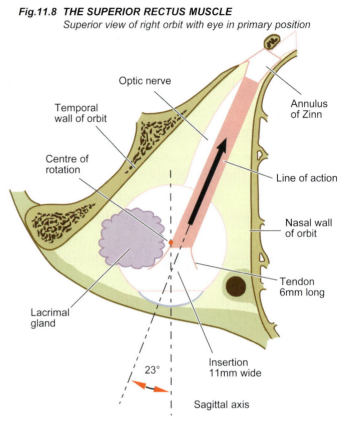

Fig.11.8 THE SUPERIOR RECTUS MUSCLE
Superior view of right orbit with eye in primary position

Optic nerve

Temporal wall of orbit

Centre of rotation

Lacrimal gland

Annulus of Zinn

Line of action

Nasal wall of orbit

Tendon 6mm long

Insertion 11mm wide

23°

Sagittal axis

The blood supply is derived from the superior muscular branch of the ophthalmic artery, and venous drainage is into the superior ophthalmic vein.

Motor innervation is supplied by the superior division of the oculomotor nerve, cranial nerve III. The nerve fibres enter the muscle from within the muscle cone about one-third of the way along its length from the annulus of Zinn.

Actions of the superior rectus

With the eye in the primary position, contraction of the superior rectus produces supraduction as its main effect, with adduction and incycloduction as secondary actions. Supraduction is produced because the line of action and the insertion of the muscle are above and anterior to the centre of rotation. As the muscle contracts (along its line of action) the distal tendon is drawn back causing the eye to rotate about the transverse axis, raising the anterior pole. Adduction and incycloduction occur because the insertion and the line of action are to the nasal side of the centre of rotation.

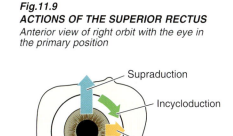

Fig.11.9
ACTIONS OF THE SUPERIOR RECTUS
Anterior view of right orbit with the eye in the primary position

As the visual axis moves nasally (adducts) the supraduction effect decreases and the effects of adduction and incycloduction increase. As the visual axis moves temporally (abduction), the movement of the globe carries the point of insertion temporally also, thus supraduction increases to a maximum at 23° of abduction and the adduction and incycloduction effects decrease. As the eye continues to abduct, the latter actions will change to abduction and excycloduction, as the line of action of the muscle is moved temporal to the centre of rotation.

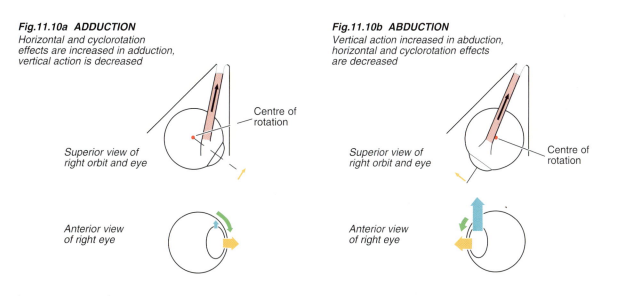

Fig.11.10a ADDUCTION
Horizontal and cyclorotation effects are increased in adduction, vertical action is decreased

Centre of rotation

Superior view of right orbit and eye

Anterior view of right eye

Fig.11.10b ABDUCTION
Vertical action increased in abduction, horizontal and cyclorotation effects are decreased

Superior view of right orbit and eye

Centre of rotation

Anterior view of right eye

THE MEDIAL RECTUS

The medial rectus arises from the medial part of the common annular tendon. It runs forward along the nasal wall of the orbit with its line of action in the horizontal plane. Like the superior rectus, its muscle sheath is continuous with the dura mater of the optic nerve at the apex of the orbit while anteriorly its medial surface is connected to the periorbita of the lacrimal bone by the medial check ligament.

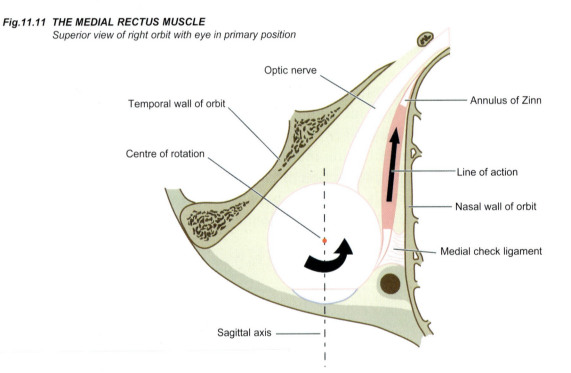

Fig.11.11 THE MEDIAL RECTUS MUSCLE
Superior view of right orbit with eye in primary position

Optic nerve

Temporal wall of orbit

Centre of rotation

Annulus of Zinn

Line of action

Nasal wall of orbit

Medial check ligament

Sagittal axis

The muscle is about 41mm long and its insertion into the sclera is by a 4mm tendon, along a 10mm insertion line whose centre is 5.5mm from the limbus.

The blood supply to the medial rectus is from the inferior muscular branch of the ophthalmic artery. Venous drainage is via the inferior ophthalmic vein.

The motor innervation to this muscle is from the inferior division of the oculomotor nerve. The fibres enter the surface of the muscle about 14mm from the annulus of Zinn.

Actions of the medial rectus

Because of its horizontal orientation this muscle is only concerned with adduction when the visual axis lies in the horizontal plane. The width of the muscle and its broad insertion make it unlikely to have any important secondary actions, although in adduction combined with extreme supraduction or infraduction, contraction of the medial rectus might possibly aid these latter movements.

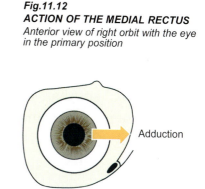

Fig.11.12
ACTION OF THE MEDIAL RECTUS
Anterior view of right orbit with the eye in the primary position

Adduction

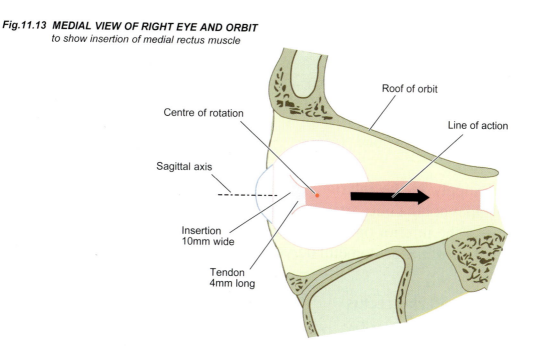

Fig.11.13 MEDIAL VIEW OF RIGHT EYE AND ORBIT
to show insertion of medial rectus muscle

Roof of orbit

Centre of rotation

Line of action

Sagittal axis

Insertion
10mm wide

Tendon
4mm long

213

THE INFERIOR RECTUS

The proximal tendon of the inferior rectus is continuous with the annulus of Zinn where it straddles the lower border of the superior orbital fissure. The body of the muscle is directed downwards and outwards at 23° to the sagittal axis, so that its line of action lies in the same vertical plane as that of the superior rectus.

The muscle is about 40mm long, and its insertion into the sclera is via a 5mm tendon along a 10mm insertion line whose centre is 6.5mm from the limbus. The sheath of this muscle is continuous with that of the inferior oblique muscle and this forms that part of the support for the globe known as the ligament of Lockwood (see Fig.14.3).

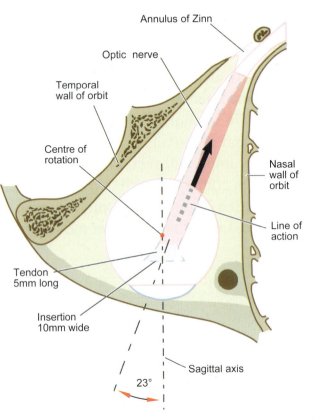

Fig.11.14 THE INFERIOR RECTUS MUSCLE
Superior view of right orbit with eye in primary position
(Muscle passes beneath globe and optic nerve)

Annulus of Zinn

Optic nerve

Temporal wall of orbit

Centre of rotation

Nasal wall of orbit

Line of action

Tendon 5mm long

Insertion 10mm wide

Sagittal axis

23°

The blood supply to the inferior rectus is derived from the inferior muscular branch of the ophthalmic artery and from the infra-orbital artery. Venous drainage is to the inferior ophthalmic vein. The motor nerve supply is from the inferior division of the oculomotor nerve.

Actions of the inferior rectus

Contraction of the inferior rectus produces infraduction, adduction and excycloduction.

Infraduction is produced because of the direction of the line of action of the muscle and because the insertion of the muscle is anterior and below the centre of rotation of the eye. Also, because the line of action is directed medially from the insertion point which is anterior to the centre of rotation, the muscle produces adduction and excycloduction.

As the eye abducts, the adduction and excycloduction effects of the inferior rectus decrease, but the infraduction that it produces becomes a maximum at 23° of abduction. With further abduction the line of action of the muscle is moved temporal to the vertical axis and the secondary actions change from adduction and excycloduction to abduction and incycloduction.

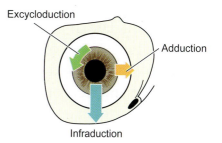

Fig.11.15
ACTIONS OF THE INFERIOR RECTUS
Anterior view of right orbit with the eye in the primary position

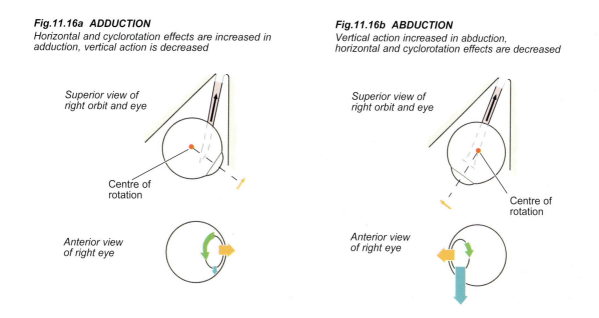

Fig.11.16a ADDUCTION
Horizontal and cyclorotation effects are increased in adduction, vertical action is decreased

Superior view of right orbit and eye

Centre of rotation

Anterior view of right eye

Fig.11.16b ABDUCTION
Vertical action increased in abduction, horizontal and cyclorotation effects are decreased

Superior view of right orbit and eye

Centre of rotation

Anterior view of right eye

THE LATERAL RECTUS

The proximal tendon of the lateral rectus is continuous with the common annular tendon where it spreads across the middle and lower parts of the superior orbital fissure and attaches to the spina recti lateralis. Like the medial rectus the line of action of the lateral rectus is principally horizontal. It runs forward to the globe along the lateral wall of the orbit. The lateral check ligament connects the muscle sheath to the periorbita at the zygomatic tubercle. The lacrimal gland lies above this muscle and rests on its tendon along the lateral surface of the globe.

The length of the lateral rectus is 41mm and it has a 9mm tendon. The insertion into the sclera is along a 9mm line whose centre is 7mm from the limbus.

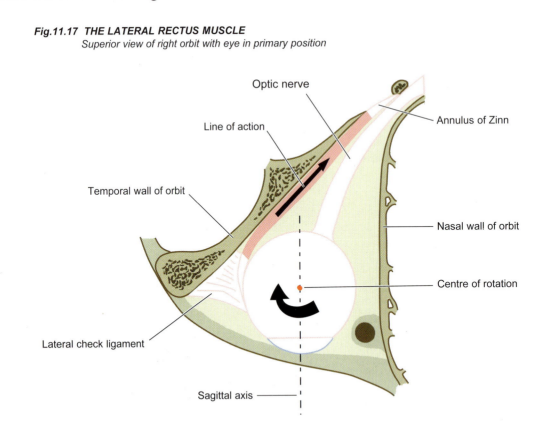

Fig.11.17 THE LATERAL RECTUS MUSCLE
Superior view of right orbit with eye in primary position

Optic nerve

Line of action

Annulus of Zinn

Temporal wall of orbit

Nasal wall of orbit

Centre of rotation

Lateral check ligament

Sagittal axis

The superior muscular branch of the ophthalmic artery and the lacrimal artery supply blood to the lateral rectus and the drainage route is via the inferior ophthalmic vein. The motor innervation is derived from the abducent nerve.

Actions of the lateral rectus

As with the medial rectus, the function of the lateral rectus is principally to move the eye about its vertical axis. Contraction of the lateral rectus produces abduction and, like the medial rectus, its secondary actions are likely to be negligible.

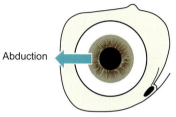

Fig.11.18
ACTION OF THE LATERAL RECTUS
Anterior view of right orbit with the eye in the primary position

Abduction

Fig.11.19 LATERAL VIEW OF LEFT EYE AND ORBIT
to show insertion of lateral rectus muscle

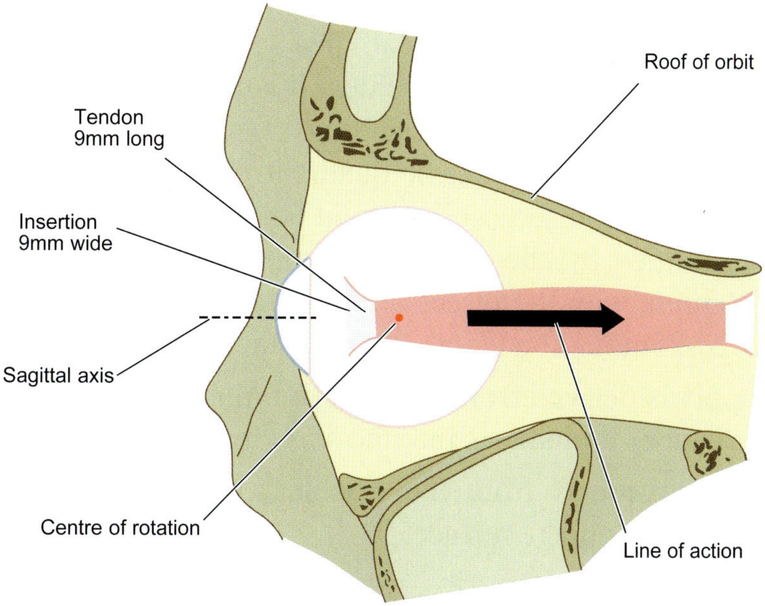

Tendon 9mm long

Insertion 9mm wide

Roof of orbit

Sagittal axis

Centre of rotation

Line of action

217

THE OBLIQUE MUSCLES

The oblique muscles are inserted into the upper and lower posterior temporal quadrants of the globe having travelled from the upper and lower nasal margins of the orbit. This places the line of action of the two muscles in a vertical plane making an angle of 51-54° to the nasal side of the sagittal plane. Each muscle passes inferiorly to the corresponding rectus muscle during its path to its insertion point.

THE SUPERIOR OBLIQUE

The proximal tendon of the superior oblique is inserted into the periorbita at the apex of the orbit, just medial and superior to the annulus of Zinn. The muscle runs along the upper edge of the nasal wall of the orbit to a point about 10mm from the trochlea where its distal tendon commences. The trochlea is a U-shaped plate of fibrocartilage attached to the superior nasal corner of the roof of the orbit, in the trochlear fossa. A synovial sheath lies between the tendon and the trochlea. As the tendon passes through the trochlea, it is reflected back towards the globe. It passes between the superior rectus and the sclera and is inserted along an 11mm line into the upper lateral posterior quadrant of the globe. From the superior aspect, the centre of the insertion lies about 6mm behind the equator and is almost completely concealed by the superior rectus. The total length of muscle and tendon is 60-65mm, with the direct (pretrochlear) part being 40mm long and the reflected part 20-25mm. The length of the distal tendon is approximately 30mm.

The blood supply is derived from the superior muscular branch of the ophthalmic artery and the venous drainage is into the superior ophthalmic vein.

The motor innervation is from the trochlear nerve which enters the superior oblique on its orbital (upper) surface.

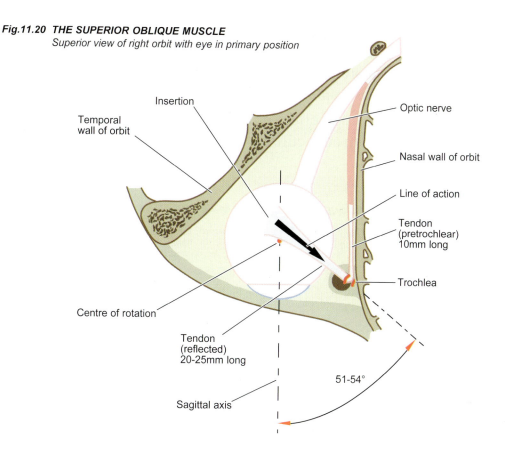

Fig.11.20 THE SUPERIOR OBLIQUE MUSCLE
Superior view of right orbit with eye in primary position

Insertion

Temporal wall of orbit

Optic nerve

Nasal wall of orbit

Line of action

Tendon (pretrochlear) 10mm long

Trochlea

Centre of rotation

Tendon (reflected) 20-25mm long

51-54°

Sagittal axis

Actions of the superior oblique

Although the body of the muscle lies parallel to the median plane, the distal tendon is reflected at the trochlea, redirecting the line of action.

Contraction of the superior oblique produces infraduction, incycloduction and abduction.

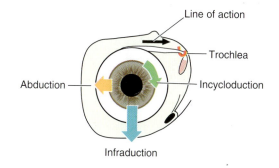

Fig.11.21 ACTIONS OF THE SUPERIOR OBLIQUE
Anterior view of right orbit with the eye in the primary position

Line of action

Trochlea

Abduction

Incycloduction

Infraduction

Infraduction occurs because the line of action lies above the centre of rotation of the eye, but it approaches its insertion from in front and nasally which causes the incycloduction. Abduction is produced because the line of action crosses behind the vertical axis towards the nasal side.

As the eye abducts the infraduction effect of the superior oblique is reduced, but the infraduction is increased with adduction.

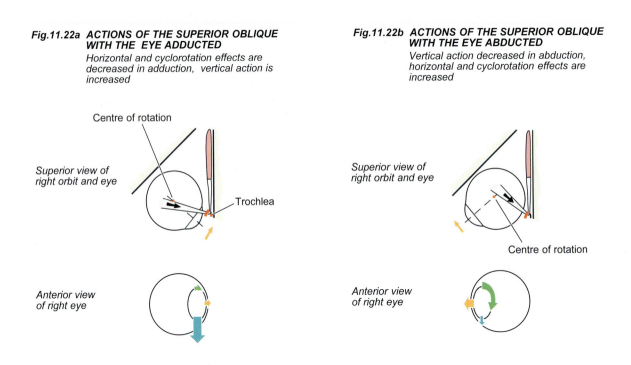

Fig.11.22a ACTIONS OF THE SUPERIOR OBLIQUE WITH THE EYE ADDUCTED
Horizontal and cyclorotation effects are decreased in adduction, vertical action is increased

Centre of rotation

Superior view of right orbit and eye

Trochlea

Anterior view of right eye

Fig.11.22b ACTIONS OF THE SUPERIOR OBLIQUE WITH THE EYE ABDUCTED
Vertical action decreased in abduction, horizontal and cyclorotation effects are increased

Superior view of right orbit and eye

Centre of rotation

Anterior view of right eye

THE INFERIOR OBLIQUE

The proximal attachment of the inferior oblique is to the lateral edge of the lacrimal fossa at the anterior nasal margin of the orbit. The muscle passes back and temporally, between the inferior rectus and the orbital floor, to insert into the sclera along a 10mm line which is level with the posterior pole of the globe. Below the globe its sheath is continuous with that of the inferior rectus.

The inferior oblique is the shortest of the extrinsic ocular muscles having a length of only 37mm. Since it lies in the same vertical plane as the reflected part of the superior oblique it also makes an angle of about 51° with the sagittal plane.

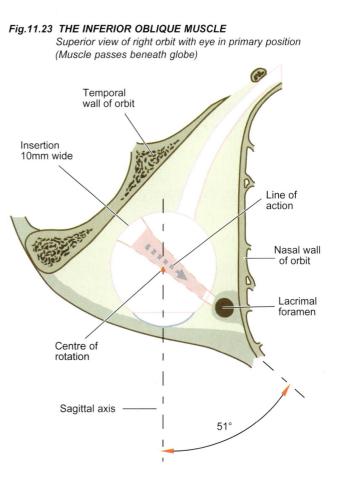

Fig.11.23 THE INFERIOR OBLIQUE MUSCLE
Superior view of right orbit with eye in primary position
(Muscle passes beneath globe)

Temporal wall of orbit

Insertion 10mm wide

Line of action

Nasal wall of orbit

Lacrimal foramen

Centre of rotation

Sagittal axis

51°

The inferior oblique receives its blood supply from the inferior muscular branch of the ophthalmic artery and from a branch of the infra-orbital artery. The drainage route is into the inferior ophthalmic vein.

The motor nerve supply is derived from the inferior division of the oculomotor (third cranial) nerve. The nerve fibres enter the upper surface of the muscle as it passes below the equator of the globe.

Actions of the inferior oblique

Contraction of the inferior oblique produces supraduction, excycloduction and abduction.

Supraduction occurs even though the muscle is attached below the globe because, like the superior oblique, its line of action is towards a point anterior and nasal to the eye and this also produces the excycloduction. The abduction effect is due to the line of action of the muscle passing behind the vertical axis towards the nasal side.

Supraduction decreases as the eye abducts and increases with adduction.

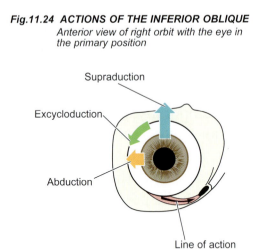

Fig.11.24 ACTIONS OF THE INFERIOR OBLIQUE
Anterior view of right orbit with the eye in the primary position

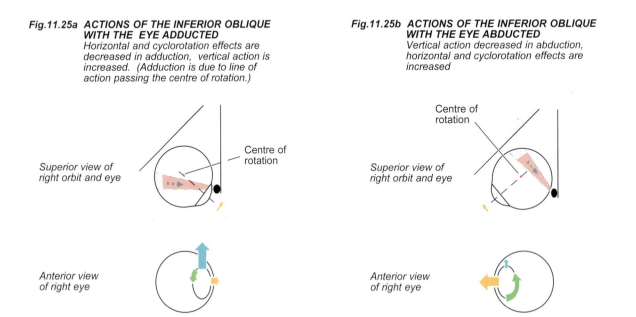

Fig.11.25a ACTIONS OF THE INFERIOR OBLIQUE WITH THE EYE ADDUCTED
Horizontal and cyclorotation effects are decreased in adduction, vertical action is increased. (Adduction is due to line of action passing the centre of rotation.)

Superior view of right orbit and eye

Centre of rotation

Anterior view of right eye

Fig.11.25b ACTIONS OF THE INFERIOR OBLIQUE WITH THE EYE ABDUCTED
Vertical action decreased in abduction, horizontal and cyclorotation effects are increased

Centre of rotation

Superior view of right orbit and eye

Anterior view of right eye

222

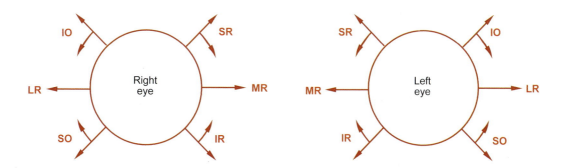

Fig.11.26 *EFFECT OF THE INDIVIDUAL MUSCLES IN MOVING THE EYE FROM THE PRIMARY POSITION*

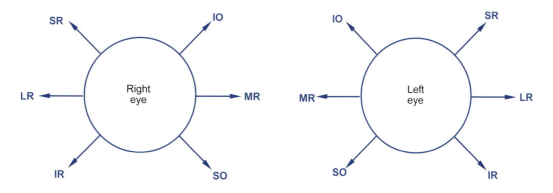

Fig.11.27 *DIRECTION OF GAZE FOR WHICH EACH MUSCLE HAS THE GREATEST EFFECT*

The actions of the individual muscles are summarised in Figs.11.26 and 11.27.

It must be emphasised that these descriptions of muscle action apply to the simple situation where a muscle is considered to act alone. Although this may be the case in horizontal movements of the eye, the production of cyclorotation or pure vertical movements requires the combined actions of pairs of muscles.

Muscle pairs are considered to be synergists if they aid each other in a particular duction or antagonists if their actions are opposed. Thus the superior rectus and inferior oblique are synergists for supraduction, while the lateral and medial recti are antagonists in horizontal duction movement.

When vertical movements are to be made, the secondary effects of the muscles used must cancel, so that there is no horizontal movement or cyclorotation. For example, in supraduction, the incycloduction effect of the superior rectus cancels the excycloduction of the inferior oblique. Also the adduction of the superior rectus muscle is cancelled by the abduction of the inferior oblique muscle.

While a given muscle is contracting, its antagonist is inhibited. This was noted by Descartes (1662) and, following the work of Sherrington (1893), became established as Sherrington's Law of Reciprocal Innervation. Breinin (1962) was able to demonstrate the law by using electrodes inserted into the extrinsic ocular muscles to record their electrical activity as the eye rotated. Electrical activity increases as the muscle contracts and the eye rotates, moving the direction of gaze towards what is called the motor field of the muscle. When the visual axis is

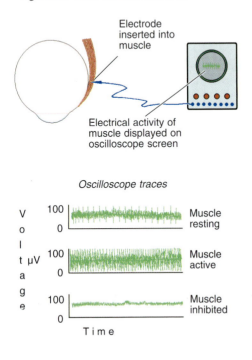

Fig.11.28a ELECTROMYOGRAPHY

Electrode inserted into muscle

Electrical activity of muscle displayed on oscilloscope screen

Oscilloscope traces

Voltage µV

Muscle resting

Muscle active

Muscle inhibited

Time

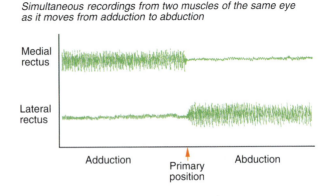

Fig.11.28b RECIPROCAL INNERVATION
Simultaneous recordings from two muscles of the same eye as it moves from adduction to abduction

Medial rectus

Lateral rectus

Adduction   Primary position   Abduction

224

moved into the motor field of its antagonist, electrical activity of the muscle (and thus its contraction) is inhibited. When the innervation is removed, it is the elasticity of the muscles that restores the eye to the primary position.

When the rotation of only one eye is considered the movement is referred to as a duction, but when both eyes move, the movements are referred to as either version (conjugate) or vergence (disjunctive) movements.

Version movements occur in tracking an object moving in the visual field while the visual axes remain at the same angle to each other. Thus both eyes must move in the same direction for a version movement. For example, for a movement where both eyes move to the right (dextroversion), the right lateral and left medial recti contract. These muscles are then called contralateral synergists for dextroversion or yoke muscles. For movement to the left or laevoversion the right

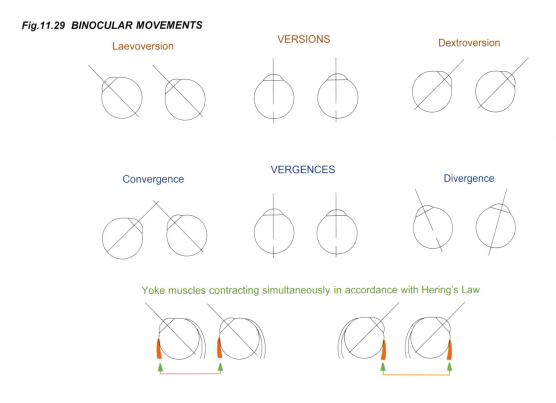

Fig.11.29 BINOCULAR MOVEMENTS

Laevoversion   VERSIONS   Dextroversion

Convergence   VERGENCES   Divergence

Yoke muscles contracting simultaneously in accordance with Hering's Law medial rectus and the left lateral rectus are the yoke muscles. In normal voluntary movements, equal and simultaneous innervation is said, by Hering's Law of Equal Innervation, to flow to the muscles of both eyes to ensure that the eyes move equal amounts to take up or maintain fixation. If, in an abnormal muscle condition, one muscle requires more innervation than usual, Hering's Law means that the contralateral synergist will also receive an excessive amount of stimulation leading to excessive rotation of the contralateral eye.

Vergence movements are those in which the visual axes swing towards each other (convergence) or apart (divergence). The same laws apply to vergences as to versions.

Normally the eyes do not make movements of greater than 10-12° from the primary position since head rotations can be made to avoid the need for large fixation or refixation (saccadic) movements.

STRUCTURE OF THE EXTRINSIC OCULAR MUSCLES

The extrinsic ocular muscles, like general skeletal muscle, are composed of striated muscle cells. However, on average, extrinsic ocular muscle cells are thinner than those of skeletal muscle having a mean diameter of only 10-15μm. Since the oculorotary muscles are relatively short, the cells of which they are composed generally extend the full length of the muscle. Two types of striated muscle cell are present, Fibrillenstruktur and Felderstruktur (see page 35).

Bundles of muscle cells are surrounded by a thin connective tissue sheath, the perimysium, and surrounding the whole muscle is the muscle sheath or epimysium. Between the cells is the connective tissue endomysium. Extrinsic ocular muscles have an abundant blood supply and the connective tissue is rich in elastic fibres.

Fig.11.30 STRUCTURE AND CONTROL OF EXTRINSIC OCULAR MUSCLE

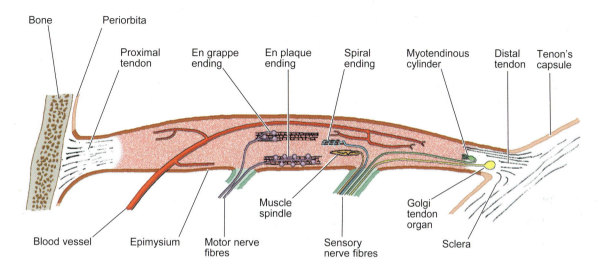

CONTROL OF EXTRINSIC OCULAR MUSCLE

To obtain consistently high visual acuity and to avoid diplopia, fixation needs to be very precise. The fine control required to produce accuracy of eye movement is provided by a very high level of innervation, both motor and sensory. Muscle cells in extrinsic ocular muscles share motor innervation with between 3 and 10 other cells. This contrasts with general skeletal muscle where up to 1000 muscle cells share branches of a motor neurone. Fast cells receive en plaque motor innervation and these cells are used for the rapid saccadic eye movements. The tonic Felderstruktur cells receive en grappe endings and may be used to hold the visual axis steady on the fixation point. The nerve fibres in all extrinsic ocular muscles enter the muscles at the junction of the middle and proximal third, and the nerve fibre bundles break into finer groups distributed distally and proximally to the appropriate cells, together with sympathetic vasomotor fibres.

Sensory structures within the extrinsic ocular muscles are also extensive; the body of the muscles contain muscle spindles, the tendons contain Golgi tendon organs and at the junction of the tendons and some muscle fibres are myotendinous cylinders (palisade endings). These receptors monitor the state of contraction of the muscle and the tension in the tendons that anchor the muscle to the globe and to the orbital wall. The signals passed to the midbrain centres from these receptors give information about the position and movement of the eye and thus the receptors are referred to as proprioceptors.

Since a high proportion of fibres in the nerves to the extrinsic ocular muscles are sensory, carrying proprioceptive information to the central nervous system, the nerves supplying the muscles must be considered as mixed. However, the pathway of the sensory fibres to the nuclei of the central nervous system is still to be fully elucidated.

Chapter 12

THE EYELIDS AND CONJUNCTIVA

The eyelids are movable folds of modified skin which play a significant role in protecting the eye, particularly the cornea. Reflex and voluntary eyelid closure forms a barrier to small foreign bodies, liquids and gases. The lids are used to reduce the amount of light, and other radiation close to the visual spectrum, entering the eye. The eyelids provide some of the constituents of the tears fluid and tears are moved by the eyelids across the cornea towards the lacrimal drainage system.

The upper eyelid extends downwards from the eyebrow (supercilia) to the upper lid margin. The lower eyelid extends from the nasojugal and malar folds of the cheek up to the lower lid margin. These folds mark the regions where the tissue of the lids is anchored to the periosteum of the facial bones.

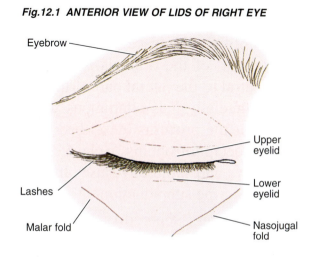

Fig.12.1 ANTERIOR VIEW OF LIDS OF RIGHT EYE

Eyebrow

Upper eyelid

Lower eyelid

Lashes

Malar fold

Nasojugal fold

THE EYEBROWS

The brows are composed of thick skin (see page 236) containing large numbers of sweat and sebaceous glands. The hairs of the brows are directed up and out medially, but are directed down and out at the upper temporal border of the orbit.

The eyebrows serve to divert sweat from the forehead away from the orbits and also play a major role in facial expression. Because of the internal association of the facial muscles that surround the orbit, lid movement is also frequently linked with brow movement which, in common with all changes in facial expression, forms part of the mechanism of non-verbal communication.

Four striated muscles are associated with movement of the eyebrows.

- The orbicularis oculi muscle
- The occipitofrontalis muscle
- The corrugator supercilii
- The procerus muscle

The orbicularis oculi has an upper orbital part which passes into the subcutaneous tissue of the eyebrow and acts as a brow depressor. The frontal belly of the occipitofrontalis muscle blends with the orbital part of the orbicularis oculi from the central to the lateral part of the brows while medially it is continuous with the fibres of the procerus (described below). The occipitofrontalis elevates the eyebrows and indirectly raises the upper eyelids during supraduction.

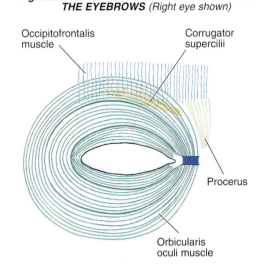

Fig.12.2 FACIAL MUSCLES ASSOCIATED WITH THE EYEBROWS (Right eye shown)

Occipitofrontalis muscle

Corrugator supercilii

Procerus

Orbicularis oculi muscle

The corrugator supercilii lies between the occipitofrontalis and the orbicularis, and runs laterally from the medial end of the superciliary arch to the middle of the eyebrow. These muscles draw the brows down and medially producing the characteristic vertical frown furrows in the lower part of the forehead between the brows.

The orbicularis, the corrugator and the occipitofrontalis muscles are supplied with motor innervation by the temporal branch of the facial nerve.

The fourth muscle concerned with eyebrow movement, the procerus, does not insert directly into the brows but is responsible for drawing down their nasal angle, producing horizontal furrows over the bridge of the nose. This muscle is pyramidal in shape (it is also known as the pyramidalis) and arises from the fascia covering the lower part of the nasal bone and the lateral nasal cartilage. It is inserted into the subcutaneous tissue between the brows. The motor nerve supply to this muscle is from the upper buccal branch of the facial nerve.

Details of the blood, lymphatic, sensory and motor nerve supply to these muscles are shown in Figs. 12.27-33.

THE EYELIDS

The upper and lower eyelids are united at each end of their free margin. The opening between the margins forms the palpebral fissure or aperture. The fissure is closed medially at the inner canthus and laterally at the outer canthus.

The inner canthus is in the form of a narrow triangular space, containing the small reddish mass of the caruncle and a fold of conjunctiva, the plica semilunaris. The inner canthus and its contents are frequently obscured in infants by an epicanthal fold of upper lid tissue, but this normally disappears as the bridge of the nose develops. In Mongolian races, this fold is present in adults and runs along the margin of the upper eyelid to the outer canthus.

The palpebral aperture changes position throughout life. In the new-born, the upper lid lies above the margin of the cornea when the eyelids are open, but with

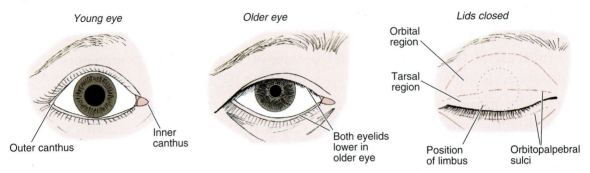

Fig.12.3 EYELID POSITION

Young eye

Older eye

Lids closed

Orbital region

Tarsal region

Outer canthus

Inner canthus

Both eyelids lower in older eye

Position of limbus

Orbitopalpebral sulci

increasing age, both lid margins move down. The upper lid covers increasing amounts of the upper cornea while increasing amounts of sclera are seen below the lower limbus. Closure of the lids during waking hours causes the lid margins to meet just above the lower limbus, but in sleep the lids meet below the cornea as supraduction of the globe occurs.

The surface of the lid is grooved by a furrow, the orbitopalpebral sulcus, which divides the eyelid into an orbital region and a tarsal region. The orbitopalpebral sulcus of the upper eyelid is the more obvious and the looser orbital tissue above may sag, forming an orbital fold which may become more evident with age. If the skin is particularly loose, it may overhang the lid margin producing a condition known as blepharochalasis.

The lid margins are about 2mm wide and 30mm long. At the outer canthus the posterior edge of the margin is against the globe but at the inner canthus the margin extends 5-6mm nasally to the surface of the eye. Thus about five-sixths of the length of the posterior eyelid margin is in contact with the globe and this five-sixths carries the eyelashes on the rounded anterior edge.

There are two or three rows of lashes (or cilia) on the edge of the lids, with about 100-150 on the upper lid and about 50-75 on the lower. On the upper eyelid the length of the lashes is 8-12mm and on the lower lid they are 6-8mm long. They are renewed every 3-5 months but if completely removed (epilated) they will regrow fully in about ten weeks.

The length of the lid margin where the eyelashes are found is known as the ciliary part while the medial region where there are no lashes is the lacrimal part. At the junction of these two regions lies the lacrimal papilla. This is a small mound with a central 0.25mm opening, the lacrimal punctum. The papillae are directed slightly backwards, so that the papilla of the upper eyelid is not normally visible, and the punctum of the lower papilla can only be seen if the lid is pulled away from the globe.

The orifices of the tarsal glands can be seen close to the posterior margin of the lids, and anterior to these, a grey, slightly pigmented line, marks the intermarginal sulcus, separating the gland orifices from the eyelashes.

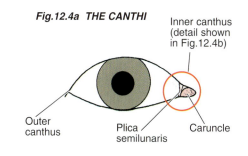

Fig.12.4a THE CANTHI

Inner canthus (detail shown in Fig.12.4b)

Outer canthus

Plica semilunaris

Caruncle

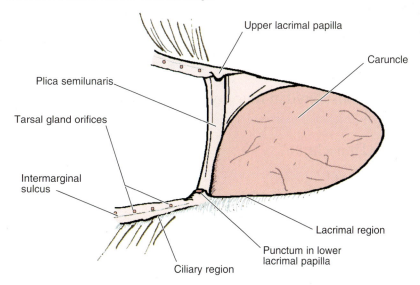

Fig.12.4b DETAIL OF INNER CANTHUS
The upper lid is pulled forward to show the margin

Upper lacrimal papilla

Caruncle

Plica semilunaris

Tarsal gland orifices

Intermarginal sulcus

Lacrimal region

Punctum in lower lacrimal papilla

Ciliary region

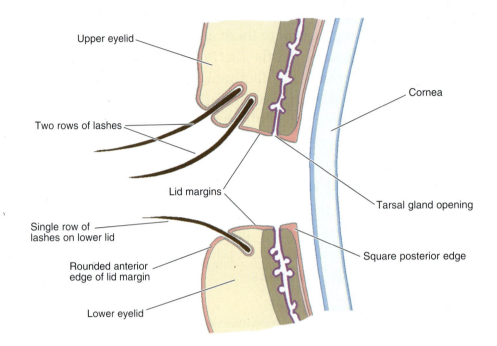

Fig.12.5 VERTICAL SECTION THROUGH LID MARGINS AND CORNEA
Note the rounded edge of the anterior lid margin and the sharper edge of the posterior margin.

Upper eyelid

Cornea

Two rows of lashes

Lid margins

Tarsal gland opening

Single row of lashes on lower lid

Rounded anterior edge of lid margin

Square posterior edge

Lower eyelid

STRUCTURE OF THE EYELIDS

The lids can be considered in four layers.

- Skin
- Striated muscle
- Fibrous layer
- Conjunctiva

Between these are layers of connective tissue, which vary in thickness with location.

Fig.12.6 SAGITTAL SECTION THROUGH UPPER EYELID

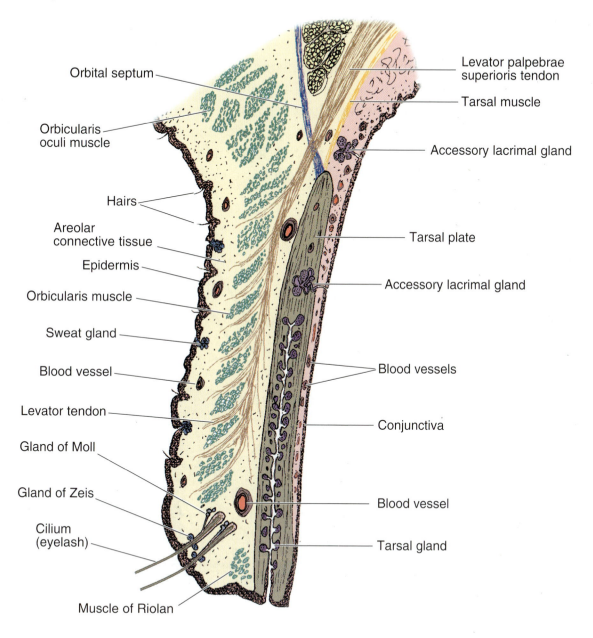

Orbital septum

Orbicularis oculi muscle

Hairs

Areolar connective tissue

Epidermis

Orbicularis muscle

Sweat gland

Blood vessel

Levator tendon

Gland of Moll

Gland of Zeis

Cilium (eyelash)

Muscle of Riolan

Levator palpebrae superioris tendon

Tarsal muscle

Accessory lacrimal gland

Tarsal plate

Accessory lacrimal gland

Blood vessels

Conjunctiva

Blood vessel

Tarsal gland

The skin

Skin in general may be divided into two main layers, the epidermis and the dermis.

The epidermis is the superficial keratinising stratified squamous epithelium composed of 4 or 5 distinct layers. In regions where the skin is subject to abrasion there are five layers, while elsewhere there are only four. The majority of the cells are keratinocytes which provide the hard protein keratin. Keratinocytes develop from the basal cell layer and the whole epidermis is constantly replaced by mitosis in a 40 day cycle.

Fig.12.7 STRUCTURE OF SKIN

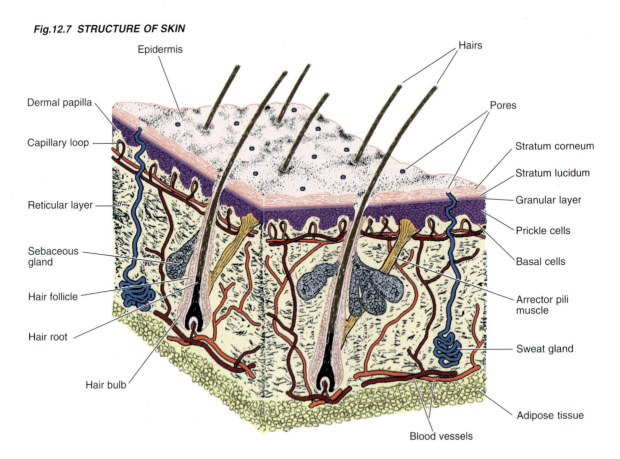

Epidermis

Hairs

Dermal papilla

Pores

Capillary loop

Stratum corneum

Stratum lucidum

Reticular layer

Granular layer

Prickle cells

Sebaceous gland

Basal cells

Hair follicle

Arrector pili muscle

Hair root

Sweat gland

Hair bulb

Adipose tissue

Blood vessels

The basal layer is a single row of columnar cells and above this is the prickle cell layer consisting of several rows of cells. Keratinisation begins in the third, granular layer in which there are 3-5 rows of cells. The fourth layer is only present in thick skin (the five layer type) and consists of dead keratinocytes which form a translucent band known as the stratum lucidum or clear layer. Finally the outermost region, known as the stratum corneum, consists of up to 30 layers of dead cell remnants filled with the hard hydrophobic keratin.

Fig.12.8 THE EPIDERMIS

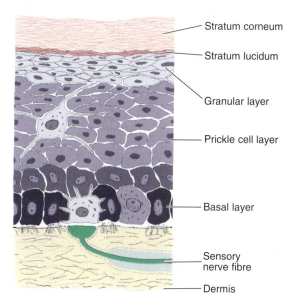

Stratum corneum

Stratum lucidum

Granular layer

Prickle cell layer

Basal layer

Sensory nerve fibre

Dermis

The dermis is below the basal layer and consists of vascular connective tissue. The ground substance is a gel containing collagen, elastin and reticulin fibres together with typical connective tissue cells; fibroblasts, mast cells and macrophages. Lymphatic vessels and nerve fibres are found in this layer.

The dermis is subdivided into a thin papillary layer and a thick reticular layer. The papillary layer consists of areolar connective tissue with papillae which project into the epidermis and contain capillary loops and pain or touch receptors (nerve endings). The reticular layer forms 80% of the dermal thickness and is mainly collagen with some elastin and reticulin. Within this layer are hair follicles and sweat and sebaceous glands. Layers of adipose tissue are usually found below the reticular layer.

Hair follicles are bag-like structures that extend from the dermis outwards to the epidermis surface, usually at an angle, and which contain the skin's hairs. The hairs originate from the hair bulb in the follicle and grow due to cell division. As the cells move towards the surface they become more and more keratinised and die. The keratin in these cells is very tough and the cells remain bound together forming the hair. (In the epidermis, the cells are not bound together and flake off, a process known as desquamation.) The hairs act as touch receptors as they have a plexus of sensory nerves wrapped around the hair bulb. Between the hair follicle and the basal epithelial layer is a bundle of smooth muscle cells, the arrector pili muscle. This is used to pull the hair upright and is under sympathetic nerve control.

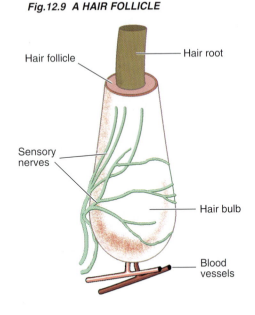

Fig.12.9 A HAIR FOLLICLE

Hair follicle

Hair root

Sensory nerves

Hair bulb

Blood vessels

The hair follicles also act as ducts for the sebaceous glands that lie below the epidermis. Sebaceous glands consist of acini filled with lipid cells which degenerate and release an oily secretion (sebum) onto the skin surface. This is a holocrine method of secretion. The oil lubricates the skin and softens the hair shaft, making it less brittle.

Sweat glands are of two types, eccrine or apocrine. The majority are eccrine glands and have a duct which extends to the surface of the epidermis. The body of the gland is a coiled structure which contains the secretory cells surrounding the central lumen. Between these and the basal lamina of the gland lie myoepithelial cells which are under sympathetic nervous control. Normally the transmitter substance at sympathetic neuro-effector junctions is noradrenaline. However, the myoepithelial cells of sweat glands have acetylcholine as the neurotransmitter and are therefore affected by drugs that block or stimulate parasympathetic activity. Secretion occurs as a merocrine process by which the cells release their product through the apical cell membrane. The secretion is 99% water with small quantities of sodium and chloride ions, metabolic waste products and little protein. Its main function is cooling but sweat is also produced as a by-product of emotional, sympathetic nervous activity.

Apocrine sweat glands are similar in structure to eccrine but are larger and they secrete into the neck of hair follicles. The apex of the cells forming these glands is lost into the lumen of the gland as a small sac along with the secretory products. The apical surface is reformed and the process repeats.

Skin of the eyelids

The skin of the eyelids is very thin, and is covered in fine hairs. It contains numerous small sweat and sebaceous glands, particularly in the nasal regions.

The epidermis is of the thin four layer type and consists of only six to seven layers of cells in total. At the anterior border of the tarsal gland orifices, the keratinised epithelium gives way to the nonkeratinised epithelium of the conjunctiva.

The dermis is thin and blends with the subcutaneous areolar tissue beneath. This layer contains no fat and is absent at the lid margins and the canthi. It is only firmly attached at the sulci, so that it readily becomes oedematous or can collect blood (ecchymosis or "black eye"). The dermis consists of a network of collagen and elastic fibres, with numerous fine blood vessels and lymphatics. The hair follicles, sebaceous and sweat glands lie in this layer.

The follicles of the eyelashes extend obliquely 1.5-2.0mm into the dermis, surrounded by an extensive elastic layer and many sensory nerve fibres. The eyelash follicles lack arrector muscles but have paired sebaceous glands opening into them and are associated with sweat glands that open either into the follicle or onto the surface of the skin.

The sebaceous glands of Zeis (1835) associated with the cilia are large and their oily secretion, which is passed into the follicle by a wide duct, lubricates the lash and prevents it from drying.

The sweat glands of Moll (1857) are in the form of unbranched tubular spirals. The cells of these glands have an apocrine mode of secretion. The secretory epithelium is surrounded by myoepithelial cells and a thick basement membrane encloses both layers of cells (Fine 1979).

In the upper lid, collagen fibres from the tendon of the levator muscle pass into the dermal layer.

Striated muscle

The orbicularis oculi muscle

Together with the fibrous layer, the orbicularis oculi forms the bulk of the thickness of the eyelid. It is a flat, oval sheet of muscle attached at its nasal and lateral extremities by the palpebral ligaments. It extends from the lid margins to the eyebrows, the cheek and on to the frontal process of the zygomatic.

There are two main areas of muscle; an orbital and a palpebral

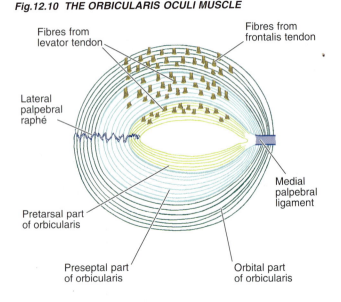

Fig.12.10 THE ORBICULARIS OCULI MUSCLE

Fibres from levator tendon

Fibres from frontalis tendon

Lateral palpebral raphé

Medial palpebral ligament

Pretarsal part of orbicularis

Preseptal part of orbicularis

Orbital part of orbicularis

part, the palpebral part being subdivided into preseptal and pretarsal portions. The bundles of muscle fibres originate at the nasal process of the frontal bone and sweep, without interruption, around the orbit to terminate at the frontal process of the maxilla. The orbicularis fibres interweave with other facial muscle fibres, in particular those of the occipitofrontalis and corrugator.

The palpebral parts of the orbicularis oculi arise from the medial palpebral ligament and pass across the upper and lower lids to join at the lateral palpebral raphé. The pretarsal portions meet at the common pretarsal tendon with which the preseptal portions blend anteriorly. This 8mm long tendon is continuous with the periosteum of the zygomatic tubercle. The orbital portion blends with the palpebral part and is not visible externally. The junction of the preseptal and pretarsal parts is marked superficially by the palpebral furrow.

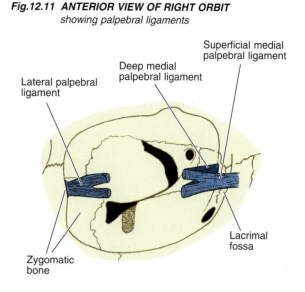

Fig.12.11 ANTERIOR VIEW OF RIGHT ORBIT
showing palpebral ligaments

Superficial medial palpebral ligament

Deep medial palpebral ligament

Lateral palpebral ligament

Lacrimal fossa

Zygomatic bone

At the lacrimal fossa, the pretarsal bundles divide to form deep and superficial endings or heads. The deep heads of both upper and lower pretarsal muscles are anchored by the deep medial palpebral ligament to the lacrimal bone behind the lacrimal fossa. This posterior section of muscle is referred to as the lacrimal part of the orbicularis or Horner's muscle. Similar divisions of the tendons of the preseptal and orbital parts have been described and these blend with the fascia of the lacrimal sac and periorbita to form a lacrimal diaphragm, putting traction on the lacrimal sac during lid closure (see pages 272 and 275).

In the upper eyelid, the bundles of the orbicularis are divided, particularly in the pretarsal region, by the fibres of the levator tendon (see Figs.12.6 and 12.10).

A small part of the pretarsal portion is isolated from the rest by the lash follicles at the lid margin. This is the ciliary bundle or muscle of Riolan (Fig.12.12) which is considered to have the function of tensioning the eyelid against the globe.

Fig.12.12 SECTION THROUGH UPPER EYELID MARGIN

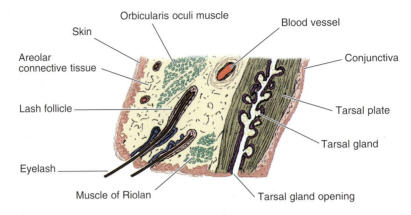

The whole of the orbicularis oculi muscle is innervated by the facial (seventh cranial) nerve. The palpebral portion is used in reflex or spontaneous blinking and in voluntary winking, while the orbital portion is used in forcible lid closure. If the eyelids are prevented from closing when forcible lid closure is attempted, the eyes rotate upwards, an effect known as Bell's phenomenon. Blinking sweeps the tears film across the cornea and aids the movement of the tears towards the lacrimal puncta.

The reflex blink is described in Chapter 17 with the other ocular reflexes and the involvement of the muscle in tears drainage is described with the lacrimal system.

Lid closure commences laterally with the upper lid moving down to meet the lower lid (which hardly moves during blinking) so that the palpebral fissure narrows progressively from the outer to the inner canthus. A blink takes about 300 milliseconds to complete and normally occurs about once every three seconds, but the rate increases if the person is agitated.

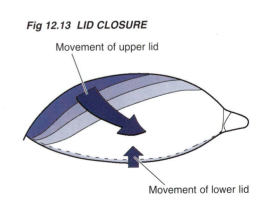

Fig 12.13 LID CLOSURE

Movement of upper lid

Movement of lower lid

The levator palpebrae superioris muscle

The levator palpebrae superioris muscle originates at the apex of the orbit where its tendon is continuous with that of the superior rectus muscle. The muscle sheaths of the superior rectus and the levator fuse except where the conjunctiva comes between them at the upper fornix. The connective tissue of the conjunctival stroma then fuses with the muscle sheaths so that it is moved as the globe or upper eyelid moves. The distal tendon of the levator expands into a wide flat sheet or aponeurosis which divides the lacrimal gland and is attached at its extremities to the medial and lateral orbital walls via expansions to the palpebral ligaments. The aponeurosis splits into two lamellae; the superior lamella sends its fibres between the bundles of the orbicularis to insert into the subcutaneous tissue anteriorly and into the anterior surface of the tarsal plate posteriorly. The inferior lamella contains smooth muscle and forms the superior tarsal or palpebral muscle (of Müller) which inserts into the superior border of the tarsal plate.

Fig.12.14 VERTICAL SECTION THROUGH ORBIT
to show levator palpebrae superioris

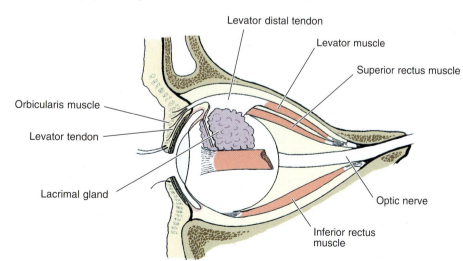

Levator distal tendon

Levator muscle

Superior rectus muscle

Orbicularis muscle

Levator tendon

Lacrimal gland

Optic nerve

Inferior rectus muscle

In the lower eyelid, there is no muscle corresponding to the levator. The smooth tarsal muscle, which is much sparser in the lower lid than in the upper, arises from the fascial expansions of the inferior rectus and inferior oblique muscles.

The position of the upper eyelid is maintained by contraction of the levator aided by the tarsal muscle. Contraction of the superior rectus muscle on voluntary supraduction is accompanied by contraction of the levator, so that both eye and lid move together. Ptosis (drooping of the eyelid) occurs if either the levator or the smooth tarsal muscle is paretic or paralysed. The small movements of the lower eyelid are produced by the tarsal muscle in conjunction with the fascial expansions of the inferior rectus and oblique muscles.

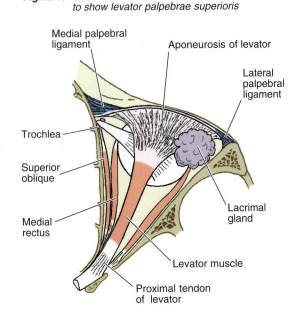

Fig.12.15 SUPERIOR ASPECT OF ORBIT
to show levator palpebrae superioris

Medial palpebral ligament

Aponeurosis of levator

Lateral palpebral ligament

Trochlea

Superior oblique

Medial rectus

Lacrimal gland

Levator muscle

Proximal tendon of levator

The levator muscle is innervated by the superior division of the oculomotor (third cranial) nerve by fibres that have passed through the superior rectus muscle. Its blood supply is from the superior muscular branch of the ophthalmic artery and the venous drainage is into the superior ophthalmic vein. The smooth tarsal muscle is innervated by the orbital sympathetic supply, and when stimulated, widens the palpebral aperture.

In the lids, a thin layer of loose areolar tissue lies in the spaces behind the muscle layer, separating it from the fibrous layer. In the upper lid, this tissue is continuous with the subaponeurotic layer of the scalp, so that haemorrhages of the scalp may leak into the eyelid.

The fibrous layer

This layer consists of the tarsal plates, which give the lids shape and firmness, and the orbital septum (septum orbitale of Henlé).

The tarsal plates are about 1mm thick and are composed of dense fibrous connective tissue. The upper plate is D-shaped, about 25mm long and 12mm high. The lower plate is the same length but only 5mm high and almost rectangular in shape. The plates are linked to the orbital margins by the orbital septum and the medial and lateral palpebral ligaments and to the smooth muscles as described above. Both upper and lower plates terminate close to the lid margins in fibrous expansions that support the cilia. At the posterior lid margin, the conjunctival epithelium is applied directly to the surface of the plate.

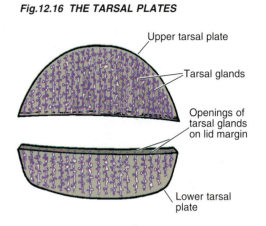

Fig.12.16 THE TARSAL PLATES

Upper tarsal plate

Tarsal glands

Openings of tarsal glands on lid margin

Lower tarsal plate

The tarsal plates contain the tarsal glands which are surrounded by connective tissue, rich in elastic fibres and containing the blood vessels, lymphatics and nerve fibres supplying the glands.

The tarsal glands (also known as Meibomian glands after Heinrich Meibom 1666) may be seen as yellow streaks within the tarsal plate through the palpebral conjunctiva. They are modified sebaceous glands and the yellow colour is due to the cholesterol contained in the fatty sebum that they secrete.

The glands are arranged as a single row, and run vertically in the tarsal plates from the lid margin, where the openings of their ducts are located, just behind the intermarginal sulcus. There are about 25 glands in the upper eyelid and about 20 in the lower. Each gland consists of cell-lined alveoli feeding short ducts opening directly into a central duct which passes the secretion on to the lid margin. Each

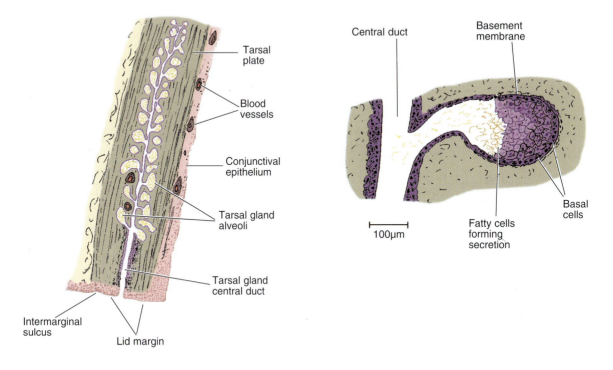

Fig.12.17 A TARSAL GLAND

Tarsal plate

Blood vessels

Conjunctival epithelium

Tarsal gland alveoli

Tarsal gland central duct

Intermarginal sulcus

Lid margin

Fig.12.18 A TARSAL GLAND ALVEOLUS

Central duct

Basement membrane

Basal cells

Fatty cells forming secretion

100µm

alveolus is enclosed in a multilaminar basement membrane, internal to which is a layer of basal or germinal cells. The rest of the alveolus is filled with fatty cells which degenerate, the cells thus forming part of the oily holocrine secretion produced by the gland. The secretion lubricates the eyelids, prevents their sticking and limits the overflow of the tears film by forming a greasy margin to the lids. The oily surface formed on the tears film by the secretion may also reduce evaporation.

Embedded in the tarsal plate, near its junction with the orbital septum, are found the accessory lacrimal glands although the majority of these glands are found in the orbital region of the conjunctiva.

The orbital septum is a weak fibrous connective tissue sheet, extending from the

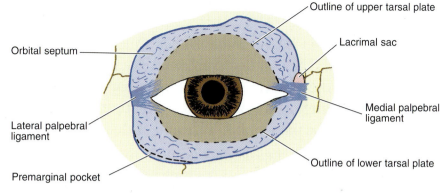

Fig.12.19 THE ORBITAL SEPTUM

Orbital septum

Outline of upper tarsal plate

Lacrimal sac

Lateral palpebral ligament

Medial palpebral ligament

Premarginal pocket

Outline of lower tarsal plate

periosteum at the orbital margin to the edge of the tarsal plates. At the medial margin of the orbit it passes behind the lacrimal sac and is continuous with the deep portion of the medial palpebral ligament which is attached to the posterior lacrimal crest. The septum then extends laterally to the lacrimal sac and forwards to become continuous with the superficial portion of the medial palpebral ligament at the anterior lacrimal crest. Elsewhere the septum follows the margin of the orbit, except for a slight deviation onto the anterior surface of the zygomatic bone (the premarginal pocket of Eisler, see page 281).

The lateral part of the septum is continuous with the lateral palpebral raphé at the junction of the upper and lower palpebral parts of the orbicularis oculi.

The septum is perforated by blood vessels, nerves and the aponeurosis of the levator.

Although the fibrous layer is protective and restrains the orbital contents, the septum orbitale may thin and weaken with age, so that fat or the lacrimal gland may protrude, deforming the eyelids.

THE CONJUNCTIVA

The inner surface of the lids is lined with a mucous membrane that forms the palpebral conjunctiva. The conjunctival tissue extends posteriorly and is reflected at the fornix to cover the anterior globe as the bulbar conjunctiva which extends to the limbus. This folding creates a bag-like structure called the conjunctival sac, open anteriorly along the palpebral fissure and closed posteriorly by the cornea.

The conjunctiva is smooth and closely applied to the tarsal plates of the eyelids but is thrown into folds in the fornix and where it reflects onto the globe, so that the dimensions of the sac may vary considerably.

The conjunctiva consists of nonkeratinised epithelium and goblet cells covering a connective tissue stroma or substantia propria. Its goblet cells provide mucin which acts as a wetting agent for the epithelial surfaces, and the glands in the stroma provide a proportion of the tears fluid. The sac-like structure prevents small foreign bodies from passing into the orbit around the globe and the vascular tarsal conjunctiva provides oxygen for the cornea when the eyelids are closed.

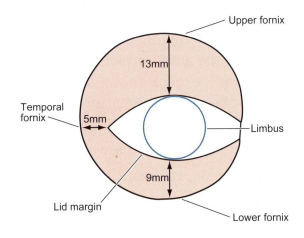

Fig.12.20 **DIMENSIONS OF THE CONJUNCTIVAL SAC**

Upper fornix

13mm

Temporal fornix

5mm

Limbus

9mm

Lid margin

Lower fornix

STRUCTURE OF THE CONJUNCTIVA

For convenience, the conjunctiva can be considered to have a number of regions. These have marked variations in structure. From lid margin to limbus the regions are:

- Marginal
- Tarsal
- Palpebral
- Fornix
- Bulbar
- Limbal

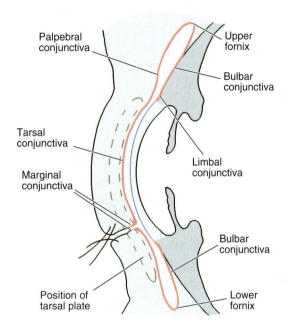

Fig.12.21 **THE REGIONS OF THE CONJUNCTIVA**

Marginal conjunctiva

The nonkeratinised conjunctival epithelium commences at the orifices of the tarsal glands, just posterior to the intermarginal sulcus. Here there are five to six layers of cells with the basal cells being columnar and the superficial squamous. There are no goblet cells in this region and the stroma is virtually absent. An increase in the number of cell layers posteriorly produces a square edge (Fig.12.22) which allows the lids to sweep the tears film across the cornea during blinking.

Tarsal conjunctiva

Moving away from the posterior margin of the eyelid the number of layers of cells reduces with the surface cells becoming more cuboidal. Behind the tarsal plate the epithelium thins to a double layer of cells with the superficial layer becoming progressively columnar and the deep layer flatter. A few goblet cells may be found. The substantia propria is extremely thin in this region and contains some lymphatic vessels and a large number of capillaries.

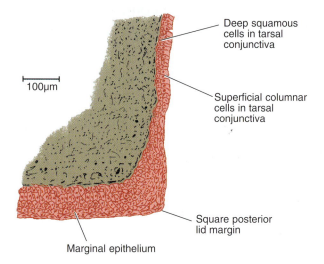

Fig.12.22 THE POSTERIOR LID MARGIN

Deep squamous cells in tarsal conjunctiva

Superficial columnar cells in tarsal conjunctiva

Square posterior lid margin

Marginal epithelium

100μm

Palpebral conjunctiva

Beyond the edge of the tarsal plates the epithelium continues as a double layer of cells with the number of goblet cells increasing. The substantia propria thickens, having an adenoid layer rich in lymphatic and blood vessels. Deep to this adenoid layer is the fibrous layer formed of a thick meshwork of collagen and elastic fibres. The substantia propria contains the accessory lacrimal glands of Krause and Wolfring (see page 267).

Fornix region

The goblet cell population reaches a maximum in the fornices, particularly the lower fornix. The fibrous layer of the conjunctiva becomes continuous superiorly with the fibres of the levator aponeurosis and inferiorly with the expansions of the inferior rectus sheath.

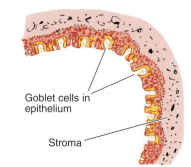

Fig.12.23 THE FORNIX REGION

Goblet cells in epithelium

Stroma

Bulbar conjunctiva

Over the globe the double layer of cells in the epithelium continues as far as the limbus but with the goblet cell numbers decreasing. The substantia propria becomes thinner and blends with the fascia bulbi (Tenon's capsule).

Limbal conjunctiva

The goblet cell population drops to nil at the limbus while the number of epithelial layers increases with the superficial cells again becoming flatter. Ten to fifteen layers of cells fill the external scleral sulcus and these cells blend gradually into the corneal epithelium. At the limbus the epithelial layers have a corrugated undersurface with the ridges running radially towards the cornea. The thickened regions of epithelium are called rete pegs and the regions of stroma between them, filled with fine blood vessels, nerves and lymphatics are the conjunctival stromal papillae. The finger-like processes thus formed, which point in towards the cornea, are called the palisades of Vogt (1921).

Fig.12.24 THE LIMBAL REGION

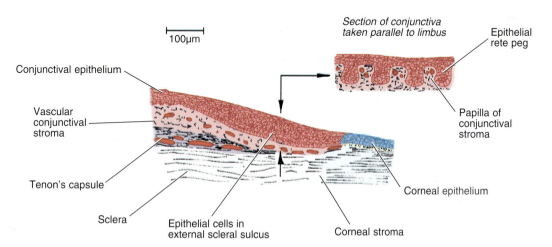

THE PLICA SEMILUNARIS AND CARUNCLE

The plica semilunaris is the fold of conjunctiva found in the inner canthus. (It may represent the remnant of the nictitating membrane or third eyelid found in some animals). It forms a 2mm deep cul-de-sac during adduction of the globe but virtually disappears during abduction.

The fatty stroma of the plica shows traces of smooth muscle and may occasionally contain cartilage. The epithelium is similar to that of the limbus in having 10-12 layers of cells but, unlike the limbus, is rich in goblet cells.

The caruncle lies medially to the plica and can easily be seen during abduction as a fleshy red mound. It is covered in stratified nonkeratinised epithelium and has a number of fine hairs. There are numerous sebaceous glands and goblet cells and sometimes sweat glands. The structure of the caruncle resembles that of the lower eyelid from which, during development, it has been cut off by the inferior lacrimal canaliculus.

Fig.12.25 ANTERIOR VIEW OF INNER CANTHUS

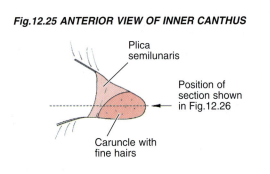

Plica semilunaris

Position of section shown in Fig.12.26

Caruncle with fine hairs

Fig.12.26 HORIZONTAL SECTION THROUGH INNER CANTHUS

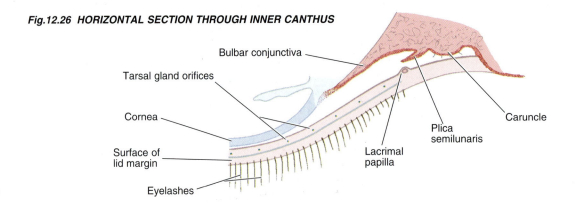

Bulbar conjunctiva

Tarsal gland orifices

Cornea

Surface of lid margin

Eyelashes

Lacrimal papilla

Plica semilunaris

Caruncle

BLOOD SUPPLY

The anterior layers of the eyelids are supplied by blood vessels from both the orbital and facial arterial systems while the posterior layers and the conjunctiva are supplied mainly by the orbital vessels.

Blood from the facial system reaches the lids from the facial, the superficial

Fig.12.27 ARTERIES TO THE EYELID REGION

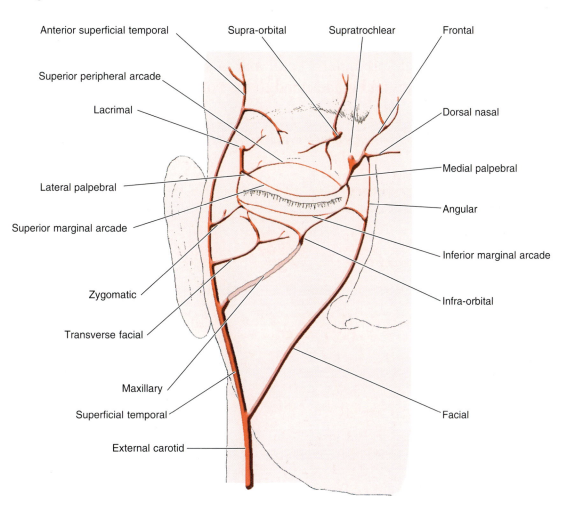

temporal and the infra-orbital arteries. From the orbital system, blood is supplied by the dorsal nasal, the supra-orbital, the frontal and the lacrimal arteries all of which are branches of the ophthalmic artery.

The lacrimal artery forms lateral palpebral branches and the dorsal nasal gives off medial palpebral branches. These, together with end branches of the supra-orbital and frontal arteries, form the marginal and peripheral palpebral arcades of the upper lid. In the lower lid, only a marginal arcade is formed.

The peripheral arcade runs along the edge of the tarsal plate while the marginal arcade lies 2-3mm away from the lid margin. The arcades are located in the areolar tissue behind the orbicularis oculi and give off branches to the skin, the muscles, the tarsal plates and glands, and to the conjunctiva. These latter vessels

Fig.12.28 VERTICAL SECTION THROUGH UPPER EYELID AND ANTERIOR GLOBE
showing arteries

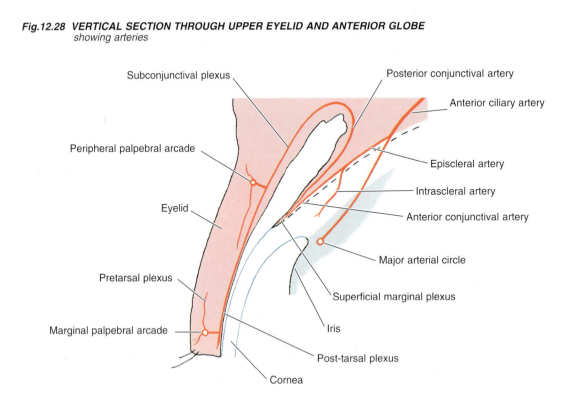

254

form the subconjunctival plexus of the eyelids which sends branches in the conjunctival stroma to the fornices. These are the posterior conjunctival arteries which anastomose with the anterior conjunctival arteries derived from the anterior ciliary arteries.

Vessels from the posterior conjunctival arteries form the pericorneal plexus in the palisade region at the limbus. The branching conjunctival vessels lie superficially and are freely movable, while the straighter vessels derived directly from the anterior ciliary arteries lie deeper in the episcleral tissue and run radially to the corneal margin. At the edge of the cornea they form the superficial marginal plexus. This gives off terminal branches which form the limbal loops at the level of the anterior limiting lamina of the cornea and recurrent vessels which run posteriorly to join the perilimbal vessels.

The caruncle is supplied with blood from the superior medial palpebral branch of the dorsal nasal artery.

The eyelids have venous arcades which receive blood from the superficial lid areas via the pretarsal plexus and from the conjunctiva via the post-tarsal plexus. In general, these correspond to the arterial arcades and drain temporally to the superficial temporal vein or medially to the angular vein, which also drains the caruncle. Superiorly blood may drain into the supra-orbital vein or inferiorly via the inferior palpebral vein to the facial vein (Fig.12.29).

The facial vein, which has no valves, communicates with the orbit via the angular branches to the superior ophthalmic vein and via the deep facial vein to the pterygoid plexus (Fig.12.30). Since these both link with the cavernous sinus, infection may pass from the facial system to the intracranial venous sinuses.

The palpebral conjunctival veins drain principally to the veins of the post-tarsal venous plexus, but in the region of the fornices, both bulbar and palpebral vessels pass directly to the superior and inferior ophthalmic veins. The bulbar conjunctiva close to the limbus drains largely into the anterior ciliary veins.

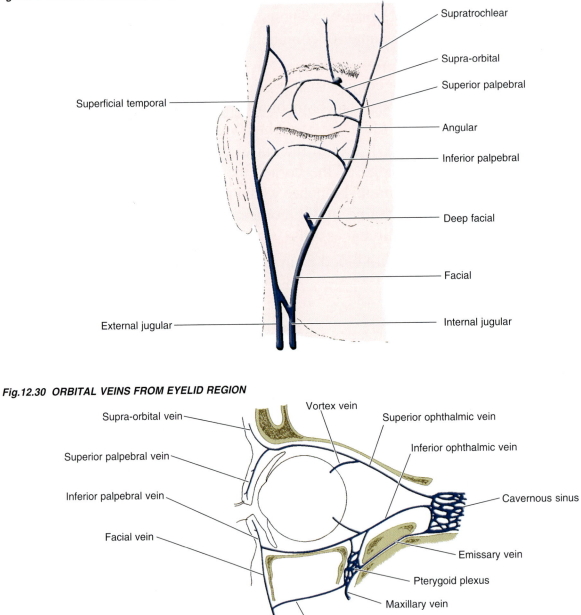

Fig.12.29 FACIAL VEINS FROM EYELID REGION

Supratrochlear

Supra-orbital

Superior palpebral

Superficial temporal

Angular

Inferior palpebral

Deep facial

Facial

External jugular

Internal jugular

Fig.12.30 ORBITAL VEINS FROM EYELID REGION

Supra-orbital vein

Vortex vein

Superior ophthalmic vein

Superior palpebral vein

Inferior ophthalmic vein

Inferior palpebral vein

Cavernous sinus

Facial vein

Emissary vein

Pterygoid plexus

Maxillary vein

Deep facial vein

256

LYMPHATIC SYSTEM

Both the eyelids and the conjunctiva have a lymphatic system.

The eyelid lymphatics divide into an anterior pretarsal system and a deep post-tarsal system that also drains the conjunctiva and the caruncle, and includes the pericorneal lymphatic channel that lies 7-8mm from the limbus. These two systems drain inferiorly to the submandibular nodes and laterally to the superficial and deep parotid nodes.

Fig.12.31 THE LYMPHATIC DRAINAGE OF THE EYELID REGION

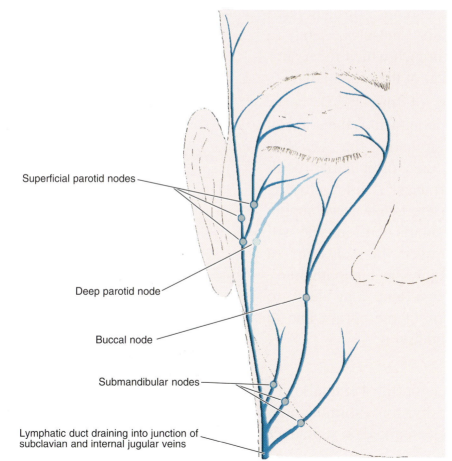

Superficial parotid nodes

Deep parotid node

Buccal node

Submandibular nodes

Lymphatic duct draining into junction of
subclavian and internal jugular veins

NERVE SUPPLY

The innervation to the eyelids is somatic motor and sensory, and autonomic. The conjunctiva receives somatic sensory and autonomic innervation.

Somatic motor nerves

The facial (seventh cranial) nerve has a temporal branch which supplies the upper part of the orbicularis oculi, the corrugator and the frontalis muscles, and a zygomatic branch which innervates the lower part of the orbicularis.

Stimulation of the facial nerve therefore contracts the facial muscles around the eyelids including the orbicularis oculi which produces lid closure. Damage to the facial nerve supply of the orbicularis oculi muscle will prevent proper lid closure (a condition known as lagophthalmos, see Glossary) and may lead to inflammation of the cornea due to exposure and drying.

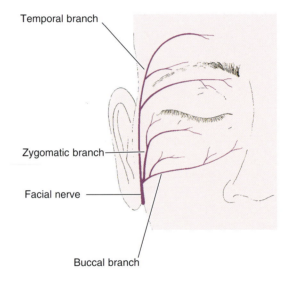

Fig.12.32
DISTRIBUTION OF FACIAL NERVE TO EYELID REGION

Temporal branch

Zygomatic branch

Facial nerve

Buccal branch

The oculomotor (third cranial) nerve supplies the levator palpebrae superioris via its superior division. Stimulation of this nerve thus produces upper lid retraction which is more marked on supraduction of the globe.

Somatic sensory nerves

The eyelids have a rich sensory nerve supply concentrated at the lid margins and lash follicles. Stimulation of these nerves produces protective rapid lid closure (blepharospasm) via reflex pathway connections to the facial nerve which causes contraction of the orbicularis oculi (see page 351).

The trigeminal (fifth cranial) nerve has two divisions that receive innervation from the eyelids; the ophthalmic and the maxillary.

The ophthalmic division receives the lacrimal, nasociliary and the frontal nerves. The frontal nerve receives the supratrochlear nerve and the supra-orbital nerve.

The lacrimal nerve serves the upper lid temporally and part of the lower lid and

Fig.12.33 SENSORY NERVES OF THE EYELID REGION

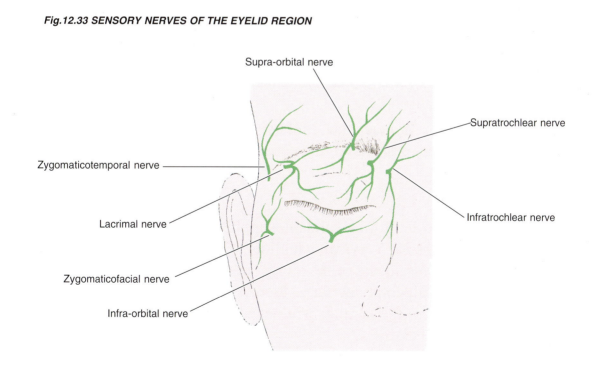

Supra-orbital nerve

Supratrochlear nerve

Zygomaticotemporal nerve

Infratrochlear nerve

Lacrimal nerve

Zygomaticofacial nerve

Infra-orbital nerve

the skin near the outer canthus. The supratrochlear nerve serves the nasal end of the upper lid and the skin of the forehead above the nose. The supra-orbital nerve serves the middle part of the upper eyelid and the skin of the forehead above the orbit. The upper and lower lid around the inner canthus and the caruncle are served by two branches of the nasociliary nerve; the external (or dorsal) nasal and the infratrochlear branches. The maxillary division of the trigeminal nerve is known as the infra-orbital nerve before it leaves the orbit via the inferior orbital fissure and the foramen rotundum. From the lower eyelid it runs below the orbital floor having passed through the infra-orbital foramen. It may also receive sensory stimuli from small areas of the upper eyelid near the inner and outer canthi.

The sensory nerves of the eyelids run through the areolar tissue between the orbicularis oculi and the tarsal plates, receiving fibres from the skin, from the conjunctiva and from the rich sensory nerve plexus around the eyelash follicles.

The conjunctiva passes its sensory information to the nerves that also serve the eyelids in its palpebral and fornix regions. Thus its innervation is via the lacrimal, frontal, nasociliary and infra-orbital branches of the ophthalmic and maxillary division of the trigeminal nerve.

In the bulbar region around the limbus, the conjunctiva passes sensory information to the ciliary branches of the nasociliary nerve.

Autonomic nerves

The smooth tarsal muscle of the eyelids is supplied by sympathetic nerve fibres originating in the superior cervical ganglion (Fig.12.34). Together with the fascial fibres of the lower lid and of the levator in the upper lid, the tarsal muscles maintain the normal palpebral aperture. Increased sympathetic activity retracts the eyelids and produces the staring, wide-eyed effect associated with terror or fright.

Fig.12.34 THE SYMPATHETIC SUPPLY TO THE EYELID REGION

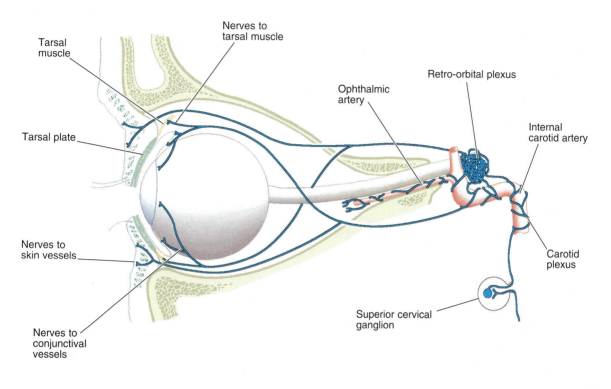

Sympathetic nerves also innervate the lid vessels which, in fright, become constricted, producing the typical blanching of the skin. The conjunctival vessels receive vasoconstrictor innervation from the same sympathetic source.

Since the parasympathetic system innervates the lacrimal gland via the rami lacrimales of the pterygopalatine ganglion (see Fig. 17.20), it is likely that similar fibres supply the accessory lacrimal glands of the eyelids.

Chapter 13

THE LACRIMAL SYSTEM

The lacrimal system supplies the tears fluid and removes unevaporated tears to the nasal meatus via a system of membranous and bony passages.

The tears fluid is formed by secretions from the lacrimal gland, the accessory lacrimal glands, the tarsal glands and the goblet cells of the conjunctiva. This fluid is moved across the cornea by lid action and passes into the membranous passages of the canaliculi, lacrimal sac and nasolacrimal duct. The lacrimal sac rests in the bony lacrimal fossa while the nasolacrimal duct is contained in the nasolacrimal canal which opens into the nasal meatus.

The tears supply nutrition and moisture to the corneal epithelium and remove waste products. They supply an anti-bacterial function and provide a lubricant for lid movement and for eye movement behind the eyelids. They also wash small foreign bodies from the cornea and conjunctival sac and provide a smooth refracting surface over the corneal epithelium.

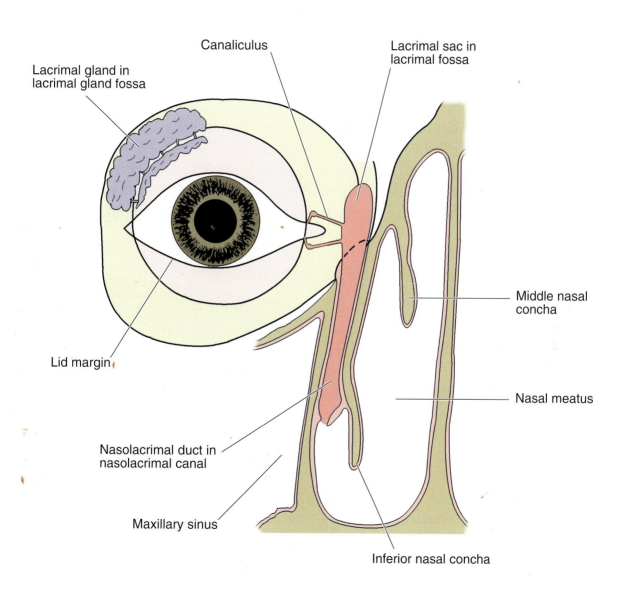

Fig.13.1 THE LACRIMAL APPARATUS
The nasal, frontal and maxillary bones are cut away to show the lacrimal sac, the nasolacrimal duct and the nasal conchae

Canaliculus

Lacrimal sac in
lacrimal fossa

Lacrimal gland in
lacrimal gland fossa

Middle nasal
concha

Nasal meatus

Lid margin

Nasolacrimal duct in
nasolacrimal canal

Maxillary sinus

Inferior nasal concha

THE LACRIMAL GLAND

The lacrimal gland is about 15mm wide, 20mm anteroposteriorly and 5mm thick. It weighs about 1gm. It is divided into two anteriorly by the aponeurosis of the levator palpebrae superioris, forming an upper orbital part and a lower palpebral part. Posterolaterally the two parts are continuous. The larger orbital part is lodged against the periorbita in the lacrimal gland fossa of the frontal bone, just inside the orbital margin.

The orbital part is in contact with the orbital septum anteriorly and with the orbital fat posteriorly. Its inferior surface rests on the levator while its lateral edge lies on the lateral rectus muscle. The inferior, palpebral part is half to one-third the size of the superior part and lies below the aponeurosis of the levator and rests against the fascia bulbi. It extends forward into the upper eyelid temporally

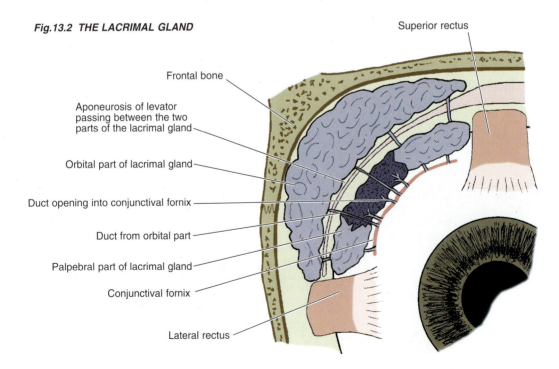

Fig.13.2 THE LACRIMAL GLAND

Superior rectus

Frontal bone

Aponeurosis of levator passing between the two parts of the lacrimal gland

Orbital part of lacrimal gland

Duct opening into conjunctival fornix

Duct from orbital part

Palpebral part of lacrimal gland

Conjunctival fornix

Lateral rectus

where it rests on the superior tarsal muscle. The palpebral part is attached to the conjunctiva at the upper temporal fornix and can be seen through the conjunctiva when the upper eyelid is everted.

The palpebral part of the gland is traversed by four or five ducts derived from the orbital part. These open into the upper and temporal conjunctival fornices together with six to eight ducts derived from the palpebral part. Removal of the palpebral part thus removes all the ducts therefore having the same effect as loss of the whole gland.

STRUCTURE OF THE LACRIMAL GLAND

The lacrimal gland consists of small lobules containing alveoli (or acini) feeding into tubules which branch in a tree-like formation from the ducts. This structure is termed tubuloracemose. The acini are lined by a double layer of cells. The superficial cells are columnar and secretory while the deep cells resting on a multilaminar basement membrane are myoepithelial (Fig.13.5). The secretory cells have large quantities of rough endoplasmic reticulum in the basal region where the secretory granules are synthesized. The secretory products are packaged by the Golgi apparatus in the apical region of the cells from where they are released to the lumen of the acinus. These cells are linked to each other by desmosomes, zonular occlusions and also by zonular adhesions. Desmosomes join them to the

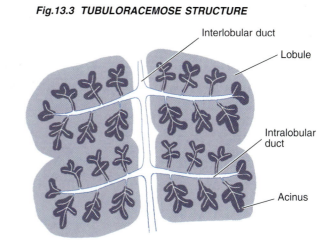

Fig.13.3 TUBULORACEMOSE STRUCTURE

Interlobular duct

Lobule

Intralobular duct

Acinus

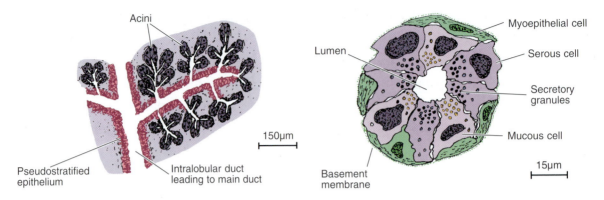

Fig.13.4 STRUCTURE OF THE LACRIMAL GLAND

Acini

Pseudostratified epithelium

Intralobular duct leading to main duct

150μm

Fig.13.5 SECTION THROUGH AN ACINUS

Myoepithelial cell

Serous cell

Secretory granules

Lumen

Mucous cell

Basement membrane

15μm

surrounding myoepithelial cells. The structure of the lacrimal gland is very similar to that of the parotid and other salivary glands.

The human lacrimal gland appears to contain both serous and mucin secreting cells.

The cells secrete steadily, but rapid bulk tears production can occur if the myoepithelial cells are stimulated to contract, forcing the secretion into the ducts. The intralobular ducts are lined with pseudostratified epithelium as are the interlobular ducts, although in the latter the epithelium is somewhat thicker. The ducts are surrounded by vascular connective tissue but there are no lymph nodes within the gland, although lymphocytes and plasma cells are present. These increase in number with age, as does the collagen content of the connective tissue.

Blood supply

Blood is supplied to the lacrimal gland by the lacrimal artery and it is drained by both superior and inferior ophthalmic veins.

Nerve supply

Sensory neurones pass to the lacrimal nerve, but only a low level of sensory innervation is present. The main function of this nerve is to carry innervation from the skin of the upper lid region.

Sympathetic nerves supply the vessels of the gland while the secretomotor innervation to the myoepithelial cells is parasympathetic. These parasympathetic fibres originate in the superior salivatory nucleus located in the lower part of the pons and travel with the facial nerve synapsing in the pterygopalatine ganglion located in the pterygopalatine fossa below the medial end of the inferior orbital fissure. The postganglionic fibres (known as the rami lacrimales) pass up through the inferior orbital fissure to the lacrimal gland (see Fig.17.20).

Fig.13.6
SAGITTAL SECTION THROUGH EYELIDS AND ANTERIOR GLOBE
showing the structures which produce tears

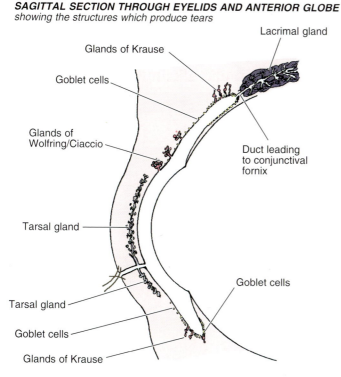

Lacrimal gland

Glands of Krause

Goblet cells

Glands of
Wolfring/Ciaccio

Duct leading
to conjunctival
fornix

Tarsal gland

Goblet cells

Tarsal gland

Goblet cells

Glands of Krause

THE ACCESSORY LACRIMAL GLANDS

The secretion from the lacrimal gland passes via the ducts to the conjunctival sac where it is combined with the secretions from the goblet cells, the tarsal glands and the accessory lacrimal glands. Details of the goblet cells and the tarsal glands may be found in Chapter 12.

The accessory lacrimal glands of Krause (1854) are located in the stroma of the palpebral conjunctiva with approximately twenty in the upper fornix and eight to ten in the lower, with the majority of these glands lying in the lateral regions of the fornices. The glands of Wolfring (1872) or Ciaccio (1876) occupy the upper part of the superior tarsal plate and there are usually three or four of these.

The structure of these accessory lacrimal glands is similar to that of the main lacrimal gland.

THE TEARS FILM

Figures quoted for tears production vary considerably but the amount produced may be close to 0.5-1.0gm per day which was the figure estimated by Schirmer (1903). The tears are essentially a clear watery salty fluid having 98-99% water content and an osmotic pressure equivalent to a 0.9% sodium chloride solution. Their pH lies between 7.3 and 7.5 which is a similar alkalinity to that of blood plasma.

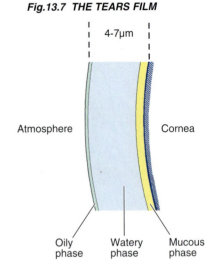

Fig.13.7 THE TEARS FILM

The tears form a layer some 4-7μm thick over the anterior surface of the cornea, spread by the action of the eyelids and surface tension.

The film can be considered as having three layers or phases; a superficial oily phase, a middle watery phase and a deep mucous phase.

The oily phase is derived from the tarsal glands and serves as a lubricant, prevents the lid margins from sticking, forms a barrier to prevent the overflow of tears at the eyelid margins, and may also reduce the evaporation of the watery phase of the tears.

The watery phase is secreted by the lacrimal gland and the accessory lacrimal glands of Krause and Wolfring. This layer enables gaseous exchange to take place between the atmosphere and the corneal epithelium. It provides a hydrating medium for the epithelial cells and carries metabolites to them. The tears contain about 0.7gm of protein per 100ml and about 20% of this is lysozyme. This protein dissolves bacterial cell walls. Other proteins present include ß-lysin which acts on bacterial cell membranes and lactoferrin which inhibits bacterial cell reproduction.

The mucous phase provides a surface coating to the lipid outer surface of the epithelial cell membranes allowing the watery phase to wet the cornea. This sticky mucous component provides bulk to the tears film and is principally secreted by the goblet cells of the conjunctiva.

THE DRAINAGE SYSTEM

The tears film is moved across the cornea by the action of the eyelids which sweep the tears nasally as they close from the superotemporal side. A tears meniscus or marginal tears strip (Fig.13.13) is formed along the posterior lid margin of both eyelids and the tears move in this meniscus to the inner canthus. Here the tears that have not evaporated are passed into the lacrimal drainage system.

THE MEMBRANOUS LACRIMAL PASSAGES

The membranous passages consist of the lacrimal canaliculi, the lacrimal sac and the nasolacrimal duct.

The entrance to each canaliculus is the lacrimal punctum, and these are situated in

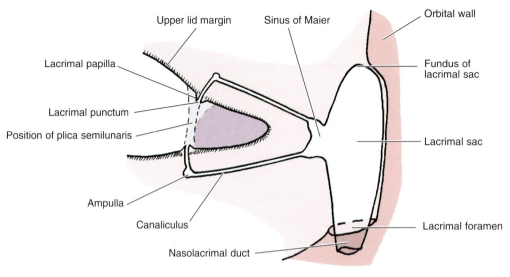

Fig.13.8 THE MEMBRANOUS PASSAGES

Upper lid margin

Sinus of Maier

Orbital wall

Lacrimal papilla

Fundus of lacrimal sac

Lacrimal punctum

Position of plica semilunaris

Lacrimal sac

Ampulla

Canaliculus

Lacrimal foramen

Nasolacrimal duct

the lacrimal papillae which are inclined slightly inwards at the junction of the ciliary and lacrimal portions of the eyelid margins. The superior punctum lies 6mm lateral to the inner canthus and is directed into the groove between the plica semilunaris and the caruncle. The inferior punctum lies 6.5mm lateral to the inner canthus and runs in the groove between the plica and the globe. The puncta are about 0.25mm in diameter but are surrounded by connective tissue rich in elastic fibres which makes them very extensible. The non-keratinised epithelium of the lid margin continues into the puncta to line the canaliculi. The tissue surrounding each punctum is relatively avascular, so that the region appears paler than the rest of the eyelid margin.

The canaliculi are about 10mm long and 0.5mm in diameter. Each has a short vertical part about 2mm long which leads from the punctum to a swelling or ampulla. From the ampulla a longer section runs medially to reach the lacrimal sac. The vertical part of the canaliculus is surrounded by fibres of the lacrimal part (Horner's muscle) of the orbicularis oculi. These fibres run parallel to the transverse part of the canaliculi which is therefore shortened as the orbicularis contracts. The canaliculi are also surrounded by connective tissue rich in elastic fibres, which increase in number towards the region of the lacrimal sac (Fig.13.9). The lumen of each canaliculus is lined with non-keratinised stratified epithelium. The two canaliculi normally unite before entering the lacrimal sac but sometimes they terminate at a small sinus (of Maier).

The lacrimal sac is about 12mm long and lies in the lacrimal fossa. It is surrounded in periorbital connective tissue which, in this region, is called the lacrimal fascia. The upper end or fundus of the sac is 4-5mm above the inner canthus and the lower end is continuous with the nasolacrimal duct. The lumen of the sac is usually flattened but it has a very variable volume due to the elasticity of its walls and it may be 5-8mm wide anteroposteriorly and 2-3mm wide laterally. The orbital septum passes laterally to the sac and joins the periosteum posteriorly.

Fig.13.9 SECTION THROUGH A JUNCTION OF A CANALICULUS WITH THE LACRIMAL SAC

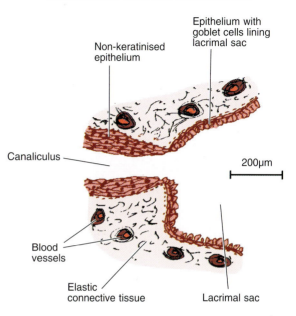

Non-keratinised epithelium

Epithelium with goblet cells lining lacrimal sac

Canaliculus

200µm

Blood vessels

Elastic connective tissue

Lacrimal sac

Fig.13.10 HORIZONTAL SECTION THROUGH ORBIT

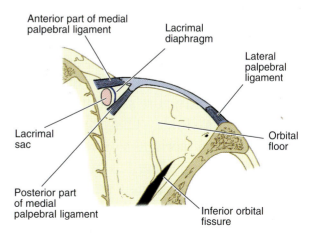

Anterior part of medial palpebral ligament

Lacrimal diaphragm

Lateral palpebral ligament

Lacrimal sac

Orbital floor

Posterior part of medial palpebral ligament

Inferior orbital fissure

The lacrimal diaphragm (Jones and Boyden 1955) is formed by the lateral lacrimal fascia and the junction of the fascia with the posterior part of the medial palpebral ligament at the level of the fundus of the lacrimal sac. The medial palpebral ligament thus anchors the anterior part of the fascia. The lateral part of the diaphragm (and hence the lacrimal sac) is stretched each time the orbicularis contracts since the deep origin of the superior and inferior preseptal parts of the orbicularis are attached to its surface.

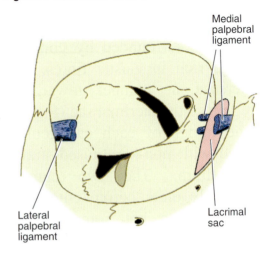

Fig.13.11 ANTERIOR VIEW OF RIGHT ORBIT

Medial palpebral ligament

Lateral palpebral ligament

Lacrimal sac

The lacrimal sac is lined with goblet and columnar cells forming a mucous membrane surrounded by a fibroelastic stroma. Outside this stroma the vessels of the anteromedial orbital blood supply form a dense capillary bed.

The nasolacrimal duct is continuous with the inferior part of the lacrimal sac and is about 18mm long and 4mm in diameter. Approximately 12mm of the duct lies in the nasolacrimal canal and the rest extends into the inferior nasal meatus. In the nasal meatus the duct lies in the mucous membrane of the lateral wall. Its inferior opening is called the ostium lacrimale (see Fig.13.17) and this normally lies just below the junction of the inferior nasal concha and the maxilla. The duct has the same structure as the lacrimal sac except that the mucous membrane lining exhibits many folds. These have been described as valves by various workers but only the plica lacrimalis or valve of Hasner (Fig.13.12) that closes the end of the duct can be considered to behave as a valve. Movement of this flap of mucous membrane is associated with changes in pressure in the duct that occur with eyelid movement, so that the valve closes when the lids close.

Fig.13.12 SECTION SHOWING 'VALVES' OF MEMBRANOUS PASSAGES

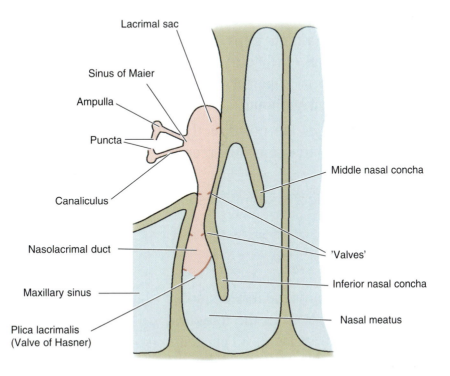

Blood supply

The upper parts of the membranous passages are supplied with blood by the lid vessels, so the lacrimal sac is supplied by the superior medial palpebral artery derived from the ophthalmic artery and by branches of the angular artery. The nasolacrimal duct and the lower part of the sac are supplied by the superior medial palpebral artery, branches of the angular artery and the infra-orbital and sphenopalatine branches of the internal maxillary artery. Venous drainage is to the angular and infra-orbital veins.

The lymphatics of the stroma drain to the submandibular or deep cervical nodes.

Nerve supply

The somatic sensory nerves from the upper parts of the drainage passages pass to the infratrochlear nerve which joins the nasociliary branch of the ophthalmic division of the trigeminal (fifth cranial) nerve. The lower part of the duct is innervated by the anterior superior alveolar nerve which is a branch of the maxillary division of the trigeminal.

The membranous passages are not directly supplied with motor innervation but the surrounding orbicularis muscles receive fibres from the facial (seventh cranial) nerve.

Sympathetic autonomic nerves supply vasomotor fibres to the blood vessels of the stroma.

The lacrimal pump

The tears are moved towards the inner canthus by the eyelids which close from the temporal side of the palpebral aperture. The tears meniscus or strip formed at the junction of each lid and the globe is thus moved towards the inner canthus. Because of the flow of tears in these strips, they are also known as the lacrimal rivers and they are interrupted some 6mm before the inner canthus by the lacrimal puncta. The puncta dip into these rivers and collect the tears fluid before it reaches the inner canthus. This makes the so-called lacrimal lake in this location a redundant element of the drainage system and Wolff has suggested that there may normally be a greater pool of tears at the outer canthus.

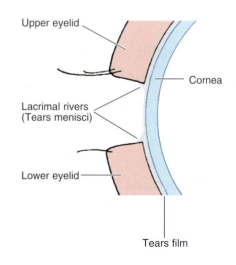

Fig.13.13 THE LACRIMAL RIVERS

Upper eyelid

Cornea

Lacrimal rivers
(Tears menisci)

Lower eyelid

Tears film

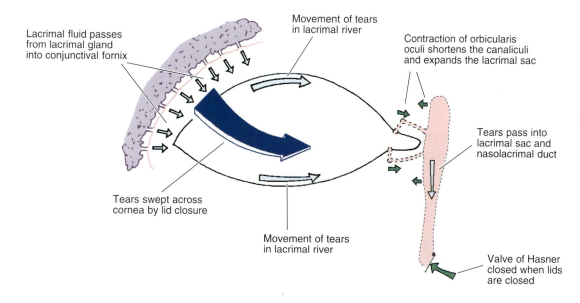

Fig.13.14 TEARS MOVEMENT

Lacrimal fluid passes from lacrimal gland into conjunctival fornix

Movement of tears in lacrimal river

Contraction of orbicularis oculi shortens the canaliculi and expands the lacrimal sac

Tears pass into lacrimal sac and nasolacrimal duct

Tears swept across cornea by lid closure

Movement of tears in lacrimal river

Valve of Hasner closed when lids are closed

Tears are drawn into the puncta by capillary action and by the expansion of the canaliculi that occurs as the orbicularis oculi relaxes and the eyelids open. Contraction of the orbicularis closes the puncta and shortens the transverse section of the canaliculi thus forcing the tears fluid in them towards the lacrimal sac. The traction produced by the preseptal part of the orbicularis expands the lacrimal sac drawing the tears into it. The expansion of the sac reduces the pressure in the nasolacrimal duct causing the valve of Hasner to close. This prevents the contents of the nasal meatus from being drawn into the duct. As the lids open again, contraction of the sac pushes the tears into the nasolacrimal duct from where they pass into the nasal meatus.

THE BONY PASSAGES

The membranous structures of the lower lacrimal sac and the upper two-thirds of the nasolacrimal duct are contained in the bony lacrimal fossa and the nasolacrimal canal.

The lacrimal fossa lies in the lower medial margin of the orbit. It forms a hollow in the anterior part of the lacrimal bone and the posterior part of the frontal process of the maxilla. The posterior lacrimal crest of the lacrimal bone curves anteriorly and forms the posterior and lateral walls of the fossa. The crest terminates in the hooklike hamular process which articulates with the lacrimal notch of the maxilla. The anterior lacrimal crest forms the anterior border of the lacrimal fossa. The fossa is about 7mm wide and 16mm high.

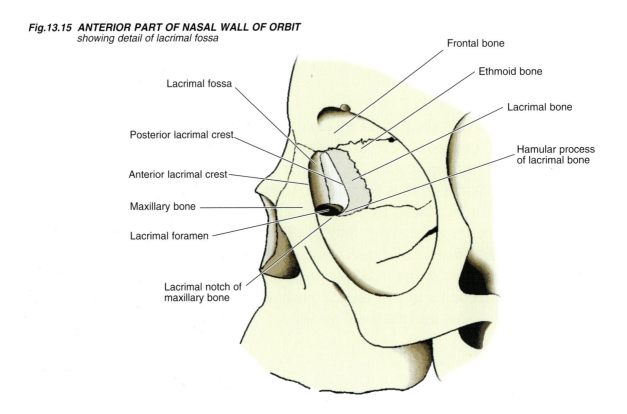

Fig.13.15 ANTERIOR PART OF NASAL WALL OF ORBIT
showing detail of lacrimal fossa

Frontal bone

Ethmoid bone

Lacrimal fossa

Lacrimal bone

Posterior lacrimal crest

Hamular process
of lacrimal bone

Anterior lacrimal crest

Maxillary bone

Lacrimal foramen

Lacrimal notch of
maxillary bone

The lacrimal fossa extends downwards through the lacrimal foramen into the nasolacrimal canal. The lateral wall of the canal is formed by the nasolacrimal groove of the maxilla. This groove runs on the medial side of the wall of the maxillary antrum and is angled back and perhaps slightly laterally, although often the canals are parallel to each other. Medially the upper part of the canal is walled by a thin descending process of the lacrimal bone and the thin ascending lacrimal process of the inferior concha. The inferior opening of the canal lies some 16mm above the floor of the nasal meatus and 14mm behind the anterior border of the inferior concha.

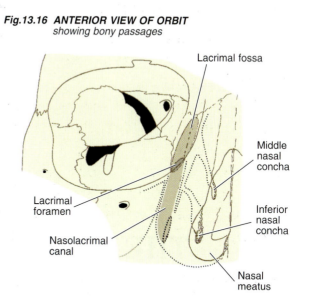

Fig.13.16 ANTERIOR VIEW OF ORBIT
showing bony passages

Lacrimal fossa

Middle nasal concha

Lacrimal foramen

Inferior nasal concha

Nasolacrimal canal

Nasal meatus

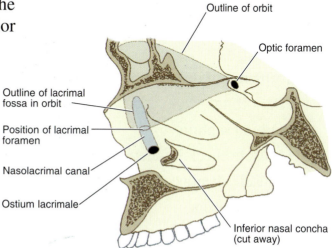

Fig.13.17 SAGITTAL SECTION THROUGH NASAL MEATUS
(Inferior concha cut away to show ostium lacrimale)

Outline of orbit

Optic foramen

Outline of lacrimal fossa in orbit

Position of lacrimal foramen

Nasolacrimal canal

Ostium lacrimale

Inferior nasal concha (cut away)

277

Chapter 14

THE ORBITAL FASCIAE

The orbital fasciae consist of sheets of connective tissue that line and support the structures within the orbit. Together with the fat that packs the interspaces, the fasciae serve to resist displacement of the globe. The smooth socket they provide for the globe allows easy eye rotation but translational movements are limited and do not normally exceed one or two millimetres.

For convenience of description the fasciae are divided into six sections.
- Periorbita
- Orbital septum
- Muscle check ligaments
- Muscle sheaths
- Bulbar fascia
- Fibro-adipose tissue (orbital fat)

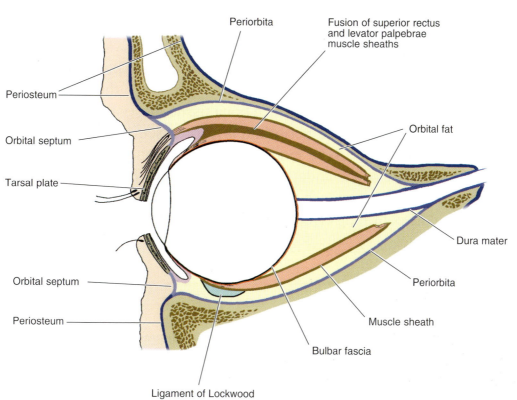

Fig.14.1 SAGITTAL SECTION THROUGH ORBIT
showing the orbital fasciae

Periorbita

Fusion of superior rectus
and levator palpebrae
muscle sheaths

Periosteum

Orbital septum

Orbital fat

Tarsal plate

Dura mater

Orbital septum

Periorbita

Periosteum

Muscle sheath

Bulbar fascia

Ligament of Lockwood

The periorbita

The periorbita lines the orbital cavity and is continuous with the periosteum of the facial bones. It is firmly attached to the underlying bone, particularly at the sutures and lines the foramina, fissures and fossae and therefore provides anchorage for structures within the orbit. At the lacrimal fossa it divides to provide a sheet of connective tissue over the lacrimal sac forming the lacrimal fascia. A similar splitting occurs at the inferior orbital fissure, which is both lined and roofed by periorbital tissue. The periorbita blends with the dura mater at the optic foramen and superior orbital fissure. It also blends with the muscle tendons and check ligaments and anchors the trochlea, the palpebral ligaments and the orbital septum.

Like periosteum, the periorbita consists of a layer of white fibrous tissue overlying fine elastic fibres. Between the periorbita and the bone are cells which form bone tissue in the developing orbit. In the adult these cells become quiescent but retain the facility to produce bone tissue, becoming active if orbital bones are damaged. Initially the periorbita is very vascular, but the vascularity decreases with age and the tissue tends to become thinner. The blood vessels communicate with those of the underlying bone providing metabolites and loss of the periorbita can therefore produce decay through lack of nutrition. Alternatively the bone, lacking the confining effect of the periorbita, may erupt or exfoliate into the surrounding tissues.

The orbital septum

The orbital septum (or septum orbitale) is a sheet of fibrous connective tissue which extends from the periphery of the tarsal plates to the margin of the orbit. At the medial edge of the orbit it runs obliquely across the lacrimal fossa, so that the upper part of the lacrimal sac lies in front of the septum. Laterally, it forms part of the lateral palpebral raphé together with the palpebral part of the orbicularis oculi (see Fig.12.10). It does not absolutely follow the

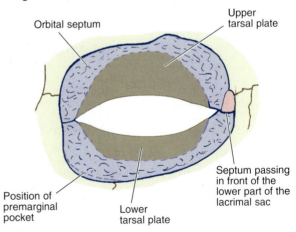

Fig.14.2 **THE ORBITAL SEPTUM**

Orbital septum

Upper tarsal plate

Position of premarginal pocket

Lower tarsal plate

Septum passing in front of the lower part of the lacrimal sac

280

lower temporal margin of the orbit, but it is attached to the periosteum of the zygomatic bone and forms a narrow fat-filled pocket, the premarginal pocket of Eisler (1930).

In the upper eyelid the orbital septum blends with the aponeurosis of the levator palpebrae superioris. In the lower lid it blends with the fibrous expansions of the inferior rectus and inferior oblique muscles. It is a relatively weak sheet which may perforate, allowing prolapse of the orbital fat or the lacrimal gland.

The muscle check ligaments

The check ligaments of the muscles are fibro-elastic connective tissue containing some smooth muscle cells. From the lateral and medial walls of the orbit they form triangular expansions to the lateral and medial recti and the bulbar fascia. These send fascial expansions to the inferior oblique and inferior rectus sheaths to form the ligament of Lockwood. Although referred to as check ligaments there is little evidence that these fibres are normally significant in restricting movement of the globe other than translation.

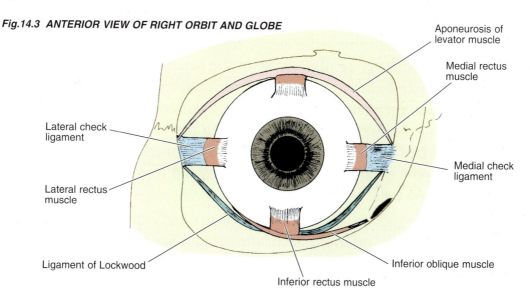

Fig.14.3 ANTERIOR VIEW OF RIGHT ORBIT AND GLOBE

Aponeurosis of levator muscle

Medial rectus muscle

Lateral check ligament

Medial check ligament

Lateral rectus muscle

Ligament of Lockwood

Inferior oblique muscle

Inferior rectus muscle

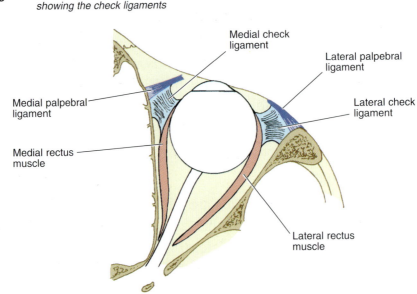

Fig.14.4 HORIZONTAL SECTION THROUGH THE ORBIT
showing the check ligaments

Medial check ligament

Lateral palpebral ligament

Medial palpebral ligament

Lateral check ligament

Medial rectus muscle

Lateral rectus muscle

The muscle sheaths

The muscle sheaths or epimysium are similar to the collagen, elastin and reticulin structures found in association with skeletal muscle elsewhere. They enclose the muscle cells and provide support for nerve fibres and blood vessels entering the muscle. The epimysium is continuous with the tendons anchoring the muscles and hence with the structures to which these are attached. Where the muscles are in close proximity to each other, their sheaths are continuous. The superior rectus and the levator muscles have continuity between their sheaths so that the upper eyelid is raised when the globe supraducts. At the upper fornix these sheaths blend with the stroma of the conjunctiva, causing the fornix to move posteriorly as the eye moves upwards.

Below the globe the sheaths of the inferior rectus and inferior oblique fuse and extend anteriorly into the inferior part of the tarsal plate and orbital septum. The sheaths of these together with fascial expansions to the medial and lateral recti, form the suspensory ligament of Lockwood (see Fig.14.3). This ligament serves to support the globe and prevents it from dropping into the maxillary antrum if the orbital floor is damaged or removed. Blunt trauma to the eye may force the globe downwards, opening the sutures of the orbital floor. When these close the muscle sheaths may be trapped preventing supraduction of the globe.

The bulbar fascia

The bulbar fascia (or Tenon's capsule) forms an external sheath to the sclera. As the tendons of the oculorotatory muscles pass through to the sclera, this sheath is reflected onto the tendon to form a sleeve around it. In the case of the superior oblique this sleeve extends as far as the trochlea while that of the inferior oblique extends a fibrous band to the orbital floor. Elsewhere the sleeves blend with the muscle sheaths and become continuous with the check ligaments.

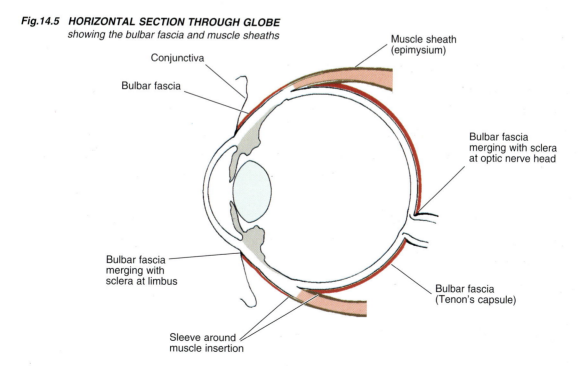

Fig.14.5 HORIZONTAL SECTION THROUGH GLOBE
showing the bulbar fascia and muscle sheaths

Muscle sheath (epimysium)

Conjunctiva

Bulbar fascia

Bulbar fascia merging with sclera at optic nerve head

Bulbar fascia merging with sclera at limbus

Bulbar fascia (Tenon's capsule)

Sleeve around muscle insertion

Fibrous trabeculae link the sclera and the capsule and it blends with the sclera at the limbus and around the optic nerve. The capsule thus moves with the globe and if the globe is removed it may be left attached to the muscles to provide a socket for a prosthetic (artificial) eye.

The orbital fat

The adipose tissue that fills the rest of the orbit is divided by sheets of fibrous tissue that extend from the periorbita to link with the muscle sheaths and the bulbar fascia. In a study using 5mm thick whole orbit sections, Koornneef (1977) has shown that the sheets of connective tissue do not form distinct compartments or surgical spaces as previously suggested. Instead there is a generally symmetrical pattern for the fascial organisation of the two orbits, within which a vast number of fat lobules are formed. The collagen septa that divide the fat are very vascular, and contain fibroblasts and some smooth muscle cells. These septa support nerves and the major blood vessels of the orbit. Their links with the muscle sheaths and the globe are strong enough to prevent supraduction of the globe if the septa become trapped in a fracture of the orbital floor (Fine 1977).

Chapter 15

THE VISUAL PATHWAY

Collectively, the retinae, optic nerves, chiasma, optic tracts, lateral geniculate bodies, optic radiations and the visual cortex constitute the visual pathway. Since details of the retina may be found in Chapter 9, only the postretinal components of the visual pathway will be described here.

Signals gathered by the ganglion cells of the retina are carried by the optic nerve to the optic chiasma. Here the axons originating in the nasal retina of one eye cross to the opposite optic tract. This cross-over of nerve fibres from one side of the central nervous system to the other is known as decussation. Some of the optic tract axons pass to the midbrain and terminate at the midbrain reflex nuclei, but the majority synapse with cells located in the lateral geniculate bodies. Axons of these cells form the optic radiations which curve around the lateral ventricles to reach the striate visual cortex. Although stimulation of the striate cortex produces simple visual sensations, perception is only achieved when the activities of the striate cortex combine with activities of other areas of the brain in a manner not yet fully understood.

Fig.15.1 THE LOCATION OF THE VISUAL PATHWAY

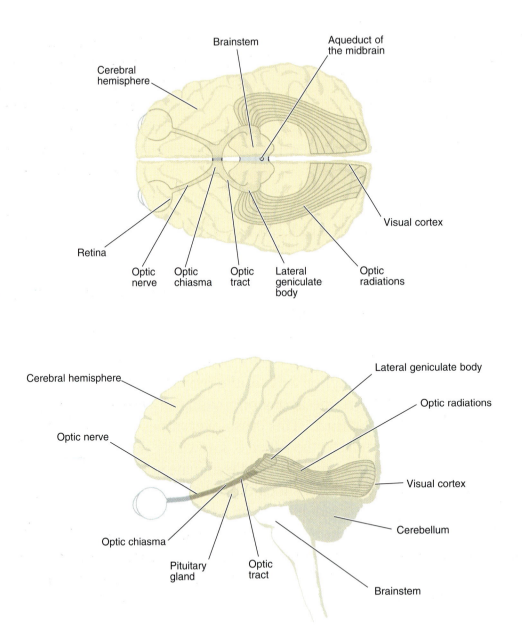

THE OPTIC NERVES

Although the axons contained in the optic nerve originate in the retina and terminate by synapsing in the lateral geniculate bodies or in the midbrain, the optic nerve extends only from the optic disc to the anterior border of the optic chiasma. Each optic nerve contains 1.1-1.3 million axons derived from the retinal ganglion cells, with each axon acquiring a myelin sheath as it leaves the lamina cribrosa. Surrounding and protecting the myelinated fibres are the three meningeal sheaths, since the optic nerve is in fact part of the central nervous system.

The total length of the optic nerve is about 4cm and this may be subdivided into intra-ocular, intra-orbital, intracanalicular and intracranial sections (Fig.15.2).

Intra-ocular section

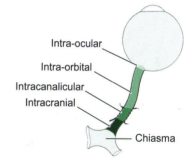

Fig.15.2 REGIONS OF THE OPTIC NERVE

Intra-ocular

Intra-orbital

Intracanalicular

Intracranial

Chiasma

The intra-ocular section is 1.0-1.5mm long and extends from the retinal surface of the optic disc to the posterior scleral foramen. The nerve therefore passes through the retina, the choroid and the sclera, accompanied by the central retinal artery and vein, before emerging from the globe.

As the nerve fibre layer of the retina converges on the optic disc it becomes thicker with the superior nasal margin of the disc having the thickest part of this layer. This thickening gives rise to the name optic papilla and in the centre of this region is a depression, the physiological cup. Since the retinal, choroidal and scleral layers do not necessarily terminate at the same point, the disc presents a variety of rings or crescents when viewed with the ophthalmoscope (see Fig.9.28).

287

The axons passing into the disc are surrounded by fibrous astrocytes and these cells form a layer 1-2μm thick across the disc surface. A thin basement membrane lies between the astrocytes and the vitreous humour. The astrocytes divide the axons into bundles or fascicles and also separate the axons from the lateral surface of the retina. This layer of astrocytes is called the intermediary tissue of Kuhnt. At the level of the choroid, collagen fibres, known as the border tissue of Elschnig, are interposed between the optic nerve and the choroidal stroma. This marks the end of the prelaminar part of the intra-ocular section of the nerve and the commencement of the laminar part. The laminar part is formed into bundles by collagen fibres derived from the surrounding sclera that comprise the sieve-like lamina cribrosa. Although weaker than the sclera, this meshwork of collagen supports the nerve fibres and strengthens a potentially vulnerable point in the outer coat of the globe. Astrocytes surrounding the axons separate them

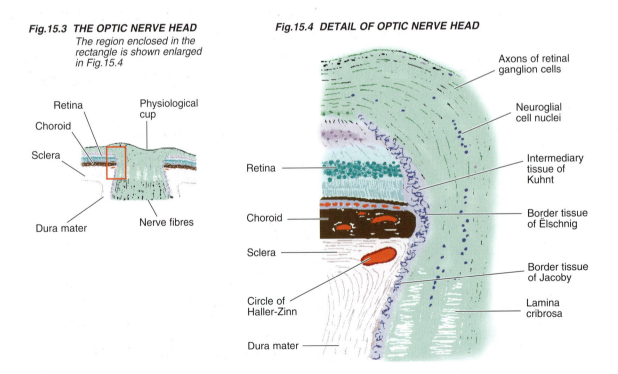

Fig.15.3 THE OPTIC NERVE HEAD
The region enclosed in the rectangle is shown enlarged in Fig.15.4

Retina
Physiological cup
Choroid
Sclera
Dura mater
Nerve fibres

Fig.15.4 DETAIL OF OPTIC NERVE HEAD

Axons of retinal ganglion cells
Neuroglial cell nuclei
Intermediary tissue of Kuhnt
Border tissue of Ëlschnig
Border tissue of Jacoby
Lamina cribrosa

Retina
Choroid
Sclera
Circle of Haller-Zinn
Dura mater

from the collagen fibres and are continuous peripherally with the glial tissue adjacent to the choroid. This region of the glial sheath is the border tissue of Jacoby. Elastic tissue, not markedly present in the rest of the sclera, has been reported in some quantities in the lamina cribrosa by Hogan et al.

In the postlaminar optic nerve, the axons are divided into about one thousand bundles by septa derived from the pia mater. These septa are composed of collagen and contain fibroblasts, blood vessels and nerve fibres. The septa provide mechanical strength and stability, and support the vessels carrying metabolites to the axons of the optic nerve. The septa commence at the posterior border of the lamina cribrosa and this marks the commencement of the myelination of the optic nerve axons. The myelination is produced by oligodendrocytes and the addition of a myelin sheath around each axon doubles the diameter of the nerve to about 3mm before it emerges from the posterior scleral foramen. The oligodendrocyte nuclei lie in columns in the optic nerve and can be differentiated from the astrocytes which are also present by their small more densely staining nuclei and cytoplasm. Microglial macrophage cells are also to be found throughout the nerve. The wrapping formed by the

Fig.15.5 LONGITUDINAL SECTION THROUGH THE OPTIC NERVE AND OPTIC NERVE HEAD

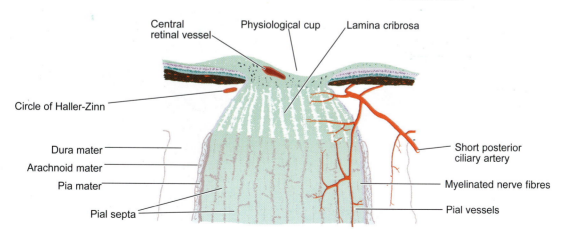

Central retinal vessel
Physiological cup
Lamina cribrosa
Circle of Haller-Zinn
Dura mater
Arachnoid mater
Pia mater
Pial septa
Short posterior ciliary artery
Myelinated nerve fibres
Pial vessels

oligodendrocytes differs from that of Schwann cells in that it lacks an outer layer of cell cytoplasm and the basement membrane is also absent. At the nodes between the oligodendrocytes the axon is exposed since the myelin sheath formed by adjacent cells is not contiguous. Unlike the myelinated nerves of the peripheral nervous system, the axons of the optic nerve do not regenerate if severed. A damaged nerve fibre will degenerate back to its ganglion cell in the retina and will produce transneuronal degeneration of the cells with which the fibre synapses in the lateral geniculate body.

The majority of the optic nerve axons have a diameter of about 1µm with a range of between 0.3µm and 3.5µm. Although the conduction rate varies depending on neurone type, peripheral nerve fibres with a similar diameter conduct at 12-30m/s.

Intra-orbital section

The orbital portion of the optic nerve extends from the globe to the optic foramen surrounded by the cone of the rectus muscles. It is about 25mm long and, since the posterior pole of the eye is only 18mm from the optic foramen, the nerve has sufficient slack to allow eye movements to occur without significant traction. Adipose tissue is packed between the muscles and the nerve

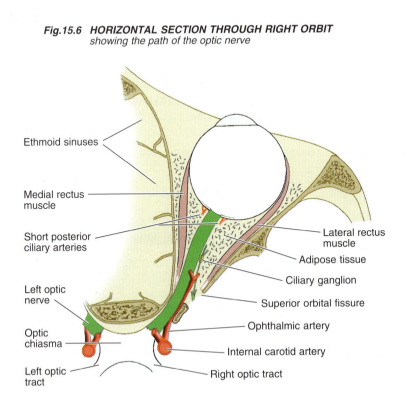

Fig.15.6 HORIZONTAL SECTION THROUGH RIGHT ORBIT
showing the path of the optic nerve

Ethmoid sinuses

Medial rectus muscle

Short posterior ciliary arteries

Left optic nerve

Optic chiasma

Left optic tract

Lateral rectus muscle

Adipose tissue

Ciliary ganglion

Superior orbital fissure

Ophthalmic artery

Internal carotid artery

Right optic tract

and this is subdivided into lobules by fibrous septa which interconnect with septa outside the cone. These fibrous sheets serve to support the nerves and blood vessels. The short ciliary arteries and nerves form a ring around the optic nerve where it leaves the globe. The ciliary ganglion lies between the nerve and the lateral rectus muscle midway between the globe and the optic foramen. The central retinal artery and vein pierce the meninges to enter the nerve from below about 10-15mm behind the globe.

As with the sheaths that enclose the brain and spinal cord, the meninges of the optic nerve consist of the tough outer dura mater which is continuous with the sclera; the arachnoid mater which lies beneath the dura, and the pia mater which closely covers the optic nerve fibres. The region between the pia and the arachnoid is filled with cerebrospinal fluid.

The dura mater is about 0.5mm thick and is composed of layers of collagen fibres, longitudinal externally and circumferential internally. Some elastic fibres are present. The arachnoid is about 10μm thick and has fine trabeculae of collagen and elastic tissue covered in meningothelial cells which resemble fibroblasts. The trabeculae extend from the arachnoid to the pia and form a fine network in the pia-arachnoid space. The pial sheath is highly vascular and

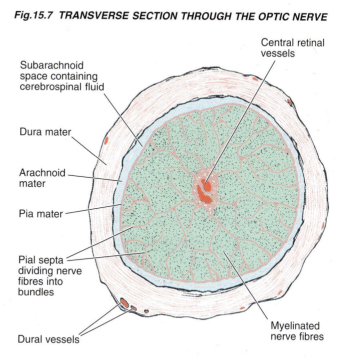

Fig.15.7 TRANSVERSE SECTION THROUGH THE OPTIC NERVE

Subarachnoid space containing cerebrospinal fluid

Central retinal vessels

Dura mater

Arachnoid mater

Pia mater

Pial septa dividing nerve fibres into bundles

Dural vessels

Myelinated nerve fibres

composed of collagen and elastic fibres. Meningothelial cells cover the surface of the pia with some regions having several layers of cells. The basal layer of these cells is separated by a basement membrane from the underlying astrocytes of the optic nerve.

Intracanalicular section

At the optic foramen in the sphenoid bone, the dura splits into two layers, one joining the periorbita and the proximal tendon of the rectus muscles and the other passing into the optic canal. The optic nerve is thus firmly anchored to the apex of the orbit and throughout its intracanalicular length. It is accompanied in the optic canal by the ophthalmic artery which lies embedded in dura, normally below the nerve but occasionally in a separate canal. Travelling with the ophthalmic artery are nerve fibres from the sympathetic retro-orbital plexus. The length of the optic canal varies so that the intracanalicular portion of the optic nerve may be between 5 and 10mm.

Intracranial section

The intracranial section of the optic nerve commences as it passes from the optic canal into the middle cranial fossa. Here the dura mater is reflected over the sphenoid bone and the nerve is then only covered by pia mater. The nerve passes posteromedially to enter the anterior border of the chiasma where it meets the optic nerve from the other orbit. Above the nerve lie the olfactory tract and the anterior cerebral arteries. At the junction of the nerve with the chiasma the internal carotid artery passes upwards along the lateral surface of the nerve, giving off the ophthalmic artery which runs along the nerve's lower lateral border.

The pial septa, which have divided the nerve into bundles along its length from the scleral foramen, end at the anterior border of the chiasma and this point is used to define the termination of the optic nerve.

Blood supply

At the optic nerve head, vessels derived from the circle of Haller-Zinn provide the capillary supply to the immediate prelaminar and laminar parts of the nerve. Recurrent vessels from the circle supply the pia mater which also receives vessels from the extraneural part of the central retinal artery and from the ophthalmic artery. Within the optic canal recurrent branches of the ophthalmic artery supply the pia. Intracranially it is supplied by the ophthalmic artery and branches of the superior hypophyseal artery.

The intra-orbital section of the nerve drains principally into the central retinal vein, while intracranially blood drains to the basal veins or to the anterior cerebral vein from the pial venous plexus.

Fig.15.8 THE ARTERIAL SUPPLY OF THE OPTIC NERVE

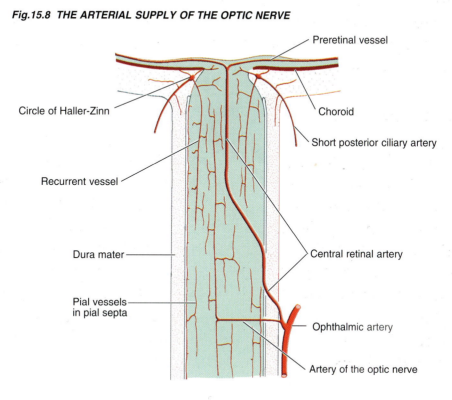

Preretinal vessel

Circle of Haller-Zinn

Choroid

Short posterior ciliary artery

Recurrent vessel

Dura mater

Central retinal artery

Pial vessels in pial septa

Ophthalmic artery

Artery of the optic nerve

Fig.15.9 THE OPTIC CHIASMA IN THE MIDDLE CRANIAL FOSSA
The roof of the right orbit is cut away to show the optic nerve and globe.
*Blood vessels labelled in **italics** form the Circle of Willis which surrounds the chiasma.*

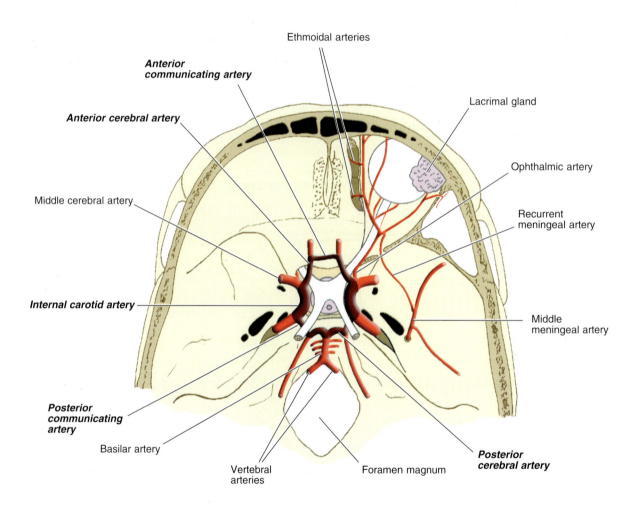

Ethmoidal arteries

Anterior communicating artery

Lacrimal gland

Anterior cerebral artery

Ophthalmic artery

Middle cerebral artery

Recurrent meningeal artery

Internal carotid artery

Middle meningeal artery

Posterior communicating artery

Basilar artery

Vertebral arteries

Foramen magnum

Posterior cerebral artery

THE OPTIC CHIASMA

The optic chiasma forms the junction between the optic nerves anteriorly and the optic tracts posteriorly. It has an oval section and is angled obliquely upwards, so that its posterior border, which lies at the angle of the anterior wall (lamina terminalis) and floor of the third ventricle, is higher than its anterior border. Below the chiasma the pituitary gland (the hypophysis cerebri) lies in the pituitary gland (hypophyseal) fossa of the sphenoid bone, while the pituitary stalk

Fig.15.10 SUPERIOR - POSTERIOR ASPECT OF THE OPTIC CHIASMA
The diaphragma sellae is cut away to show the cavernous sinus

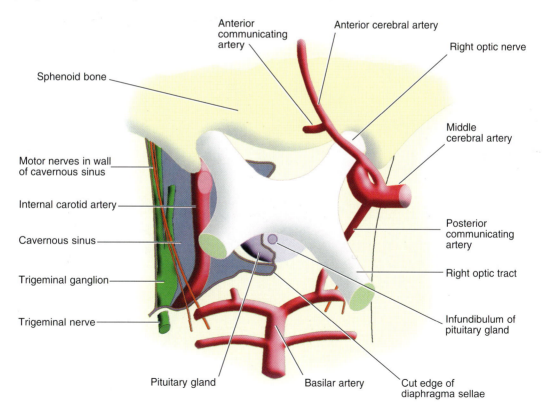

Anterior communicating artery

Anterior cerebral artery

Right optic nerve

Sphenoid bone

Middle cerebral artery

Motor nerves in wall of cavernous sinus

Internal carotid artery

Cavernous sinus

Posterior communicating artery

Trigeminal ganglion

Right optic tract

Trigeminal nerve

Infundibulum of pituitary gland

Pituitary gland

Basilar artery

Cut edge of diaphragma sellae

(infundibulum) normally passes behind the chiasma to reach the floor of the third ventricle. The chiasma and pituitary gland are separated by a fold of dura, the diaphragma sellae. Laterally the chiasma is close to the internal carotid arteries and the anterior perforated substance of the olfactory region of the cortex.

The chiasma is approximately 12mm wide, 8mm from front to back and some 4mm thick. Apart from its area of continuity with the lamina terminalis and floor of the third ventricle, the optic chiasma is covered in pia mater and suspended in cerebrospinal fluid.

Fig.15.11 SAGITTAL SECTION THROUGH THE OPTIC CHIASMA AND SURROUNDING STRUCTURES

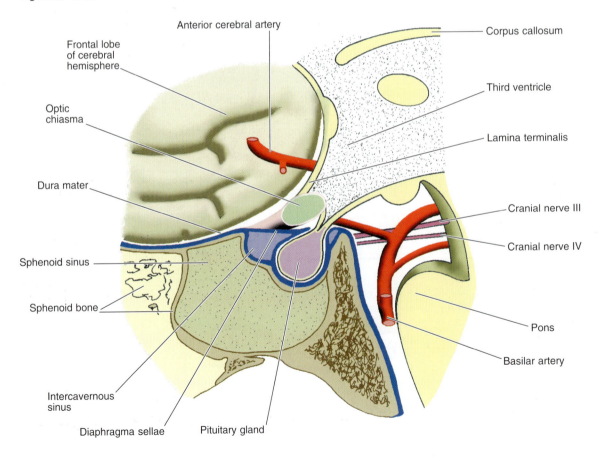

296

Blood supply

The blood supply to the optic chiasma is from the anterior cerebral, internal carotid, superior hypophyseal and the anterior and posterior communicating arteries.

Venous drainage is to the basal and anterior cerebral veins.

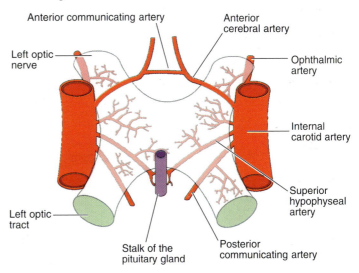

Fig.15.12 BLOOD SUPPLY TO THE CHIASMA

Anterior communicating artery

Anterior cerebral artery

Left optic nerve

Ophthalmic artery

Internal carotid artery

Superior hypophyseal artery

Left optic tract

Stalk of the pituitary gland

Posterior communicating artery

THE OPTIC TRACTS

The optic tracts run from the posterolateral angles of the optic chiasma around the lateral surface of the cerebral peduncles to reach the lateral geniculate bodies. Each tract is in the form of a flattened band of fibres which lies obliquely against the peduncle so that its lateral border lies above the medial border.

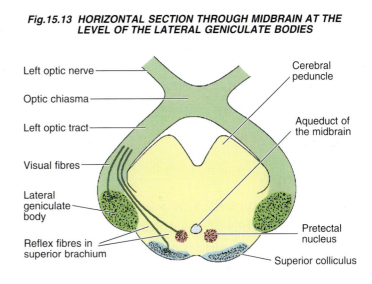

Fig.15.13 HORIZONTAL SECTION THROUGH MIDBRAIN AT THE LEVEL OF THE LATERAL GENICULATE BODIES

Left optic nerve

Cerebral peduncle

Optic chiasma

Left optic tract

Aqueduct of the midbrain

Visual fibres

Lateral geniculate body

Reflex fibres in superior brachium

Pretectal nucleus

Superior colliculus

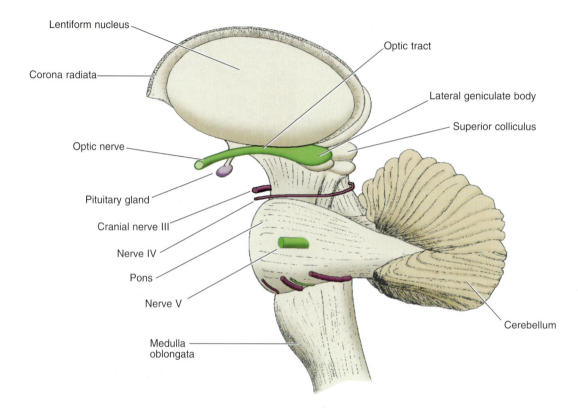

Fig.15.14 THE LATERAL ASPECT OF THE BRAINSTEM

Lentiform nucleus

Corona radiata

Optic tract

Lateral geniculate body

Superior colliculus

Optic nerve

Pituitary gland

Cranial nerve III

Nerve IV

Pons

Nerve V

Cerebellum

Medulla oblongata

Via its lateral root, the optic tract carries axons to the lateral geniculate body and passes axons to the pretectal nucleus and superior colliculus via the superior brachium.

Blood supply

The tract receives its blood supply from the pial sheath which derives its vessels from the branches of the anterior choroidal artery (see Fig.15.23), itself a branch of the internal carotid artery. Venous drainage is to the basal vein.

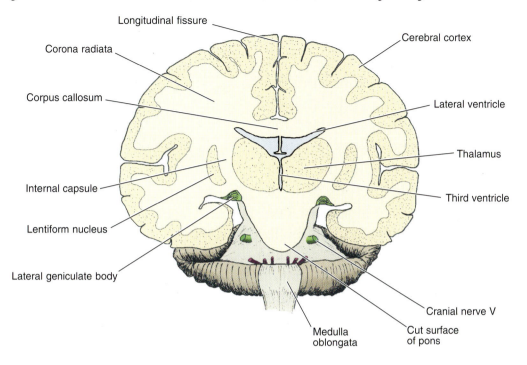

Fig.15.15 CORONAL SECTION THROUGH CEREBRAL HEMISPHERES *showing lateral geniculate bodies*

Longitudinal fissure

Cerebral cortex

Corona radiata

Corpus callosum

Lateral ventricle

Thalamus

Internal capsule

Third ventricle

Lentiform nucleus

Lateral geniculate body

Cranial nerve V

Medulla oblongata

Cut surface of pons

THE LATERAL GENICULATE BODIES

The name geniculate for these structures derives from their location at the knee-like fold in the visual pathway that occurs between the optic tracts and the radiation fibres. In coronal section, their upper surface is convex medially and concave laterally, while the lower surface is also concave, forming the hilum, with a spur at the lateral border. The dorsal lateral end or pulvinar of the thalamus and the fibres of the internal capsule overhang the lateral geniculate bodies (see Fig.15.15) and the medial surface of the temporal lobe covers the inferior and lateral aspects. The lateral geniculate bodies are on the surface of the brain stem below the dorsal end of the lentiform nucleus (Fig.15.14)

Coronal section reveals a laminar structure with six layers of cells alternating with myelinated nerve fibre laminae. Degeneration studies in primates have shown that axons from the ipsilateral retina terminate in the second, third and fifth layers, while the contralateral retina sends axons to layers one, four and six. Lesions of the visual cortex produce degeneration of cells in all six layers on the same side, provided

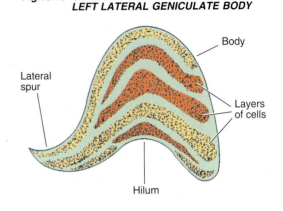

Fig.15.16 CORONAL SECTION THROUGH THE LEFT LATERAL GENICULATE BODY

Body

Lateral spur

Layers of cells

Hilum

that the cortical lesion damages all the layers of the visual cortex. There appears to be the same number of fibres reaching the lateral geniculate bodies from the optic tracts as the number of radiation fibres leaving and thus there is no significant convergence or divergence. However, there are also cells within the lateral geniculate bodies that do not project to the visual cortex and which may

Fig.15.17 NEURONE CONNECTIONS WITHIN THE LATERAL GENICULATE BODY

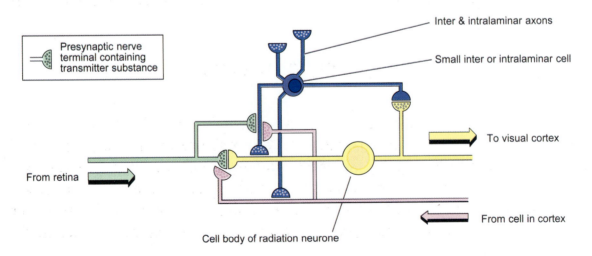

Presynaptic nerve terminal containing transmitter substance

Inter & intralaminar axons

Small inter or intralaminar cell

To visual cortex

From retina

From cell in cortex

Cell body of radiation neurone

provide intralaminar and possibly interlaminar communications between those cells which do project (Fig.15.17). Additionally, centrifugal corticogeniculate fibres have been found to synapse with the projection cells.

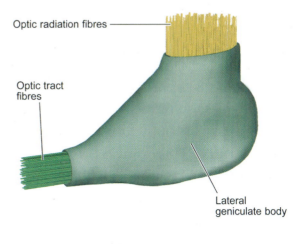

Fig.15.18 THE LATERAL GENICULATE BODY

Optic radiation fibres

Optic tract fibres

Lateral geniculate body

The optic tract fibres enter the lateral geniculate body anteriorly with some fibres entering through the hilum, while the radiation fibres leave the lateral geniculate body from the upper surface or head.

Blood supply

Blood is supplied to the lateral geniculate bodies by the anterior and posterior choroidal arteries, the latter branching from the posterior cerebral artery (see Fig.15.23).

THE OPTIC RADIATIONS

The neurones that form the optic radiations (of Gratiolet, 1854) travel to the occipital lobe of the brain to synapse with cells in the striate region of the visual cortex. The fibres pass through the posterior part of the internal capsule and fan out around the lateral wall and posterior horn of the lateral ventricle. The lower fibres have a down and forward loop before turning backwards. This part of the radiations forms the temporal loop of Meyer (1907) and passes forward in the temporal lobe, in some cases as far as the coronal plane of the optic chiasma.

Blood supply

The radiations are supplied with blood by the anterior choroidal artery, the deep optic branch of the middle cerebral artery, and posteriorly by the calcarine branch of the posterior cerebral artery (see Fig.15.23).

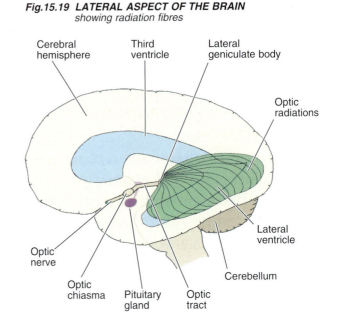

Fig.15.19 *LATERAL ASPECT OF THE BRAIN*
showing radiation fibres

Cerebral hemisphere

Third ventricle

Lateral geniculate body

Optic radiations

Optic nerve

Optic chiasma

Pituitary gland

Optic tract

Lateral ventricle

Cerebellum

THE VISUAL CORTEX

The optic radiation fibres terminate in the occipital lobes of the cerebral hemispheres and virtually the whole of these lobes form the visual cortex. Part of the cortex which lies along the calcarine fissure medially and extends around the posterior pole to the lunate sulcus laterally is marked by the distinct white line or stria of Gennari. The stria is

Fig.15.20 *THE LOCATION OF THE VISUAL CORTEX*

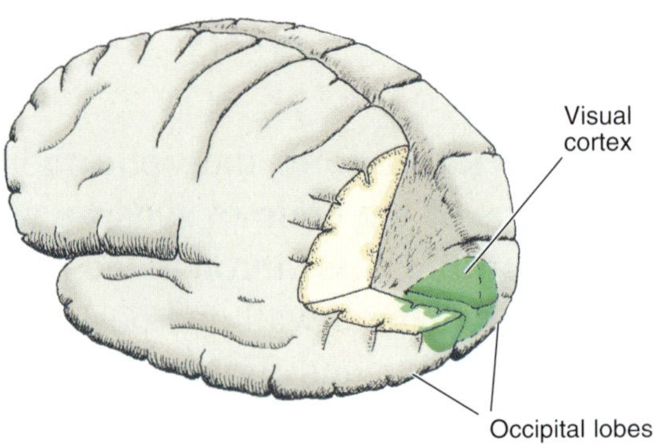

Visual cortex

Occipital lobes

produced by the myelinated radiation fibres and the region is referred to as the striate cortex. The white line is most obvious in the cortex along the lower edge of the calcarine fissure.

Brodmann, who mapped the cortex in cytoarchitectural surveys (1903-25) labelled the striate cortex as area 17. The surrounding parastriate and peristriate visual areas were numbered 18 and 19. Although the optic radiation fibres were thought to terminate solely in the striate cortex, there is evidence that, in cat and monkey, axons from the lateral geniculate bodies also terminate in areas 18 and 19.

Fig.15.21 **THE OCCIPITAL LOBE OF THE RIGHT CEREBRAL HEMISPHERE**

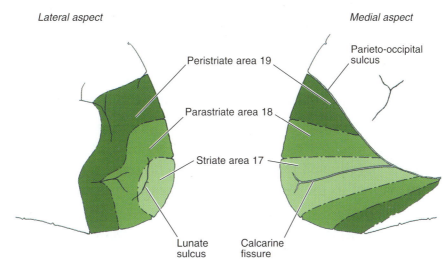

Lateral aspect

Medial aspect

Peristriate area 19

Parieto-occipital sulcus

Parastriate area 18

Striate area 17

Lunate sulcus

Calcarine fissure

In each hemisphere the striate cortex covers an area of about 3000mm^2 and is only 1.5mm thick; elsewhere the cerebral cortex is up to 4.5mm thick. The combined areas of the parastriate and peristriate regions is approximately 8000mm^2.

Brodmann's numbering system extends into the cortex which he described as having six layers. The six zones of differing cell and fibre density may be

Fig.15.22 SECTION THROUGH THE VISUAL CORTEX

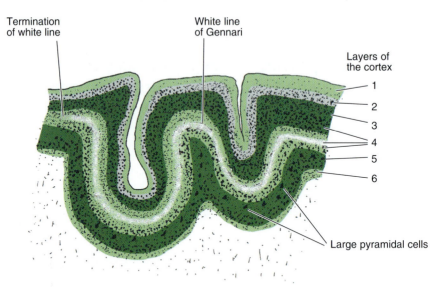

Termination
of white line

White line
of Gennari

Layers of
the cortex

1
2
3
4
5
6

Large pyramidal cells

difficult to appreciate in light micrographs since there is overlap of cell types.

A detailed description of the cortex and its functions is beyond the scope of this text but the primary visual area is notable for the white line (of Gennari) in layer IV formed by the myelinated radiation fibres. The large pyramidal cells of layer V are taken to project to the superior colliculi and to the ocular motor nuclei of the brainstem.

Although it is well established that stimulation of the striate cortex produces visual sensations, results for the parastriate and peristriate regions are more variable so that definite functions cannot reasonably be allocated to those areas. Similarly, many of the projection and association pathways found in experimental animals have not been established in man, although it is probable that area 18 is involved in coordinating eye movement and that area 19 provides a centre for the interpretation of combined visual stimuli. Additionally both halves of the visual cortex are in communication via a fibre pathway which passes between the cerebral hemispheres in the splenium of the corpus callosum.

Blood supply

The visual cortex receives its main blood supply from the posterior cerebral artery via the calcarine artery and from anastomoses with the middle cerebral artery. Venous drainage is to vessels which traverse the dura mater to reach the straight, the transverse or the superior sagittal sinus.

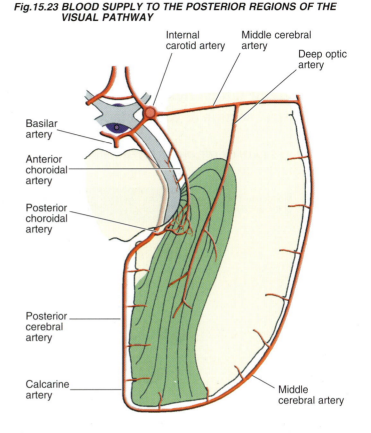

Fig.15.23 BLOOD SUPPLY TO THE POSTERIOR REGIONS OF THE VISUAL PATHWAY

Internal carotid artery

Middle cerebral artery

Deep optic artery

Basilar artery

Anterior choroidal artery

Posterior choroidal artery

Posterior cerebral artery

Calcarine artery

Middle cerebral artery

VISUAL FIELD REPRESENTATION

The route taken by the axons from a particular part of the retina to the visual cortex is well established and this means that lesions of the visual pathway can, in general, be localised by the changes that they produce in the visual field. The effect of such lesions is projected into the visual field and may give rise to areas of the field in which there is no vision or in which objects are only seen with reduced acuity. Damage to the neurones may also cause areas of the visual fields to appear coloured abnormally.

Fig.15.24 shows the general organisation of the pathway. The small central circular region in the upper part of the figure is the foveal field which subtends about 5°. The colours used in this diagram will be used in the sections that follow to show the representation of the visual field in that part of the visual pathway. The field of vision for each eye extends approximately 100° temporally and 60° nasally giving a total field of 200° of which the central 120° is the binocular field. Only a small section of each monocular field is represented in the diagram.

Fig.15.24 THE PATH OF THE FIBRES IN THE VISUAL PATHWAY

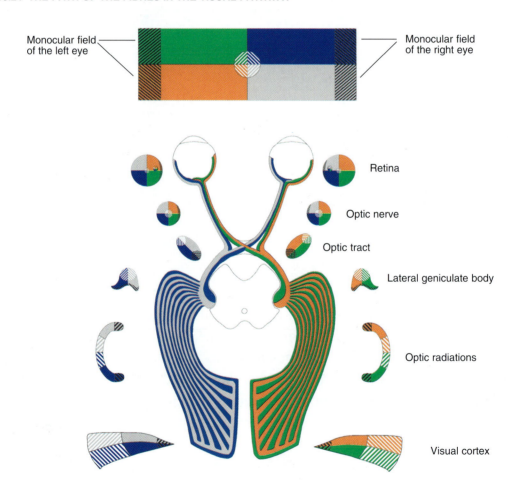

Monocular field of the left eye

Monocular field of the right eye

Retina

Optic nerve

Optic tract

Lateral geniculate body

Optic radiations

Visual cortex

Fig.15.25 THE 'RETINAL IMAGE' (as seen from behind the eye)

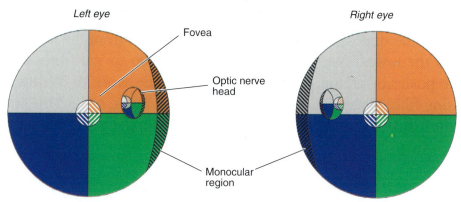

The optic nerve

Fig.15.26 shows the representation of the visual field in the optic nerve viewed from the posterior aspect (a) close to the globe and (b) close to the optic foramen. Initially the foveal fibres lie close to the lateral surface of the nerve but, nearer to the optic foramen, they move centrally. For clarity the central retinal artery and vein have been omitted from diagram (a).

Fig.15.26 THE OPTIC NERVES

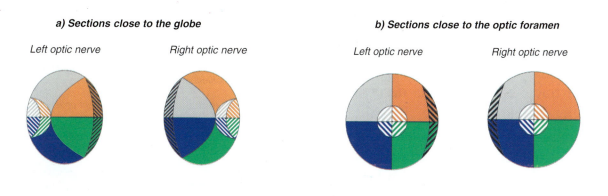

The optic chiasma

In the chiasma semi-decussation occurs as some 53% of the axons in the optic nerves cross to the opposite optic tract. Crossing fibres from the peripheral nasal retinae lie in the lowest part of the chiasma, while the foveal fibres cross above these in the posterior region. Diagrams based on the work of Wilbrand (1926) show crossing fibres looping into the opposite optic nerve or into the tract on the same side during decussation, but the validity of this concept has been questioned.

Fig.15.27 THE PATH OF NERVE FIBRES THROUGH THE CHIASMA (SEMI-DECUSSATION)

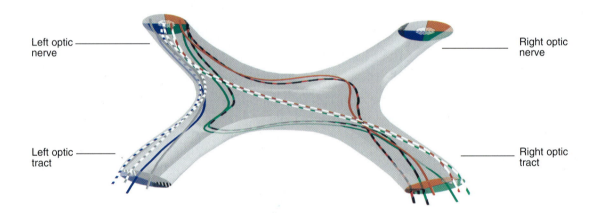

Left optic nerve

Right optic nerve

Left optic tract

Right optic tract

The optic tract

The tracts contain axons derived from both retinae with the foveal fibres situated in the upper lateral section. The arrangement of the fibres in the rest of the visual pathway is similar to that of the optic tracts with only a minor modification in the optic radiations.

Fig.15.28 SECTIONS THROUGH THE OPTIC TRACTS
(posterior aspect)

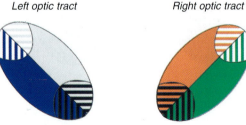

Left optic tract

Right optic tract

The lateral geniculate body

As with the optic tracts, the lateral geniculate bodies have the foveal fibres located in the upper laminae and the upper retinal fibres located medially. Only 90% of the tract fibres reach the lateral geniculate bodies, the other 10% pass to the superior colliculi and the pretectal nuclei via the superior brachia.

The optic radiations

A coronal section through the radiations shows that they have the same organisation of nerve fibres as the optic tracts and the lateral geniculate bodies if these are opened out along the junction of the upper and lower fibre groups (Fig.15.30b).

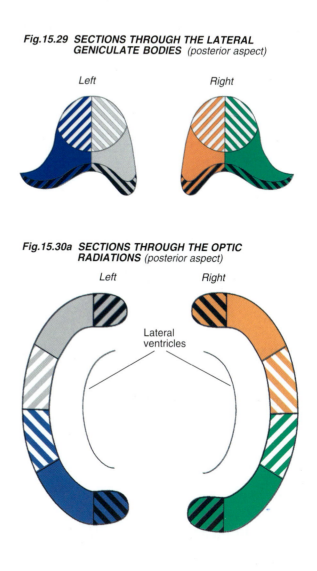

Fig.15.29 **SECTIONS THROUGH THE LATERAL GENICULATE BODIES** *(posterior aspect)*

Left   Right

Fig.15.30a **SECTIONS THROUGH THE OPTIC RADIATIONS** *(posterior aspect)*

Left   Right

Lateral ventricles

Fig.15.30b
SECTIONS OF LEFT OPTIC TRACT AND RADIATIONS
showing the relationship of the retinal representations

The foveal fibres now lie centrally and the upper and lower monocular fibres lie at the upper and lower extremities of the radiations respectively.

309

Fig.15.31 *THE VISUAL CORTEX* *(medial aspect)*

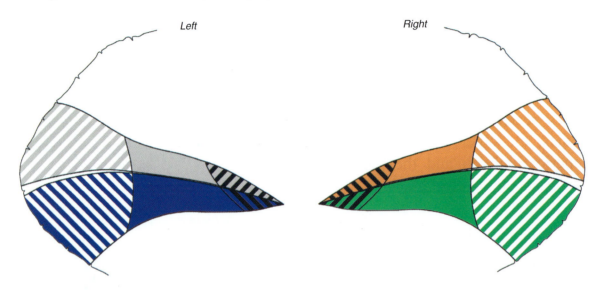

Left

Right

The visual cortex

The visual field is represented in the cortex as shown in Fig.15.31. The foveal projection covers about half the cortex, so that a 3mm^2 region of the retina projects to 1500mm^2 in the striate cortex. The peripheral retina projects to the anterior region of the cortex with the monocular area principally occupying the anterior inferior border of the calcarine fissure.

The visual association areas 18 and 19 show similar representations to those of area 17 in cat and monkey. These cortical areas project to the thalamus and also to the brainstem motor nuclei producing eye and head movements, particularly from stimulation of areas 17 and 18. Areas 17, 18 and 19 are connected with each other and with the visual areas in the other hemisphere via the splenium of the corpus callosum, as well as with other parts of the cerebral cortex.

Chapter 16

THE ORBITAL BLOOD SUPPLY

The orbits are supplied with blood via arteries derived from both the internal and the external carotid arteries. Since both orbits have a similar vascular organisation, only the supply to the right orbit will be described here.

The venous drainage from the orbits is described later in this chapter.

THE INTERNAL CAROTID ARTERY

The internal carotid artery enters the middle cranial fossa via the carotid canal of the temporal bone. It then runs forward in the carotid groove through the cavernous sinus and turns upwards to divide into the anterior and middle cerebral arteries. As the internal carotid emerges from the cavernous sinus it gives off the ophthalmic artery and reduces in diameter from about 3mm to 2mm. The ophthalmic artery runs along the lower lateral border of the optic nerve and enters the orbit by the optic canal embedded in dura mater, or sometimes via a separate

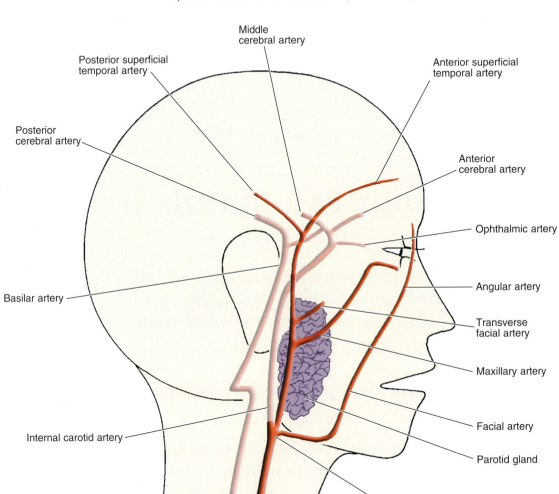

Fig.16.1 ARTERIAL SUPPLY TO THE ORBITAL REGION
Superficial vessels are shown dark, deep vessels are paler

Middle
cerebral artery

Posterior superficial
temporal artery

Anterior superficial
temporal artery

Posterior
cerebral artery

Anterior
cerebral artery

Ophthalmic artery

Basilar artery

Angular artery

Transverse
facial artery

Maxillary artery

Internal carotid artery

Facial artery

Parotid gland

Vertebral artery

External carotid artery

Common carotid artery

canal in the lesser wing of the sphenoid. Once inside the orbit, the ophthalmic artery runs for a few millimetres lateral to the optic nerve and then normally crosses above the optic nerve and, having given off a number of branches, reaches the medial orbital wall. It then passes forward between the medial rectus and superior oblique muscles and divides to form its terminal branches, the supratrochlear and dorsal nasal arteries.

Fig.16.2 SAGITTAL SECTION THROUGH THE ORBIT *showing the orbital arteries*

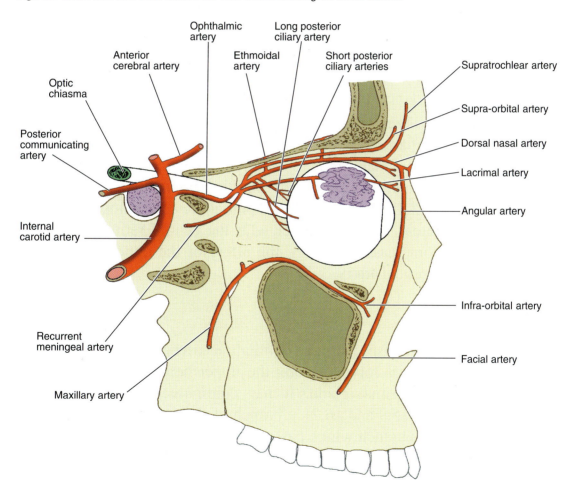

BRANCHES OF THE OPHTHALMIC ARTERY

The central retinal artery

The central retinal artery is the first, and one of the smaller branches, which leaves the ophthalmic artery while it is temporal to the optic nerve. The central retinal artery runs below the nerve for a few millimetres and, when about 10-12mm from the globe, passes through the dura and arachnoid sheaths of the optic nerve. After passing a few more millimetres forward in the subarachnoid space, it pierces the pia mater and runs axially through the nerve into the globe. At the optic nerve head, it divides into the superior and inferior retinal (or papillary) arteries which each give off a temporal and nasal branch. These subdivide to form the typical pattern of preretinal vessels (Fig.9.30).

Vessels derived from the ophthalmic artery close to the central retinal artery, or from the central retinal artery itself while it is outside the optic nerve, supply the pia and travel with the pial septa to supply the optic nerve anteriorly and posteriorly. Alternatively, the optic nerve may be supplied by the artery of the optic nerve (see Fig.15.8). This leaves the ophthalmic artery close to the central retinal artery and enters the nerve either with the central retinal artery or just posterior to it. In some cases however, the artery of the optic nerve may be a branch of the central retinal artery.

The lacrimal artery

The lacrimal artery also arises from the ophthalmic artery on the temporal side of the optic nerve. It passes forward along the upper border of the lateral rectus muscle towards the lacrimal gland. It has communication with the middle meningeal artery (Figs.15.9 and 16.2), a branch of the external carotid artery, by its recurrent meningeal branch which passes out of the orbit through the superior orbital fissure (or it may leave the orbit via the meningeal foramen (Fig.5.11a) in the greater wing of the sphenoid). Thus the middle meningeal may form an alternative to the ophthalmic artery as the main blood supply to the orbit. It and similar branches of the carotid arteries supply the dura mater and the bone in the posterior part of the orbit and in the middle cranial fossa.

Zygomatic branches pass from the lacrimal artery through the zygomaticofacial and zygomaticotemporal foramina to anastomose with the deep temporal and transverse facial arteries, which are branches of the external carotid.

The lacrimal artery then passes through the lacrimal gland which it supplies, and divides into two lateral palpebral arteries. These in turn anastomose with the medial palpebral arteries to form the palpebral arcades, usually two in the upper eyelid and one in the lower.

The muscular arteries

The muscular branches are given off by the ophthalmic artery in the section that passes over the optic nerve. These branches are variable but generally comprise a larger inferior group which supply the medial and inferior recti and inferior oblique muscles. The superior group supply the levator palpebrae superioris, the superior and lateral recti, and the superior oblique muscles, although the lateral and superior recti and the levator may receive vessels from the lacrimal artery. The branches to the recti from both groups pass forward along the muscles which they supply, finally becoming the anterior ciliary arteries which anastomose within the globe at the major arterial circle.

The posterior ciliary arteries

The posterior ciliary branches are also given off by the ophthalmic artery while it is above the optic nerve. These show considerable variation, but usually divide into about twenty short posterior ciliary arteries which enter the globe in a ring around the optic nerve. They then anastomose within the sclera to form the

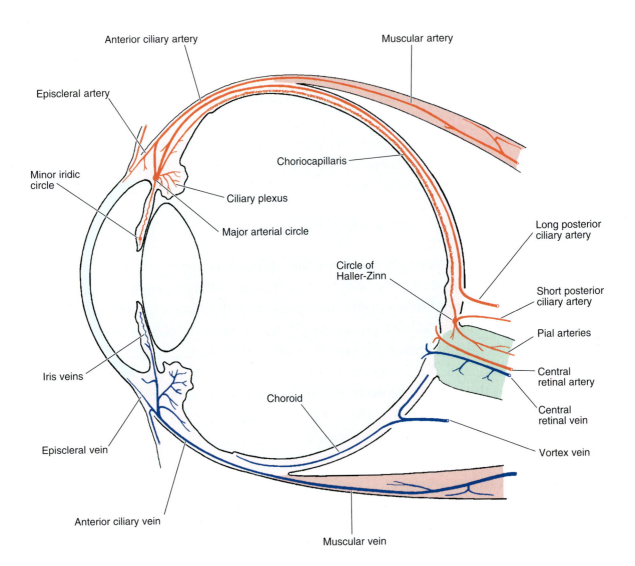

Fig.16.3 THE ARTERIES AND VEINS OF THE GLOBE
*The arteries are shown in the upper half of the diagram
and the veins in the lower half*

Anterior ciliary artery

Muscular artery

Episcleral artery

Choriocapillaris

Minor iridic
circle

Ciliary plexus

Major arterial circle

Long posterior
ciliary artery

Circle of
Haller-Zinn

Short posterior
ciliary artery

Pial arteries

Iris veins

Central
retinal artery

Choroid

Central
retinal vein

Episcleral vein

Vortex vein

Anterior ciliary vein

Muscular vein

316

posterior arterial circle of Haller-Zinn. From this, branches pass forward to form the vessels of the choroid and choriocapillaris, while recurrent vessels supply the optic nerve head. Two other branches of the ophthalmic artery, the two long posterior ciliary arteries, pass into the sclera close to the optic nerve and run forward in the suprachoroid to anastomose with the anterior ciliary arteries at the major arterial circle.

The supra-orbital artery

The supra-orbital artery leaves the ophthalmic artery on the medial side of the optic nerve and passes forward along the medial edge of the levator muscle. It supplies the levator and superior rectus and leaves the orbit via the supra-orbital notch to supply the upper eyelid and forehead.

The ethmoidal arteries

The anterior and posterior ethmoidal arteries leave the ophthalmic artery to pass through the ethmoidal foramina to reach the anterior cranial fossa. Here they supply the dura mater and give off branches which supply the ethmoidal and frontal sinuses and the nasal cavity.

The medial palpebral arteries

The two medial palpebral arteries originate from the ophthalmic artery just anterior to the trochlea and pass into the eyelids to anastomose with the other lid vessels to form the palpebral arcades. The inferior medial palpebral artery also joins a branch of the facial artery (from the external carotid artery) to supply the tissue surrounding the nasolacrimal duct.

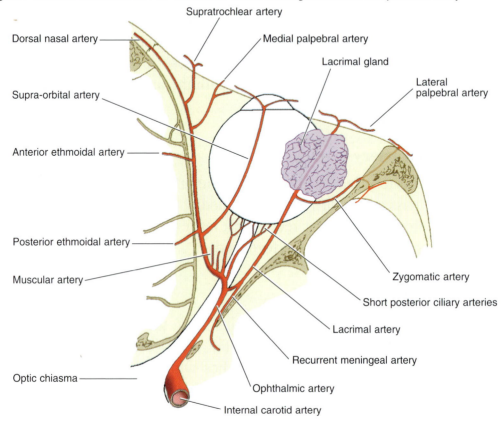

Fig.16.4 THE SUPERIOR ASPECT OF THE RIGHT ORBIT *showing branches of the ophthalmic artery*

Supratrochlear artery

Dorsal nasal artery

Medial palpebral artery

Lacrimal gland

Supra-orbital artery

Lateral palpebral artery

Anterior ethmoidal artery

Posterior ethmoidal artery

Muscular artery

Zygomatic artery

Short posterior ciliary arteries

Lacrimal artery

Recurrent meningeal artery

Optic chiasma

Ophthalmic artery

Internal carotid artery

The supratrochlear and dorsal nasal arteries

The two terminal branches of the ophthalmic artery are the supratrochlear and the dorsal nasal arteries. The supratrochlear (or frontal) artery leaves the orbit to supply the medial part of the forehead, anastomosing above the nose with the supratrochlear artery of the other orbit. The dorsal nasal artery supplies a small branch to the upper part of the lacrimal sac and then leaves the orbit between the trochlea and the medial palpebral ligament. It anastomoses with the terminal angular branch and the lateral nasal branch of the facial artery.

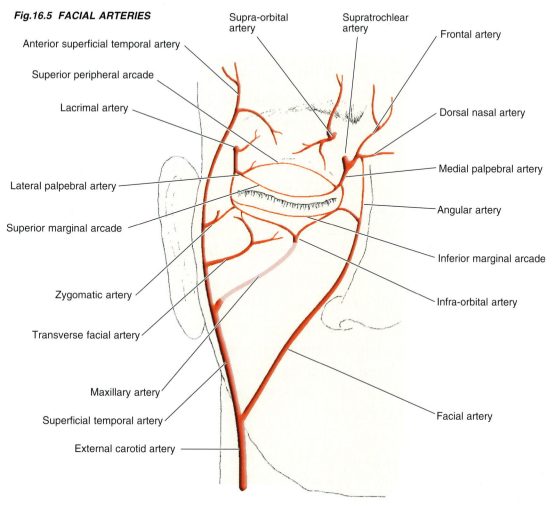

Fig.16.5 FACIAL ARTERIES

Supra-orbital artery

Supratrochlear artery

Frontal artery

Anterior superficial temporal artery

Superior peripheral arcade

Lacrimal artery

Dorsal nasal artery

Medial palpebral artery

Lateral palpebral artery

Angular artery

Superior marginal arcade

Inferior marginal arcade

Zygomatic artery

Infra-orbital artery

Transverse facial artery

Maxillary artery

Superficial temporal artery

Facial artery

External carotid artery

THE EXTERNAL CAROTID ARTERY

The external carotid artery runs up the neck and divides into the superficial temporal and the maxillary arteries as it passes through the parotid (salivary) gland which separates it from the internal carotid artery (see Fig.16.1). Various branches of the external carotid artery supply the orbit and its adnexa.

BRANCHES OF THE EXTERNAL CAROTID ARTERY

The facial artery

The facial artery branches from the external carotid just below the angle of the mandibular bone. It runs forward beneath this bone and then across its surface to reach the frontal process of the maxillary bone in the region of the medial palpebral ligament. Here it is generally termed the angular artery and it anastomoses with the supratrochlear (or frontal) branch and the dorsal nasal branch of the ophthalmic artery, supplying the forehead, the nose, the medial parts of the eyelids and the lacrimal sac. Its lateral nasal branch supplies the nose and also anastomoses with the dorsal nasal branch of the ophthalmic artery.

The superficial temporal artery

The superficial temporal artery passes upwards in front of the ear to divide into anterior and posterior branches. The anterior branch passes above the orbit and anastomoses with the supra-orbital and supratrochlear arteries and with the anterior superficial temporal artery from the opposite side to supply the muscles and skin of the forehead and brows.

The transverse facial artery

The superficial temporal artery gives off the transverse facial artery while still in the parotid gland. Terminal branches of the transverse facial artery anastomose with the infra-orbital artery to supply the lower eyelid.

The maxillary artery

The maxillary artery is the larger of the terminal branches of the external carotid artery. It passes behind the neck of the mandibular bone and into the pterygopalatine fossa below the orbit. Its infra-orbital branch runs into the orbit through the inferior orbital fissure and thence to the infra-orbital groove and canal where it gives off branches to the inferior oblique and inferior rectus muscles and the lacrimal sac. Emerging onto the face via the infra-orbital foramen it supplies the lower eyelid, anastomosing with the inferior medial and lateral palpebral arteries to form the inferior palpebral arcade.

VENOUS DRAINAGE

The orbit is drained by vessels which pass into the cavernous sinus posteriorly, into the pterygoid plexus inferiorly and into the facial veins anteriorly.

Fig.16.6 SAGITTAL SECTION THROUGH THE ORBIT *showing the orbital veins*

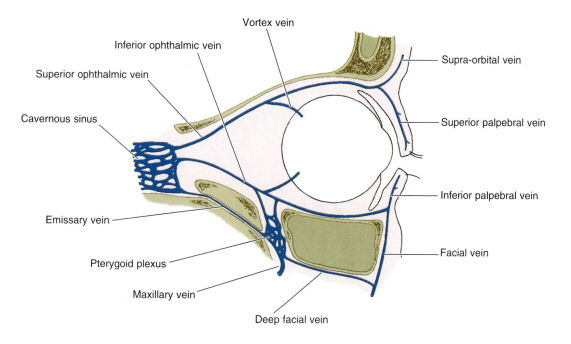

Blood leaves the anterior part of the globe by the episcleral vessels which unite to form the anterior ciliary veins. Posteriorly, blood leaves the choroid and drains from the posterior part of the ciliary body via the vortex veins (Fig.16.3). These drain to the superior and inferior ophthalmic veins which unite at or just before the cavernous sinus which they reach by passing through the superior orbital fissure.

Fig.16.7 VENOUS DRAINAGE OF ORBITAL REGION

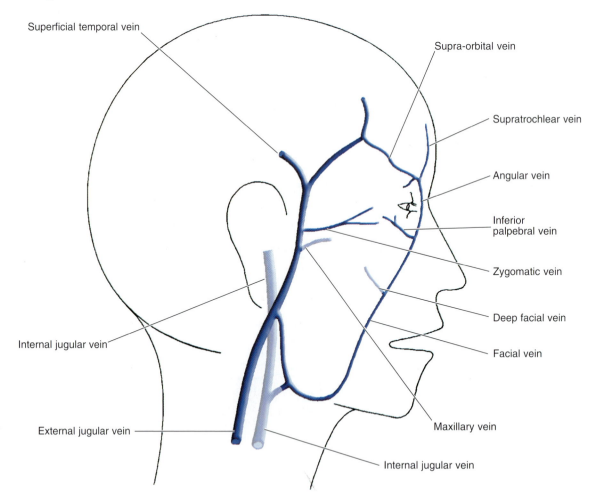

The superior ophthalmic vein is formed behind the medial part of the upper eyelid by branches of the facial (or angular) and supra-orbital veins. Its course through the orbit parallels that of the ophthalmic artery and it receives corresponding branches, including the central retinal vein, which drains the preretinal layers.

The inferior ophthalmic vein commences in the inferior medial part of the orbit, receiving vessels from structures along its path towards the superior orbital fissure. It communicates with the pterygoid plexus by vessels passing through the inferior orbital fissure and with the facial vein through the infra-orbital canal.

The cavernous sinuses lie on each side of the body of the sphenoid just behind the superior orbital fissure. Each has the internal carotid artery, the oculomotor, the trochlear and the abducent nerves, and the ophthalmic and maxillary divisions of the trigeminal nerve passing through it or running in its lateral wall (Fig.15.10). The two sinuses are interconnected by the anterior and posterior intercavernous sinuses. The cavernous system may drain into the internal jugular veins via the inferior petrosal sinuses. However, since the system is valveless, they may also drain forward into the superior ophthalmic vein or into emissary veins to the pterygoid plexus and thence to the facial system. The blood that drains through the pterygoid system passes by way of the deep facial vein to the facial vein which in turn drains to the internal jugular vein.

Blood from the eyelids and forehead may drain medially by the supra-orbital vein to the facial vein and to the internal jugular, or temporally to the superficial temporal vein and thence to the external jugular vein.

Since the facial and ophthalmic systems are also valveless, blood flows in a direction which is largely dependent upon posture, and infection may therefore easily spread from the facial to the intracranial regions or vice versa.

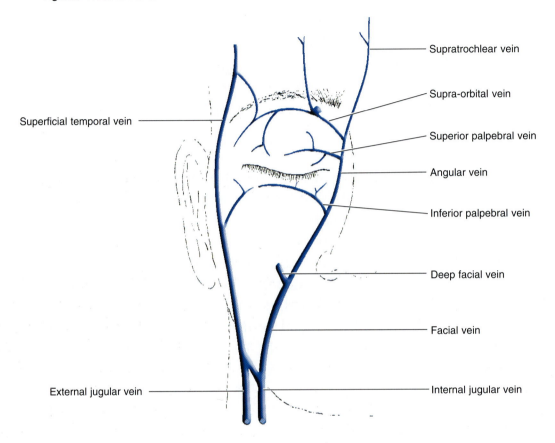

Fig.16.8 FACIAL VEINS

Supratrochlear vein

Supra-orbital vein

Superior palpebral vein

Superficial temporal vein

Angular vein

Inferior palpebral vein

Deep facial vein

Facial vein

External jugular vein

Internal jugular vein

Chapter 17

THE ORBITAL NERVE SUPPLY

Motor nerves

The orbital structures receive motor nerves from the motor nuclei located in the brainstem. These nuclei are presumed to receive axons for voluntary eye and lid movement from the frontal eye field of the cerebral cortex. This is located in part of Brodmann's area 8 and extends into areas 6 and 9 (see Fig.17.1) and stimulation in this part of the cortex produces head and eye movement. Such movements are also produced in experimental animals by stimulation of the visual cortex (areas 17 and 18). Reflex eye movement is brought about by stimulation of the motor nuclei either by fibres which descend from the cerebral cortex or by fibres ascending from the vestibular nuclei.

Sensory nerves

Somatic sensory nerve fibres from the orbit pass to the principal sensory nucleus of the trigeminal nerve. From this, postsynaptic axons travel to the thalamus where a second relay occurs. The information is then passed to the primary sensory areas 1, 2 and 3 of the postcentral gyrus.

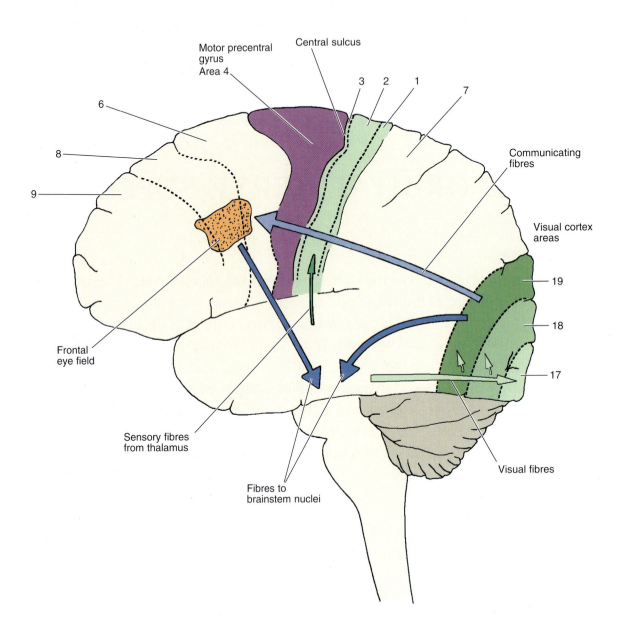

Fig.17.1 LATERAL ASPECT OF BRAIN
showing Brodmann's areas relating to the visual system

Motor precentral gyrus Area 4

Central sulcus

3 2 1

7

6

8

9

Communicating fibres

Visual cortex areas

19

18

17

Frontal eye field

Sensory fibres from thalamus

Fibres to brainstem nuclei

Visual fibres

Autonomic nerves

Autonomic motor innervation to the orbit is supplied by the sympathetic system from fibres originating in the superior cervical ganglion and by the parasympathetic system via fibres from either the visceral nucleus or the superior salivatory nucleus. The pathways are described on pages 329, 341 and 348.

THE OCULOMOTOR NERVE (N III)

The nucleus of origin of this nerve lies close to the floor of the third ventricle just anterior to the aqueduct of the midbrain, at the level of the superior colliculi.

The axons of the third nerve pass through the midbrain and the red nucleus (which contains cells relaying information between the cerebellum and thalamus) to emerge in the interpeduncular fossa (Fig.17.3). The nerve passes between the posterior cerebral and superior cerebellar arteries and runs forward passing lateral to the posterior communicating artery. It enters the cavernous sinus near its roof and then passes towards its lateral wall. The nerve divides into a superior and inferior branch and enters the orbit through the superior orbital fissure, passing within the common annular tendon of the rectus muscles.

Within the annulus, the two branches are separated by the nasociliary branch of the ophthalmic nerve. The superior division supplies the superior rectus muscle and the levator palpebrae, while the inferior branch divides into three to supply the inferior

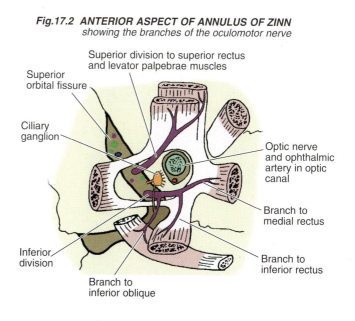

Fig.17.2 ANTERIOR ASPECT OF ANNULUS OF ZINN
showing the branches of the oculomotor nerve

Superior division to superior rectus and levator palpebrae muscles

Superior orbital fissure

Ciliary ganglion

Optic nerve and ophthalmic artery in optic canal

Branch to medial rectus

Inferior division

Branch to inferior rectus

Branch to inferior oblique

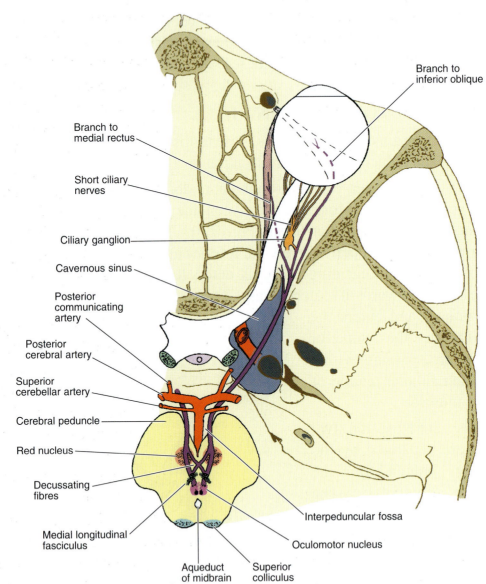

Fig.17.3 HORIZONTAL SECTION THROUGH THE MIDDLE CRANIAL FOSSA AND RIGHT ORBIT
showing the oculomotor nerve

Branch to
inferior oblique

Branch to
medial rectus

Short ciliary
nerves

Ciliary ganglion

Cavernous sinus

Posterior
communicating
artery

Posterior
cerebral artery

Superior
cerebellar artery

Cerebral peduncle

Red nucleus

Decussating
fibres

Medial longitudinal
fasciculus

Aqueduct
of midbrain

Superior
colliculus

Oculomotor nucleus

Interpeduncular fossa

rectus, medial rectus and inferior oblique muscles.

Each oculomotor nucleus provides innervation to the ipsilateral medial rectus, inferior rectus and inferior oblique, to the contralateral superior rectus and to both levator muscles. Decussating fibres cross to the opposite side of the midbrain before the oculomotor nerves emerge from between the cerebral peduncles.

The oculomotor nucleus receives axons from several sources (see Fig.17.33). Voluntary eye movements may originate from cells in the cortex anterior to the precentral gyrus, in particular Brodmann's area 8, and from some parts of areas 6 and 9. The fibres from these travel in the corticonuclear tracts (page 56). Fibres from the superior colliculi pass in the tectobulbar tracts (page 59) to the oculorotatory nuclei of cranial nerves III, IV and VI and it is probable that the visual cortex projects to these nuclei by collicular connections. The medial longitudinal fasciculus sends fibres to the nuclei of nerves III, IV, VI and VIII (vestibular) thus interconnecting them. The oculomotor nucleus also receives fibres from the parasympathetic pretectal nuclei whose cells synapse with axons from the retinae travelling in the superior brachia.

The parasympathetic supply to the iris sphincter and ciliary muscle originates in the cells of the visceral nucleus of the oculomotor nerve (also known as the Edinger Westphal nucleus). This lies in the midline along the dorsal aspect of the third nerve nucleus. Its fibres travel along the route of the oculomotor nerve with its branch to the inferior oblique muscle, as far as the ciliary ganglion. Here the autonomic fibres leave the nerve to enter the ciliary ganglion by its motor root. The ganglion is a 2mm diameter disc-like structure lying between the optic nerve and the lateral rectus muscle. Within the ganglion, the parasympathetic fibres synapse but the ciliary ganglion also contains sympathetic and sensory fibres passing through it without synapsing (Fig.17.4). The postganglionic parasympathetic fibres, which are myelinated (unusual for such fibres), pass in the short ciliary nerves to the globe. They travel in the suprachoroid to reach the iris sphincter to produce miosis, and to the ciliary muscle to produce accommodation.

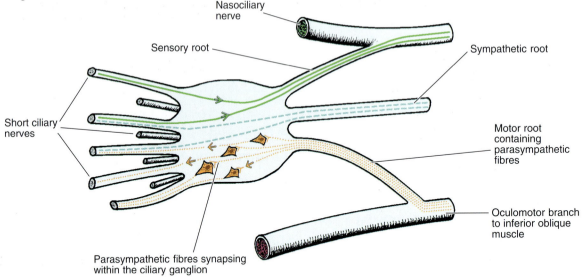

Fig.17.4 THE CILIARY GANGLION

Nasociliary nerve

Sensory root

Sympathetic root

Short ciliary nerves

Motor root containing parasympathetic fibres

Oculomotor branch to inferior oblique muscle

Parasympathetic fibres synapsing within the ciliary ganglion

Loss of the oculomotor nerve of one side near its superficial origin at the brainstem has several consequences. The affected eye loses the ability to accommodate, and the pupil of that eye is dilated. The pupil only responds to direct acting miotic drugs and not to light or to attempts to accommodate. Ptosis (drooping of the upper eyelid) occurs due to loss of innervation to the levator muscle. The failure of innervation to the oculorotatory muscles causes the eye to be deviated downwards and outwards. Loss of somatic innervation to three of the rectus muscles may also lead to slight proptosis (protrusion of the eyeball).

Diplopia (double vision) occurs due to the deviation of the affected eye. The image seen by this eye appears above and crossed to the temporal side of the image seen by the unaffected eye. The top of the image is

Fig.17.5 EFFECT OF PARALYSIS OF THE RIGHT OCULOMOTOR NERVE
Left eye fixating, right eye deviated down and out with ptosis and mydriasis

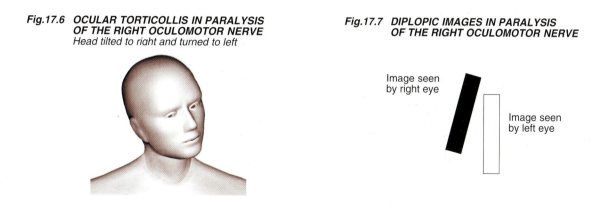

Fig.17.6 OCULAR TORTICOLLIS IN PARALYSIS OF THE RIGHT OCULOMOTOR NERVE
Head tilted to right and turned to left

Fig.17.7 DIPLOPIC IMAGES IN PARALYSIS OF THE RIGHT OCULOMOTOR NERVE

Image seen by right eye

Image seen by left eye

also tilted towards the affected side. A compensatory head tilt (ocular torticollis) may occur with the chin raised and the head tilted towards the affected side, but turned towards the normal side. Fig.17.7 shows the effect on the images. The dark bar is that seen by the affected eye which in this case is the right. The eye is abducted by the action of the unaffected lateral rectus. The superior oblique which is also unaffected causes incycloduction and the head is tilted right to compensate for this. Only slight vertical effects occur since the superior oblique produces little movement when the eye is abducted. However, any movement will be downwards and thus the image for the affected eye is projected up. The loss of innervation to the medial rectus may induce a head turn to the left into the motor field of this muscle and the slight upward tilt of the chin moves the head into the motor field of the now defective inferior oblique.

THE TROCHLEAR NERVE (N IV)

The nucleus of origin of the fourth nerve lies close to the aqueduct of the midbrain at the level of the inferior colliculi. The nerve fibres pass laterally, close to the mesencephalic nucleus of the trigeminal nerve (Fig.17.25), and then turn down and back to emerge below the inferior colliculus on the opposite side of the brainstem. Thus there is total decussation of this nerve, and it is the only cranial

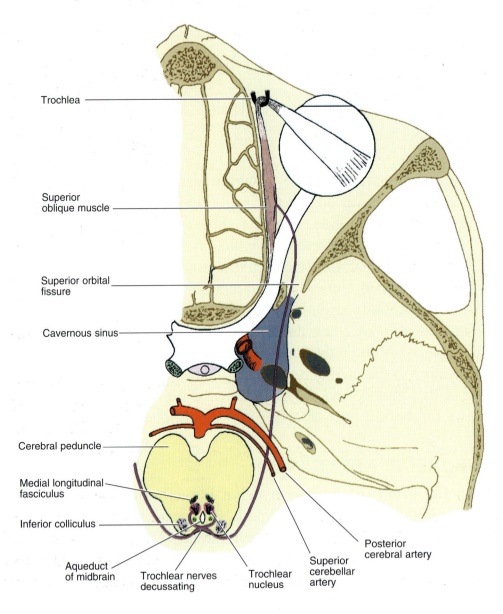

Fig.17.8 HORIZONTAL SECTION THROUGH THE MIDDLE CRANIAL FOSSA AND RIGHT ORBIT
showing the trochlear nerve

Trochlea

Superior
oblique muscle

Superior orbital
fissure

Cavernous sinus

Cerebral peduncle

Medial longitudinal
fasciculus

Inferior colliculus

Aqueduct
of midbrain

Trochlear nerves
decussating

Trochlear
nucleus

Superior
cerebellar
artery

Posterior
cerebral artery

nerve to leave the brainstem from its posterior surface. The nerve passes laterally, around the cerebral peduncles, and runs between the posterior cerebral and superior cerebellar arteries into the cavernous sinus. It then travels in the lateral wall of the sinus above the ophthalmic division of the trigeminal nerve. Initially it lies below and lateral to the oculomotor nerve but then crosses above it to enter the orbit through the superior orbital fissure outside the common annular tendon of the rectus muscles. The nerve enters the orbital surface of the superior oblique muscle above and just anterior to the origin of the superior rectus and levator muscles.

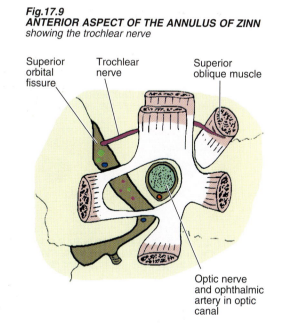

Fig.17.9
ANTERIOR ASPECT OF THE ANNULUS OF ZINN
showing the trochlear nerve

Superior orbital fissure

Trochlear nerve

Superior oblique muscle

Optic nerve and ophthalmic artery in optic canal

Stimulation of the trochlear nucleus of one side of the brainstem results in the contraction of the contralateral superior oblique.

The trochlear nerve receives axons from the corticonuclear and tectobulbar tracts as described in the section above on the oculomotor nerve. There is communication with the nuclei of cranial nerves III, IV and VIII via the medial longitudinal fasciculus which runs vertically in the brainstem, anterior to the trochlear nucleus.

Loss of function of the fourth nerve prevents infraduction when the eye is adducted. Uncrossed diplopia results with the image seen by the affected eye displaced towards the affected side. The image also lies below and with its top tilted towards the image seen by the other, unaffected eye. An ocular torticollis may result with the head turned and tilted towards the unaffected side and with the chin lowered. With a defect of the right trochlear nerve, turning the head down and towards the left (Fig.17.11) places the face towards the motor field of the defective superior oblique (down and in). Since the unopposed inferior oblique produces excycloduction, the head must also tilt to the left to compensate. The appearance of the images when the head is in the primary position is due to the action of the inferior oblique producing excyclo-duction and supraduction.

Fig.17.10 EFFECT OF PARALYSIS OF THE RIGHT TROCHLEAR NERVE
Left eye fixating, right eye deviated up and in

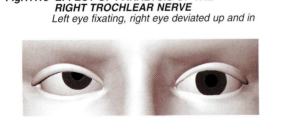

Fig.17.11 OCULAR TORTICOLLIS IN PARALYSIS OF THE RIGHT TROCHLEAR NERVE
Head turned down and to left and tilted left

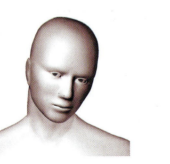

Fig.17.12 DIPLOPIC IMAGES IN PARALYSIS OF THE RIGHT TROCHLEAR NERVE

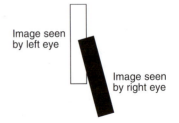

Image seen by left eye

Image seen by right eye

THE ABDUCENT NERVE (N VI)

The nucleus of the abducent nerve lies in the anterior wall of the fourth ventricle, near the midline. Medial to the nucleus is the medial longitudinal fasciculus and posteriorly the facial nerve fibres produce a bulge in the wall of the ventricle called the facial colliculus (Fig.17.13). Two groups of cells form the abducent nucleus; large multipolar cells whose axons make up the sixth nerve and small multipolar cells whose axons pass into the medial longitudinal fasciculus.

Fig.17.13 HORIZONTAL SECTION THROUGH THE MIDDLE CRANIAL FOSSA AND RIGHT ORBIT
showing the path of the abducent nerve

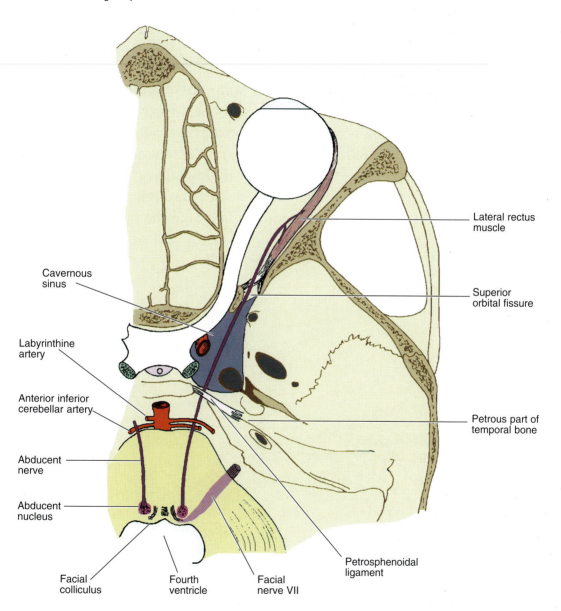

Lateral rectus muscle

Cavernous sinus

Superior orbital fissure

Labyrinthine artery

Anterior inferior cerebellar artery

Petrous part of temporal bone

Abducent nerve

Abducent nucleus

Petrosphenoidal ligament

Facial colliculus

Fourth ventricle

Facial nerve VII

The sixth nerve fibres pass obliquely downwards through the pons to emerge at the pons-medullar junction. (The seventh and eighth cranial nerves also emerge along this junction but the sixth is the most medial, see Fig.3.4). The abducent nerve passes upwards behind the anterior inferior cerebellar artery and forward between this and the labyrinthine artery. Having pierced the dura just lateral to the dorsum sellae of the sphenoid bone, the sixth nerve angles sharply over the ridge of the petrous portion of the temporal bone. Here it runs beneath the petrosphenoidal ligament and is considered to be at risk from damage by the sharp edge of the temporal bone if extreme downward movement of the cranial contents occurs. In the cavernous sinus, the nerve travels laterally to the internal carotid artery before entering the orbit. The nerve passes through the superior orbital fissure within the annulus of Zinn where it lies lateral to the oculomotor nerve. It

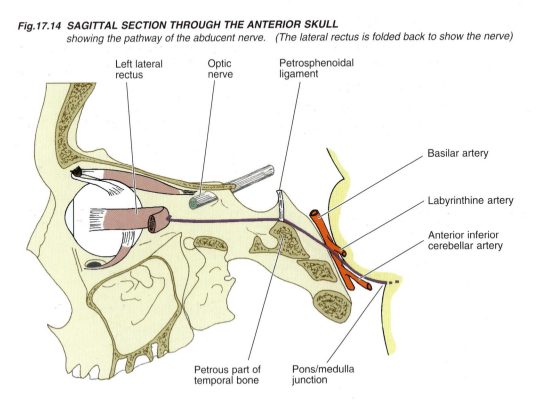

Fig.17.14 SAGITTAL SECTION THROUGH THE ANTERIOR SKULL
showing the pathway of the abducent nerve. (The lateral rectus is folded back to show the nerve)

Left lateral rectus

Optic nerve

Petrosphenoidal ligament

Basilar artery

Labyrinthine artery

Anterior inferior cerebellar artery

Petrous part of temporal bone

Pons/medulla junction

penetrates the lateral rectus within the muscle cone about 15mm from the apex of the orbit.

In common with the fourth nerve, the abducent nerve nucleus receives axons from the corticonuclear and the tectobulbar tracts and the medial longitudinal fasciculus.

Damage to the sixth nerve will result in inability to abduct the affected eye and this will produce uncrossed diplopia. The chin may be lowered and in severe cases the head will also be turned towards the affected side to move the face towards the motor field of the affected lateral rectus. The head down position may be adopted since this makes divergence easier.

Fig.17.15 ANTERIOR VIEW OF THE ANNULUS OF ZINN
showing the abducent nerve

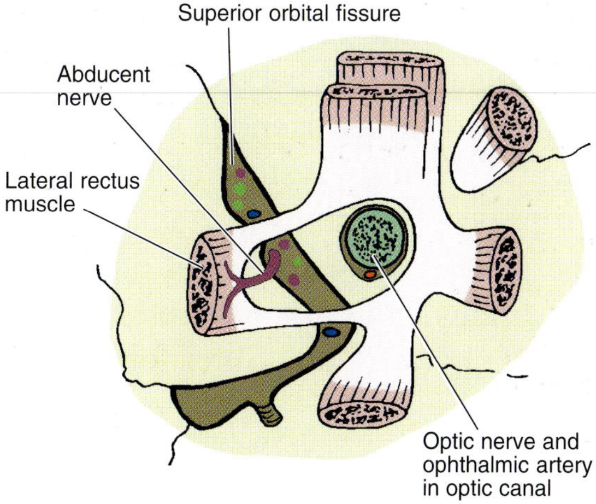

Superior orbital fissure

Abducent nerve

Lateral rectus muscle

Optic nerve and ophthalmic artery in optic canal

Fig.17.16 EFFECT OF PARALYSIS OF THE RIGHT ABDUCENT NERVE
Left eye fixating, right eye deviated inwards

Fig.17.17 OCULAR TORTICOLLIS IN PARALYSIS OF THE RIGHT ABDUCENT NERVE
Head turned to right

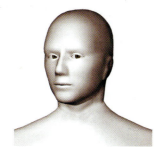

Fig.17.18 DIPLOPIC IMAGES IN PARALYSIS OF THE RIGHT ABDUCENT NERVE

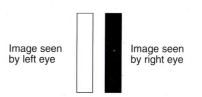

Image seen by left eye

Image seen by right eye

Axon population in nerves III, IV and VI

There seems to be little general agreement on the number of axons in the nerves controlling the oculorotatory muscles and this stems from the discovery of the mixed nature of what used to be considered to be purely motor nerves. The vast number of proprioceptive structures found in extrinsic ocular muscles must have central nervous system connections but no definite pathway for the sensory, proprioceptive fibres in cranial nerves III, IV and VI has been agreed in man. If the sensory fibres pass out of the nerve before it reaches the brainstem (in the cavernous sinus for example) the proximal count will be less than the distal. Wolff quotes 24 000 fibres for N III, 3500 for N IV and 7000 for N VI.

THE FACIAL NERVE (N VII)

The facial nerve has two roots; a motor root which supplies the facial striped muscles and a sensory root which receives taste fibres from the tongue and soft palate. The sensory root also carries preganglionic parasympathetic fibres to the lacrimal, submandibular and sublingual glands and to the glands of the nasal, palatine and possibly conjunctival mucous membranes. Only the connections to the muscles associated with the orbit and the parasympathetic route to the lacrimal gland will be considered here.

The motor nucleus of the seventh nerve lies in the lower part of the pons, lateral and anterior to the sixth nerve nucleus where it receives fibres from the corticonuclear tract. Fibres from the facial nerve nucleus pass behind the abducent nucleus before travelling forward through the pons to emerge at the pons-medulla junction, lateral to the abducent nerve. The course of the fibres behind the sixth nerve nucleus produces a bulge in the wall of the fourth ventricle, the facial colliculus. On their forward path, the fibres are joined by axons from the parasympathetic superior salivatory nucleus. Outside the pons, these fibres transfer to the nervus intermedius (sensory root) of the facial nerve. This may accompany the vestibulocochlear rather than the facial nerve into the internal

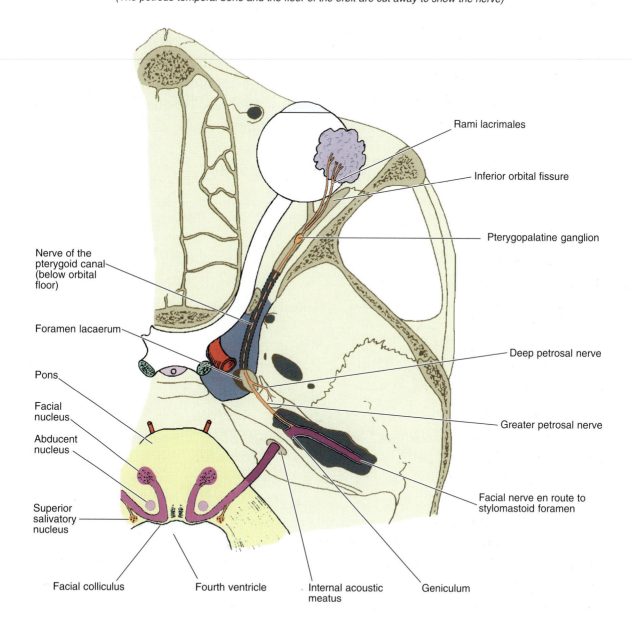

Fig.17.19 HORIZONTAL SECTION THROUGH MIDDLE CRANIAL FOSSA AND RIGHT ORBIT
showing the path of the facial nerve.
(The petrous temporal bone and the floor of the orbit are cut away to show the nerve)

Rami lacrimales

Inferior orbital fissure

Pterygopalatine ganglion

Nerve of the pterygoid canal (below orbital floor)

Foramen lacaerum

Deep petrosal nerve

Pons

Facial nucleus

Greater petrosal nerve

Abducent nucleus

Superior salivatory nucleus

Facial nerve en route to stylomastoid foramen

Facial colliculus

Fourth ventricle

Internal acoustic meatus

Geniculum

acoustic meatus, together with the labyrinthine artery. Within the petrous part of the temporal bone, the seventh nerve has a complicated path, turning first laterally and back on itself, then running downwards to emerge from the skull at the stylomastoid foramen. From here it passes forwards to the parotid gland where it divides and spreads out over the face and jaw to supply the voluntary muscles (see Fig.12.32). The orbital region is supplied by the temporal, the zygomatic and buccal branches of the nerve. The temporal branch crosses the zygomatic arch and supplies the occipitofrontalis, the orbicularis oculi and the corrugator

Fig.17.20 SAGITTAL SECTION THROUGH THE SKULL
showing the pathway of the parasympathetic fibres to the lacrimal gland

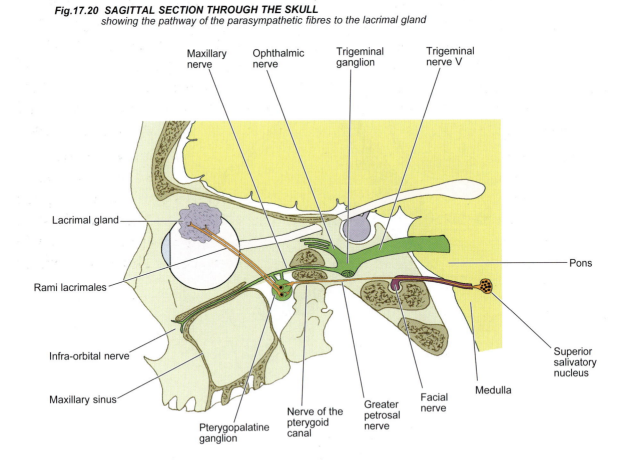

muscles. The zygomatic branch also crosses the zygomatic bone to supply the orbicularis. The buccal branch passes across the face to innervate the procerus muscle.

The parasympathetic fibres leave the facial nerve at its first bend within the temporal bone, the geniculum. These fibres travel in the greater petrosal nerve running below the trigeminal ganglion to enter the foramen lacaerum. Together with fibres from the sympathetic carotid plexus it passes through the pterygoid canal in the sphenoid where it is known as the nerve of the pterygoid canal. The parasympathetic axons synapse in the pterygopalatine ganglion, which lies in the pterygopalatine fossa, hanging below the maxillary nerve. The postganglionic fibres were originally described as reaching the lacrimal gland by a communicating branch of the fifth nerve between the zygomatic and lacrimal nerves. However, Ruskell (1971) has demonstrated that in monkey, parasympathetic fibres (which he termed rami lacrimales) run directly (and independently from N V) from the pterygopalatine ganglion to the lacrimal gland.

Damage to the facial nerve supply to the orbicularis oculi will prevent correct lid closure, a condition known as lagophthalmos (or lagophthalmus). Epiphora (excess tearing) may occur as the flaccid lower eyelid falls away from the globe and the cornea may ulcerate from the development of exposure keratitis. Loss of parasympathetic supply to the lacrimal gland reduces the lacrimal secretion to approximately one-twentieth of the normal amount; the cornea, however, appears to remain adequately moist.

SENSORY NERVES

All the orbital and ocular structures are innervated by cranial nerve V, the trigeminal. Virtually all the sensory innervation is to the ophthalmic nerve, the superior division of the fifth nerve, although some passes to the maxillary nerve, the intermediate division.

Fig.17.21 THE DISTRIBUTION OF THE THREE MAIN BRANCHES OF THE TRIGEMINAL NERVE

The ophthalmic nerve receives sensory stimulation from three orbital branches; the nasociliary nerve, the frontal nerve and the lacrimal nerve.

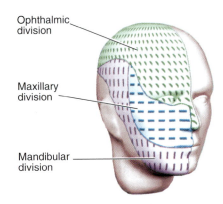

The nasociliary nerve commences in the skin and nasal cartilages at the base of the nasal bone as the external nasal branch which runs back in the nasal cavity and is joined by the two internal nasal branches to form the anterior ethmoidal nerve. This passes up through the cribriform plate of the ethmoid bone, runs back in a groove along its surface and descends to the orbit via the anterior ethmoidal foramen. Here it is joined by the infratrochlear nerve which has travelled from the region of the inner canthus, transmitting stimuli from the eyelids, the skin of the nose and the conjunctiva, caruncle and lacrimal sac. Together the anterior ethmoidal and infratrochlear nerves form the nasociliary nerve. These transmit stimuli from the cornea and conjunctiva and from the anterior globe. The nasociliary then receives the posterior ethmoidal nerve (when present) from the ethmoid and sphenoid sinuses via the posterior ethmoid foramen. Moving back along the medial wall of the orbit, the nasociliary nerve is joined by the two or three long ciliary nerves. Finally it is joined by the sensory root of the ciliary ganglion and passes over the ophthalmic artery and optic nerve to leave the orbit via the annulus of Zinn and the superior orbital fissure.

Fig.17.22 *THE ORBITAL DISTRIBUTION OF THE TRIGEMINAL NERVE*

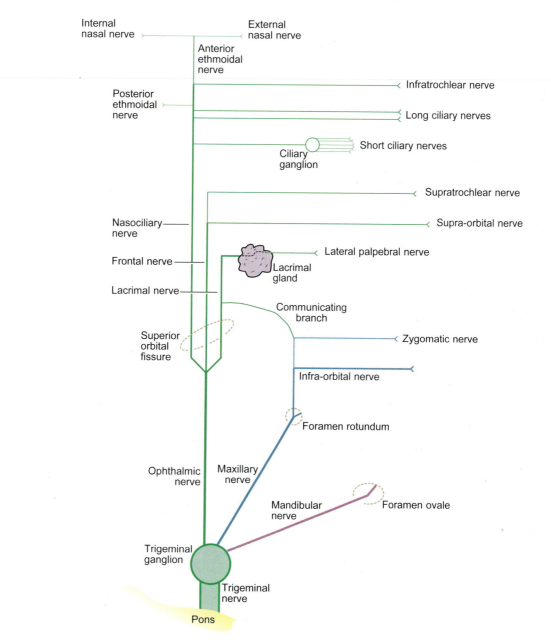

Internal nasal nerve

External nasal nerve

Anterior ethmoidal nerve

Posterior ethmoidal nerve

Infratrochlear nerve

Long ciliary nerves

Short ciliary nerves

Ciliary ganglion

Supratrochlear nerve

Nasociliary nerve

Supra-orbital nerve

Frontal nerve

Lateral palpebral nerve

Lacrimal gland

Lacrimal nerve

Communicating branch

Superior orbital fissure

Zygomatic nerve

Infra-orbital nerve

Foramen rotundum

Ophthalmic nerve

Maxillary nerve

Mandibular nerve

Foramen ovale

Trigeminal ganglion

Trigeminal nerve

Pons

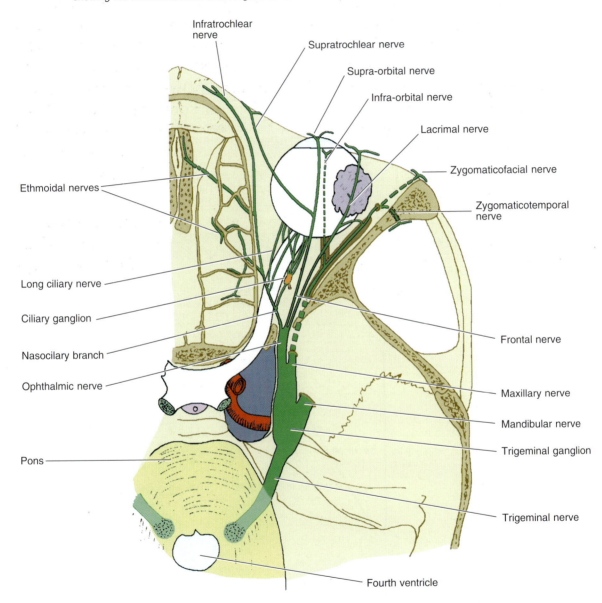

Fig.17.23 HORIZONTAL SECTION THROUGH THE MIDDLE CRANIAL FOSSA AND RIGHT ORBIT
showing the orbital branches of the trigeminal nerve

Infratrochlear nerve

Supratrochlear nerve

Supra-orbital nerve

Infra-orbital nerve

Lacrimal nerve

Zygomaticofacial nerve

Zygomaticotemporal nerve

Ethmoidal nerves

Long ciliary nerve

Ciliary ganglion

Nasocilary branch

Ophthalmic nerve

Frontal nerve

Maxillary nerve

Mandibular nerve

Trigeminal ganglion

Pons

Trigeminal nerve

Fourth ventricle

The major terminal branch of the frontal nerve is the supra-orbital nerve. This enters the orbit by the supra-orbital notch, having received branches from the forehead and scalp. It carries sensory stimuli from the upper eyelid and conjunctiva and travels back into the orbit between the levator and the orbital roof. About midway back to the apex of the orbit it is joined by the supratrochlear nerve. This has come into the orbit between the trochlea and supra-orbital notch bringing sensory information from the medial part of the forehead and from the conjunctiva and upper eyelid. The combined supratrochlear and supra-orbital nerves form the large frontal nerve which travels back between the levator and roof of the orbit to leave through the superior orbital fissure above the annulus of Zinn.

The lacrimal nerve is the smallest of the three branches and transmits sensory information from the skin covering the zygomatic bone and temporal parts of the upper eyelid. Passing back through the lacrimal gland it is joined by a few twigs

Fig.17.24 ANTERIOR ASPECT OF ANNULUS OF ZINN
showing the orbital branches of the trigeminal nerve

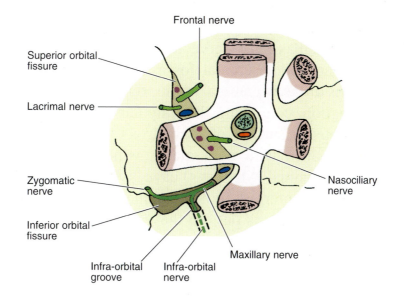

345

from the gland and conjunctiva and possibly a communicating branch from the zygomaticotemporal branch of the maxillary division of the trigeminal nerve. The lacrimal nerve travels back along the upper edge of the lateral rectus muscle accompanied by the lacrimal artery. It leaves the orbit by the superior orbital fissure and unites with the frontal and nasociliary nerves to form the ophthalmic nerve.

The maxillary nerve is formed by the union of the zygomatic nerve, the infra-orbital nerve and branches from the upper jaw and nasal mucosa.

The infra-orbital nerve passes back along the infra-orbital canal carrying sensory information from the cheek, the upper lip, the lower eyelid and, further into the canal, from the teeth of the upper jaw.

The zygomatic nerve, which joins the infra-orbital nerve in the pterygopalatine fossa, receives sensory information from the temporal fossa via its zygomaticotemporal branch, from the lateral region of the cheek by the zygomaticofacial branch and from the lacrimal gland via a communicating branch from the lacrimal nerve.

In the pterygopalatine fossa, the pterygopalatine ganglion is suspended from the maxillary nerve. The maxillary nerve leaves the fossa through the foramen rotundum to enter the middle cranial fossa. Here it joins the ophthalmic and mandibular divisions of the trigeminal at the trigeminal (Gasserian or semilunar) ganglion. The ganglion, containing the unipolar sensory cell bodies, lies in a depression in the anterior surface of the petrous temporal bone, the trigeminal impression. This is lined with dura mater, which also covers the ganglion, enclosing it in the trigeminal (Meckel's) cave. Medially is the posterior part of the cavernous sinus and inferiorly is the foramen lacaerum. Sympathetic fibres from the internal carotid plexus pass to the ganglion and it also receives fibres from the tentorium cerebelli.

The fibres of the sensory cells of the trigeminal ganglion pass into the pons in the sensory root of the trigeminal and travel in a dorsomedial direction to reach the

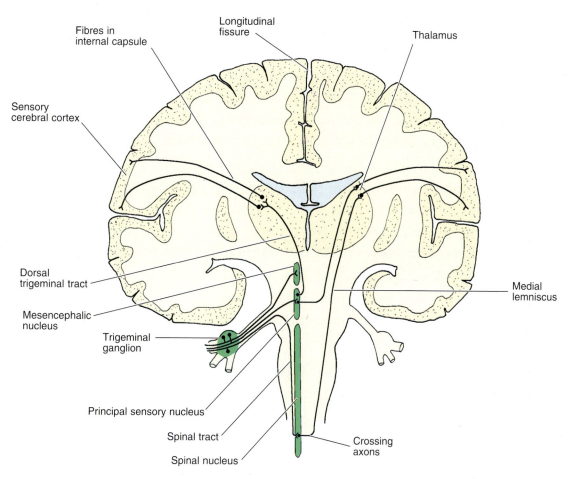

Fig.17.25 CORONAL SECTION THROUGH BRAIN
showing the trigeminal nerve pathways to the sensory cortex

Fibres in
internal capsule

Longitudinal
fissure

Thalamus

Sensory
cerebral cortex

Dorsal
trigeminal tract

Medial
lemniscus

Mesencephalic
nucleus

Trigeminal
ganglion

Principal sensory nucleus

Spinal tract

Crossing
axons

Spinal nucleus

principal sensory nucleus of the fifth nerve. Close to the nucleus, some 50% of the fibres divide into ascending and descending branches. The descending fibres form the spinal tract of the trigeminal nerve which synapse with the spinal nucleus of the trigeminal nerve as they move downwards.

The upper end of the principal sensory nucleus receives tactile and pressure information from the eye and orbit, while the lower end of the nucleus of the spinal tract receives pain and temperature information from the eye and orbit. Above the principal sensory nucleus is the mesencephalic nucleus, and fibres which ascend to this carry proprioceptive information from the extrinsic ocular muscles.

Most of the fibres from cells in the trigeminal nuclei cross to the opposite side of the brainstem before passing upwards in the medial lemniscus to relay in the thalamus and then travelling to the postcentral gyrus of the cerebral cortex. Some however, pass directly from the principal sensory nucleus to the thalamic nuclei without crossing.

Loss of sensory innervation is potentially dangerous since some of the important protective reflexes depend upon its integrity. Complete loss of sensory innervation is particularly serious for the cornea which may degenerate from neuroparalytic keratitis. Thus operative treatment for the relief of such painful conditions as herpes zoster ophthalmicus is designed to remove the pain component without loss of tactile innervation.

AUTONOMIC SUPPLY

The parasympathetic supply to the orbit via the oculomotor nerve and the facial nerve pathways have been described (pages 329 and 341).

The neurones that supply the sympathetic motor innervation to the eye and orbit have their cell bodies in the superior cervical ganglion, which forms the upper part of the spinal sympathetic chain. Postganglionic unmyelinated fibres form a plexus about the internal carotid artery and ascend with it into the middle cranial fossa. Here they form a retro-orbital sympathetic plexus from which fibres pass into the orbit accompanying blood vessels and somatic nerves. Some of those that pass to the globe do so via the sympathetic root of the ciliary ganglion and hence enter the eye in the short ciliary nerves (Fig.17.4). Those passing to the iris dilatator and to the anterior part of the globe travel in the long ciliary nerves.

The most widely distributed sympathetic nerve terminals in the ocular structures serve vasoconstrictor functions and the system also innervates the sweat glands of the skin, but some specific groups of smooth muscle are supplied by the sympathetic system. Sympathetic control is responsible for pupil dilation by contraction of the dilatator pupillae processes of the iris. Lid retraction is produced by contraction of the smooth muscle cells of the tarsal muscles innervated by the sympathetic supply.

Fig.17.26 THE SYMPATHETIC SUPPLY TO THE ORBITAL REGION
(See also Fig.12.34)

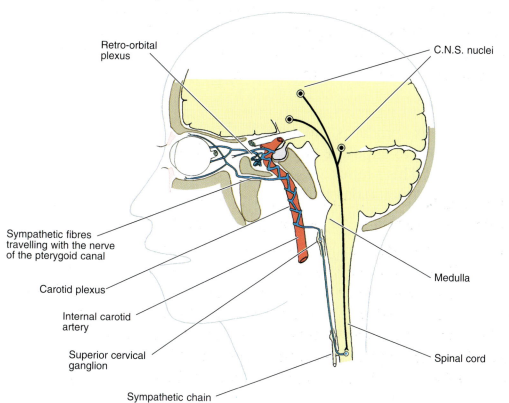

Retro-orbital plexus

C.N.S. nuclei

Sympathetic fibres travelling with the nerve of the pterygoid canal

Carotid plexus

Internal carotid artery

Superior cervical ganglion

Sympathetic chain

Medulla

Spinal cord

THE REFLEX PATHWAYS

The visual system has a number of associated protective and regulatory reflex mechanisms. The facial orbicularis muscle produces lid closure, the extrinsic ocular muscles produce lid and eye movement, and pupil and accommodation changes are brought about by the intrinsic ocular muscles. For some of these reflexes, neural pathways have not been conclusively determined, and only the probable interconnections can be given.

THE LID REFLEXES

A protective lid closure reflex occurs in response to a wide range of stimuli. The facial nerve nucleus, which controls the orbicularis oculi and hence the mechanism of eyelid closure, has connections with the superior colliculi, the trigeminal nuclei and the acoustic centres.

The dazzle reflex

The dazzle reflex produces lid closure in response to exposure to a bright light. This reflex is mediated by optic tract axons that pass to the superior colliculi and then by association fibres that travel to the facial nerve nucleus.

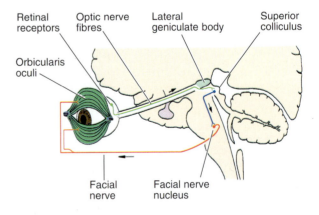

Fig.17.27 PATHWAY FOR THE DAZZLE REFLEX

Retinal receptors · Optic nerve fibres · Lateral geniculate body · Superior colliculus · Orbicularis oculi · Facial nerve · Facial nerve nucleus

The menace reflex

The menace reflex produces lid closure if an object suddenly appears or moves close to the eyes. The reflex (Fig.17.28) involves the occipital lobes and the lid movement centres of the precentral gyrus, which are connected to the facial nerve nucleus by the corticobulbar tracts.

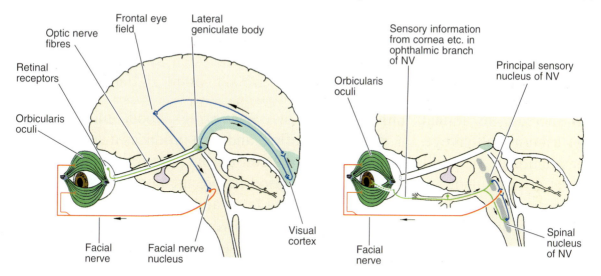

Fig.17.28 PATHWAY FOR THE MENACE REFLEX

Frontal eye field

Optic nerve fibres

Lateral geniculate body

Retinal receptors

Orbicularis oculi

Facial nerve

Facial nerve nucleus

Visual cortex

Fig.17.29 PATHWAY FOR THE SENSORY REFLEX

Sensory information from cornea etc. in ophthalmic branch of NV

Orbicularis oculi

Principal sensory nucleus of NV

Facial nerve

Spinal nucleus of NV

The sensory reflex

Sensory or tactile reflex lid closure occurs if the cornea, conjunctiva or eyelid margin is touched. The afferent pathway is the nasociliary branch of the trigeminal (fifth cranial) nerve and this reflex is also referred to as the trigeminal reflex. The connections between the fifth and seventh nerve nuclei occur via interneurones at the level of the fourth ventricle.

The auropalpebral reflex

The facial nucleus is also connected to the auditory nerve nucleus. A loud noise produces a reflex blink, which also leads to conjugate eye movement towards the apparent source of the sound.

351

THE PUPILLARY REFLEXES

Changes in pupil diameter occur in response to changes in retinal luminance, to accommodation, to emotion and to pain.

The light reflexes

An increase in retinal luminance for one eye brings about miosis (pupil constriction) in that eye, the direct light reflex, and also produces a simultaneous constriction of the pupil of the other eye, the consensual light reflex. As with all neural activity, there is a delay or latent period before the pupil constricts. The latent period varies inversely with luminance level and may be 0.2-0.5 seconds, the longer latent period corresponding to a lower luminance. The afferent pathway is via optic tract axons that pass into the superior brachium and travel to the pretectal nucleus situated in the upper part of the midbrain. From cells in this nucleus, some axons pass to the visceral nucleus of cranial nerve III on the same side to produce the direct reflex, and some decussate either in front of the aqueduct or via the posterior commissure to reach the contralateral visceral nucleus. The efferent axons follow the parasympathetic pathway to the ciliary

Fig.17.30 PATHWAY FOR MIOSIS DUE TO AN INCREASE IN RETINAL LUMINANCE

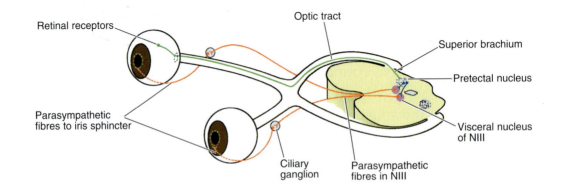

Retinal receptors

Optic tract

Superior brachium

Pretectal nucleus

Parasympathetic fibres to iris sphincter

Visceral nucleus of NIII

Ciliary ganglion

Parasympathetic fibres in NIII

ganglion and thence, after synapsing, to the iris sphincter via the short ciliary nerves.

Reduction in retinal luminance produces mydriasis (pupil dilation) by stimulation of cells situated in the superior cervical ganglion. The efferent axons from this ganglion follow the sympathetic pathway via the internal carotid plexus to the orbital sympathetic system and to the iris dilatator. It may be that optic tract axons, communicating with the pretectal nucleus, have their information relayed to the interstitial nucleus. From this, fibres descending in the interstitiospinal tract synapse at a ciliospinal centre in the upper thoracic region and from here axons pass into the sympathetic chain to reach the superior cervical ganglion. Although this is the pathway shown in Fig.17.31 it is only hypothetical.

The size of the pupil in any particular luminance is a result of a balance between the activity of the parasympathetic system controlling the iris sphincter and the sympathetic controlling the iris dilatator.

Fig.17.31 PATHWAY FOR MYDRIASIS DUE TO A DECREASE IN RETINAL LUMINANCE

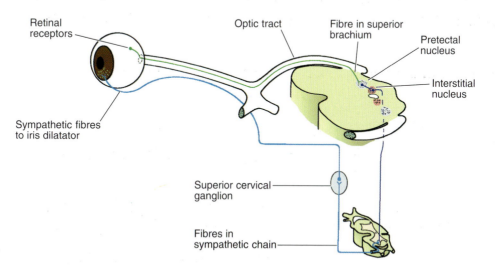

Retinal receptors

Optic tract

Fibre in superior brachium

Pretectal nucleus

Interstitial nucleus

Sympathetic fibres to iris dilatator

Superior cervical ganglion

Fibres in sympathetic chain

The near reflex

The pupils constrict when the eyes accommodate or converge. These events normally occur in near vision and each form a part of the near reflex. Miosis reduces spherical aberration and also decreases the blur circle size, thus increasing the depth of field in near vision. The afferent pathway for this miosis is uncertain, but is assumed to be cortical since in the abnormal condition of Argyll-Robertson pupil, the pupil constricts in near vision but not in response to light. The efferent pathway is the parasympathetic outflow from the visceral nucleus of the oculomotor nerve.

Pain and fear reflexes

Pain will cause pupil dilatation and the pupils dilate and the eyelids are retracted in response to fear. However, irritation of the cornea, conjunctiva or eyelids results in pupil constriction. This is due to dilation of the iris vessels assumed to be the result of the axon reflex, similar to that produced in skin capillaries when a cutaneous sensory nerve is stimulated.

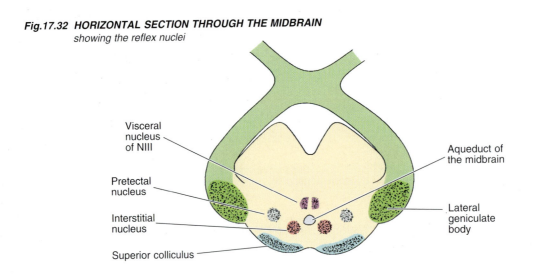

Fig.17.32 HORIZONTAL SECTION THROUGH THE MIDBRAIN
showing the reflex nuclei

Visceral nucleus of NIII

Pretectal nucleus

Interstitial nucleus

Superior colliculus

Aqueduct of the midbrain

Lateral geniculate body

EYE MOVEMENT REFLEXES

The oculorotatory muscles are controlled by the brainstem nuclei which communicate with each other by the medial longitudinal fasciculus. These nuclei also receive information from the cerebral cortex, the cerebellum and other brainstem nuclei, resulting in reflex eye movement in response to retinal and postural stimulation.

The psycho-optical reflexes act to ensure that images of objects, important or potentially important to the observer, fall on the fovea. Retinal signals provide the main stimulus for eye movement to initiate and maintain fixation and to produce the binocular movements used in response to fusional demands.

The postural reflexes move the eyes in response to body movement to assist in maintaining their alignment and to stabilise the retinal image during head movement.

The psycho-optical reflexes

The fixation reflex

The fixation reflex turns the visual axis towards an object in the visual field that attracts the attention of the visual system. Although there is a delay or latent period of about 200ms before eye movement occurs, the movement of the visual axis is rapid and similar to that of voluntary eye movement when the eye may turn at a rate of up to 700° per second. These movements are referred to as saccades. To decelerate the eye at the end of such a movement the saccadic inducing signal is reversed, sometimes producing a slight reverse saccade movement which gives the impression of initial overshoot. Fixation is never absolutely maintained, and the visual axis strays from the object, so that the eye is constantly in motion with small, rapid tremors of about 17" of arc and jerky movements or flicks of about 5' of arc which apparently compensate for slow drifts, and on which slow, irregular movements are superimposed.

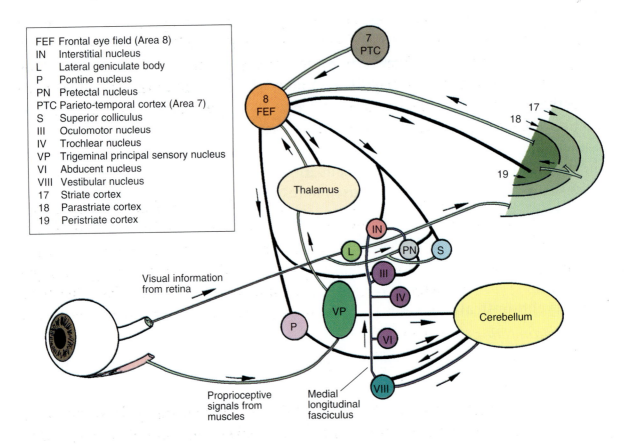

Fig.17.33 THE COMPLEX PATHWAYS INVOLVED IN THE CONTROL OF EYE MOVEMENTS

FEF Frontal eye field (Area 8)
IN   Interstitial nucleus
L   Lateral geniculate body
P   Pontine nucleus
PN   Pretectal nucleus
PTC Parieto-temporal cortex (Area 7)
S   Superior colliculus
III Oculomotor nucleus
IV   Trochlear nucleus
VP   Trigeminal principal sensory nucleus
VI   Abducent nucleus
VIII Vestibular nucleus
17   Striate cortex
18   Parastriate cortex
19   Peristriate cortex

Thalamus

Cerebellum

Visual information from retina

Proprioceptive signals from muscles

Medial longitudinal fasciculus

The pursuit reflex

If the object moves, the refixation or pursuit reflex enables the eye to follow it. Unlike the jerky movement in the initial fixation, this tracking movement is normally smooth, provided that the object does not move faster than 30-40° per second. As with voluntary movement, head turn is initiated if the object lies much more than 10° from the visual axis, and, except in downwards gaze, eye movements rarely exceed 30° from the primary position.

The tracking reflex

The tracking reflex can be observed in optokinetic or train nystagmus. If a series of resolvable objects move across the visual field, they will each be tracked for a short distance and then fixation will be transferred to the next object. This involuntary eye movement may be exploited by using a rotating striped drum to objectively measure visual acuity, since if the eye can resolve the stripes, optokinetic nystagmus will be observed.

The fusion reflex

The fusion reflex is invoked when both eyes are used to observe a particular object. Corrective eye movements occur to avoid the lack of clarity and double vision that results if the images seen with each eye do not lie on corresponding points of the retinae. Diplopia does not occur provided that the images for the two eyes lie on points which correspond to within about 10'. The dissimilarity of the retinal images due to the separation of the two eyes is used by the visual system to provide information for stereopsis.

Postural reflexes

The reflexes which rotate the eyes to stabilise the retinal image in response to changes in head position are termed the static reflexes while those that respond to changes in movement (acceleration/deceleration) are called the statokinetic reflexes.

The static reflex

The static reflexes occur as a result of afferent information from the otolith system of the labyrinth of the inner ear. The otoliths are small crystals of calcium carbonate which lie in the polysaccharide jelly covering the maculae of the saccule and utricle. Projecting into the jelly are the cilia of hair cells and these cells make contact with bipolar neurones whose cell bodies are located in the vestibular ganglion. Gravity causes the otoliths to bend the cilia and produce a change in the signal carried by the vestibular neurones. These signals combined with information

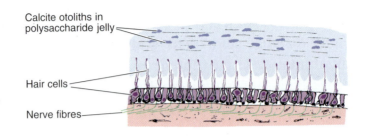

Fig.17.34 HAIR CELLS OF SACCULE AND UTRICLE

Calcite otoliths in polysaccharide jelly

Hair cells

Nerve fibres

from receptors located in the neck muscles and the head-neck joint cause change in the muscle tone of the vertically acting rectus and the oblique muscles. Thus chin elevation or depression will produce compensatory eye movement to maintain fixation. The effect has also been called the 'doll's eye phenomenon' after the way that the weighted eyes of a doll move as the body is moved. Although vertical ductions may be effected voluntarily, cycloductions cannot be

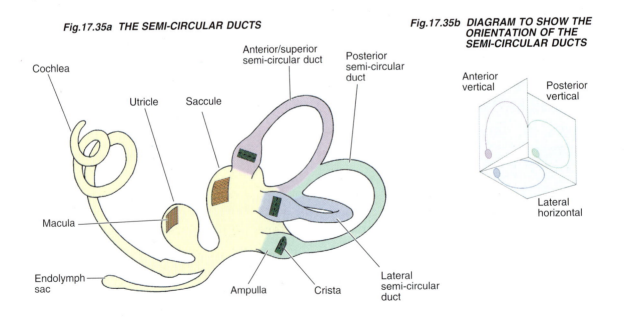

Fig.17.35a THE SEMI-CIRCULAR DUCTS

Cochlea

Utricle

Saccule

Anterior/superior semi-circular duct

Posterior semi-circular duct

Macula

Endolymph sac

Ampulla

Crista

Lateral semi-circular duct

Fig.17.35b DIAGRAM TO SHOW THE ORIENTATION OF THE SEMI-CIRCULAR DUCTS

Anterior vertical

Posterior vertical

Lateral horizontal

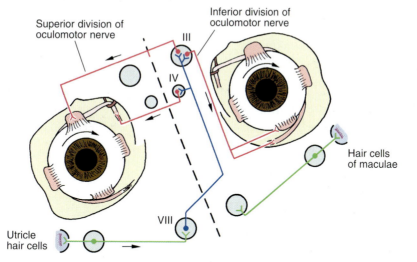

Fig.17.36 THE HEAD TILT REFLEX

Superior division of oculomotor nerve

Inferior division of oculomotor nerve

III

IV

Hair cells of maculae

VIII

Utricle hair cells

performed at will but if the head is tilted to one side, the reflex signal to the extrinsic ocular muscles produces a compensatory cyclorotation of the eyes. However, the amount of cyclorotation produced is usually only about 10% of the angle of head tilt.

The statokinetic reflexes

The three semi-circular canals of the inner ear are lined with membranous ducts. Each duct terminates in a swelling or ampulla in the wall of which lies the transverse ampullary crest or crista. This crest is covered in hair cells and is

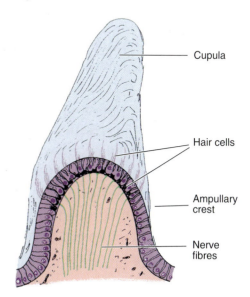

Fig.17.37 HAIR CELLS OF THE AMPULLAE

Cupula

Hair cells

Ampullary crest

Nerve fibres

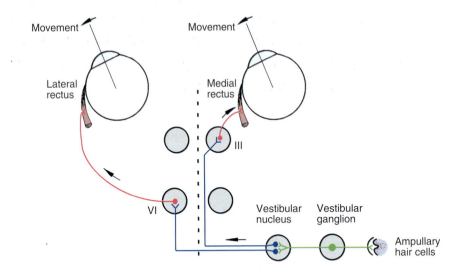

Fig.17.38 PATHWAY FOR THE HORIZONTAL STATO-KINETIC REFLEX

surrounded by a mound of proteinous jelly, the cupula. Acceleration and deceleration of the endolymph in the ducts moves the cupula and hence moves the cilia of the hair cells. These changes are signalled to the vestibular nucleus to produce compensatory eye movements which stabilise the retinal image as the head starts to rotate. This mechanism responds within about 10ms but in sustained rotation the slower optokinetic reflex is used to stabilise the image and to negate the unpleasant vestibular effects which would occur when the movement stops. Szentagothai (1950) found that the ampullary cells of one labyrinth communicated with the medial rectus, the superior rectus and the superior oblique muscle of the ipsilateral eye and the lateral rectus, the inferior rectus and the inferior oblique muscle of the contralateral eye. Thus turning the head to the right stimulates the right vestibular nucleus and inhibits the left and produces a reflex movement of both eyes towards the left.

Similar effects are produced by head rotations in other planes since the three semi-circular canals are mutually perpendicular (Fig.17.35b). The initial slow compensatory eye movement is followed by a rapid recovery movement in the opposite direction and this oscillation is referred to as vestibular nystagmus. It is important to note that it is the change in movement that produces the nystagmus.

Caloric stimulation of the canals with warm and cold water or electrical stimulation may also be used to elicit nystagmus.

Chapter 18

THE DEVELOPMENT OF THE EYE

The growth of the fertilised ovum into a human foetus is a complex process. An understanding of the development of the embryonic and foetal eye may clarify some of the structural arrangements in the adult eye and can also help to explain some anomalies of ocular development that may be encountered in practice.

Immediately after fertilisation, cell division is slow, it takes some 36 hours for the fertilised ovum to become two cells. At this stage, if the two-celled structure, the blastomere, is split, both cells may survive, producing identical twins. Seventy-two hours after fertilisation cell division has produced a mass of 8-12 cells, the morula. By day 5 a blastocyst has been formed, this is a 100µm diameter hollow

Fig.18.1 THE FERTILIZED OVUM

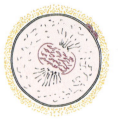

Fig.18.2 THE BLASTOMERE

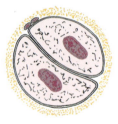

Fig.18.3 THE MORULA

Fig.18.4 THE BLASTOCYST

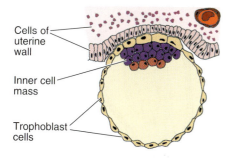

Cells of uterine wall

Inner cell mass

Trophoblast cells

Fig.18.5 THE IMPLANTED BLASTOCYST

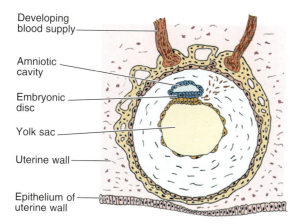

Developing blood supply

Amniotic cavity

Embryonic disc

Yolk sac

Uterine wall

Epithelium of uterine wall

sphere with a single layer of cells surrounding the fluid-filled interior. The surface cells, known as trophoblasts, will be involved in the placental structure, while a few cells adhering internally (the inner cell mass) will become the embryonic disc.

The blastocyst, which has been floating in the uterine fluid, becomes anchored to the wall of the uterus and is covered in uterine epithelial cells, a process known as implantation. This enables the developing embryo to obtain nutrients from the maternal blood supply, initially by diffusion and later by the development of the highly vascular placenta.

During the second week post-fertilisation the inner cell mass becomes organised to surround two spaces, the amniotic cavity and the yolk sac. The amniotic cavity is surrounded by a single layer of ectodermal cells and the yolk sac is surrounded by a single layer of endoderm. During the third week, mesoderm, which is destined to form the bulk of the body's connective tissue, grows between the two layers.

Fig.18.6 *THE EMBRYONIC DISC*

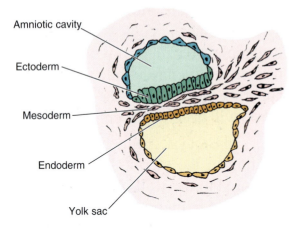

Amniotic cavity

Ectoderm

Mesoderm

Endoderm

Yolk sac

Fig.18.7
SURFACE VIEW OF THE EMBRYONIC DISC
(Amniotic cavity removed)

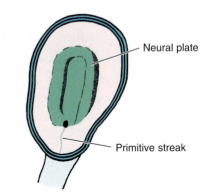

Neural plate

Primitive streak

The, now trilaminar, structure is the embryonic disc and the embryo evolves by elongation of this disc with differential rates of growth in the cell layers along the edges of the disc producing significant folds and swellings. The invading mesoderm rapidly forms a rod-like structure, the notochord, which supports the developing embryo and will later create a framework for the spinal column. At this stage the embryo is about 2mm long.

Along the length of the notochord, from the level of the future midbrain, blocks of mesoderm form pairs of

Fig.18.8 *SECTION THROUGH THE EMBRYO*

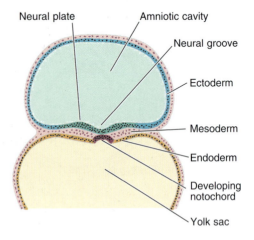

Day 17

Neural plate

Amniotic cavity

Neural groove

Ectoderm

Mesoderm

Endoderm

Developing notochord

Yolk sac

somites, from which the spinal vertebrae, muscles and skin will develop.

The ectoderm thickens centrally to form the neural plate (by day 17) along the edge of which further growth produces the neural folds. This creates an axial depression, the neural groove. By day 22, continuing growth brings the edges of the neural folds together, resulting in the formation of the neural tube in the central region of the embryo.

Fig.18.9 *THE 24 DAY EMBRYO*

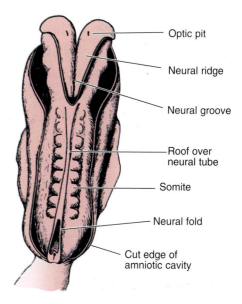

Optic pit

Neural ridge

Neural groove

Roof over neural tube

Somite

Neural fold

Cut edge of amniotic cavity

Fig.18.10
DEVELOPMENT OF THE NEURAL TUBE
(Sections through the central region of the embryo)

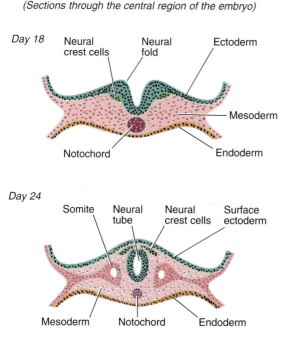

Day 18

Neural crest cells — Neural fold — Ectoderm

Mesoderm

Notochord — Endoderm

Day 24

Somite — Neural tube — Neural crest cells — Surface ectoderm

Mesoderm — Notochord — Endoderm

Neural crest cells, which in general provide sensory and autonomic neurones and their ganglia, separate from the neural and surface ectoderm and migrate laterally to lie in the mesoderm between the neural tube and the surface cells.

The eye and its associated structures will develop from the surface and neural ectoderm, the neural crest cells and the mesoderm.

The surface ectoderm will provide the corneal epithelium, the crystalline lens, the lacrimal and accessory lacrimal glands, the conjunctiva and the epidermis of the lids.

The neural ectoderm differentiates into the retina, the neurones and glia of the optic nerve, the iris sphincter and the iris and ciliary epithelium. The mesoderm provides the extrinsic ocular muscles and endothelium of the vessels. However the bulk of the connective tissues of the eye and orbit are derived from the neural crest cells, including the corneal, scleral, iris and choroidal stromal cells, the ciliary muscle, the orbital fat, cartilage and bones, the orbital nerves and meninges.

Fig.18.11 THE EARLY DEVELOPMENT OF THE BRAIN

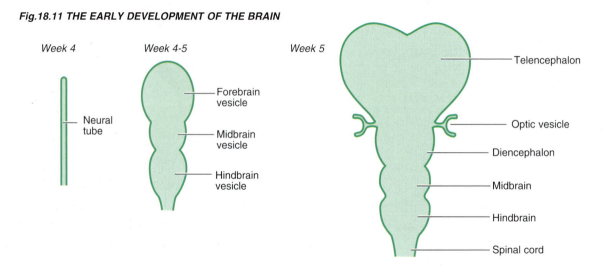

Development of the neural tube at the future head end of the embryo produces the brain vesicles, initially three; the forebrain, midbrain and hindbrain. Further growth will divide the forebrain into the telencephalon (cerebral hemispheres) and the diencephalon (thalamus) and it is at the junction of these that the eye and its associated structures will be formed. Extension and folding of the hindbrain will produce the pons, the cerebellum and the medulla oblongata.

As the forebrain develops, and prior to closure of the neural groove, the neural

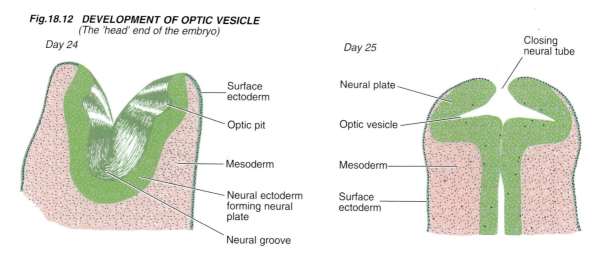

Fig.18.12 DEVELOPMENT OF OPTIC VESICLE
(The 'head' end of the embryo)

Day 24

- Surface ectoderm
- Optic pit
- Mesoderm
- Neural ectoderm forming neural plate
- Neural groove

Day 25

- Closing neural tube
- Neural plate
- Optic vesicle
- Mesoderm
- Surface ectoderm

ridges at each side of the groove develop optic pits in the region that will mark the junction of the telencephalon and diencephalon. By day 25 growth along the lateral walls of the neural plate produces the laterally directed optic vesicles and neural crest cells grow between these and the surface ectoderm displacing the mesoderm.

The area between the forebrain cavity and the optic vesicles constricts, forming the optic stalk. Differential growth rates at the perimeter of the optic vesicles causes an indentation to form at the lower edge of the vesicle and optic stalk (Fig.18.14b). As the outer rim of the vesicle continues its growth, the central area

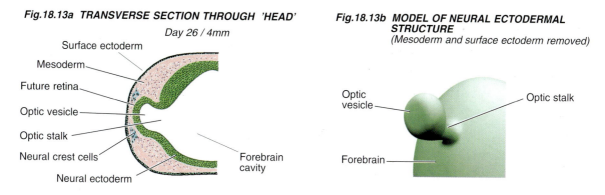

Fig.18.13a TRANSVERSE SECTION THROUGH 'HEAD'

Day 26 / 4mm

- Surface ectoderm
- Mesoderm
- Future retina
- Optic vesicle
- Optic stalk
- Neural crest cells
- Neural ectoderm
- Forebrain cavity

Fig.18.13b MODEL OF NEURAL ECTODERMAL STRUCTURE
(Mesoderm and surface ectoderm removed)

- Optic vesicle
- Optic stalk
- Forebrain

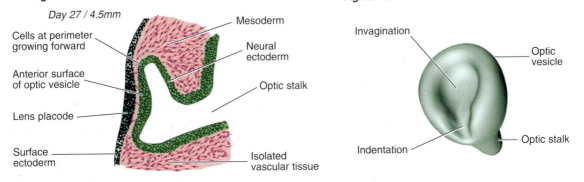

Fig.18.14a LENS PLACODE FORMATION

Day 27 / 4.5mm

Cells at perimeter growing forward

Anterior surface of optic vesicle

Lens placode

Surface ectoderm

Mesoderm

Neural ectoderm

Optic stalk

Isolated vascular tissue

Fig.18.14b INVAGINATION OF OPTIC VESICLE

Invagination

Optic vesicle

Indentation

Optic stalk

grows less rapidly. This produces an invagination of the anterior surface of the vesicle and the lengthening indentation forms a groove along the lower edge of the optic stalk. Eventually, what was the anterior layer of cells will be in contact with the posterior, inner, surface of the vesicle and these combined layers will form the retina (Fig.18.18a).

The edges of the groove in the lower surface come together to form the optic (embryonic, choroidal) fissure which starts to close early in the fifth week (9mm)

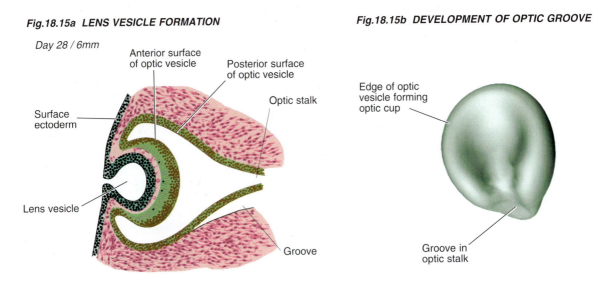

Fig.18.15a LENS VESICLE FORMATION

Day 28 / 6mm

Surface ectoderm

Lens vesicle

Anterior surface of optic vesicle

Posterior surface of optic vesicle

Optic stalk

Groove

Fig.18.15b DEVELOPMENT OF OPTIC GROOVE

Edge of optic vesicle forming optic cup

Groove in optic stalk

and is normally sealed at the 13mm stage by the end of the fifth week. Failure of this fissure to close completely results in a coloboma which may be visible in the iris, choroid or retina.

At day 26 the surface ectoderm in front of the optic vesicle thickens, forming the lens placode. As the lens placode invaginates it forms the lens vesicle (Fig.18.15a), which separates from the surface ectoderm (Fig.18.18a) at the 33 day (10mm) stage by which time the lens is about 0.2mm in diameter and the capsule has started to form.

As the lens separates from what will become the cornea, the posterior cells elongate and their nuclei move towards the anterior surface. The elongated cell processes are the primary lens fibres which fill the lens vesicle by day 42 (18mm stage). Division of the equatorial cells of the lens and the successive elongation of their processes increases the volume of the lens and generates the lens sutures which are visible at 8 weeks (Fig.10.20).

Fig.18.16 DEVELOPMENT OF THE LENS

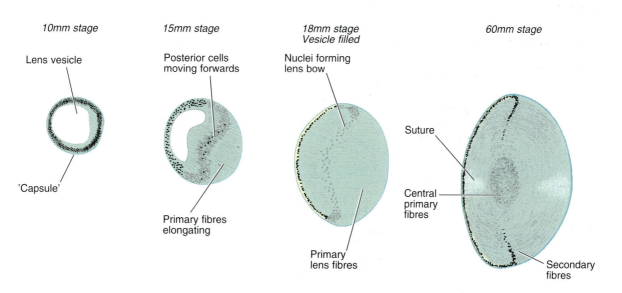

10mm stage

Lens vesicle

'Capsule'

15mm stage

Posterior cells moving forwards

Primary fibres elongating

18mm stage
Vesicle filled

Nuclei forming lens bow

Primary lens fibres

60mm stage

Suture

Central primary fibres

Secondary fibres

The separation of the lens from the surface ectoderm marks the start of the development of the cornea, which at this stage consists of two layers of epithelial cells. By the end of week 6 (18mm) a derivative of the neural crest cells, the mesenchyme, has formed two layers of endothelial cells behind the epithelial cell basement membrane. By the end of week 7 (24mm) further mesenchyme expansion has created a layer between the epithelium and the endothelium which by week 8 (30mm) consists of about eight layers of flattened cells with collagen fibres starting to appear. During week 12 the cornea is approximately 2mm in diameter and by 4 months it is about 4.5mm in diameter, by which time both the anterior and posterior limiting laminae are visible. By month 5 corneal nerve endings are found widely distributed amongst the epithelial cells. The cornea is initially translucent but transparency develops with development of the lamellae of the stroma. At birth the cornea is about 10mm in diameter.

Fig.18.17 DEVELOPMENT OF THE CORNEA

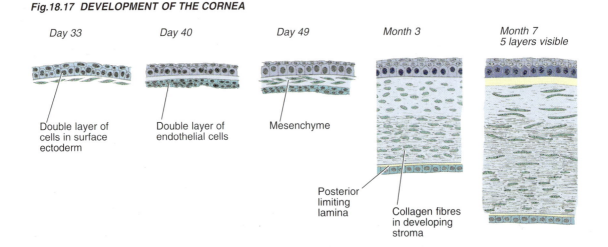

Day 33 — Double layer of cells in surface ectoderm

Day 40 — Double layer of endothelial cells

Day 49 — Mesenchyme — Posterior limiting lamina

Month 3 — Collagen fibres in developing stroma

Month 7 — 5 layers visible

At 7 weeks (21mm) the anterior chamber becomes a definitive fluid-filled space (Fig.18.19) bounded by the corneal endothelium and the mesenchyme tissue which will form the iris. By about the fourth month the canal of Schlemm is formed (Fig.18.23) and the trabecular meshwork starts to differentiate.

Circumferential condensations in the mesenchyme layer, backwards from the limbus near the future insertion of the rectus muscles, start to produce the sclera during the seventh week (Fig.18.19). These reach the posterior pole of the eye by week 12 (65mm) with the sclera being fully differentiated by the fifth month.

The extrinsic ocular muscles start to develop from the orbital mesoderm during week 4. At 5 weeks the nerve supply to the muscles is in place and the rectus muscle cone is forming around the optic nerve. There is a progressive forward differentiation of the muscles. At 10 weeks Tenon's capsule has started to form around the globe and towards the end of the third month the muscle tendons are embedded in the sclera. The trochlea forms at the orbital margin during the 20-30mm stage, appearing before the frontal bone has ossified. As the orbital bone development lags behind the development of the globe, the superior oblique muscle initially makes an obtuse angle. The levator is the last muscle to appear, starting its development shortly before the 30mm stage. Initially it is medial to the superior rectus (at the 60mm stage) and only takes its place above it in the fourth month. Congenital ptosis may be due to late development of this muscle.

The orbital bones are derived from neural crest cells and differentiate during the third month. The formation of the bones is closely related to the growth of the optic cup. The orbital margin is circular at 6 months and at this stage the margin only extends to the equator of the globe. At birth, the orbital margin is still relatively round and the lacrimal fossa faces forwards. As the skull develops the orbit widens and the lacrimal fossa rotates to face laterally. While the orbit virtually doubles in size between birth and adulthood, the globe is nearly three-quarters of its adult size at birth, its diameter increasing by an average of only 0.1mm per year up to the age of 15. The angle between the orbital axes is initially 180° and gradually converges, until in the adult it becomes about 45°.

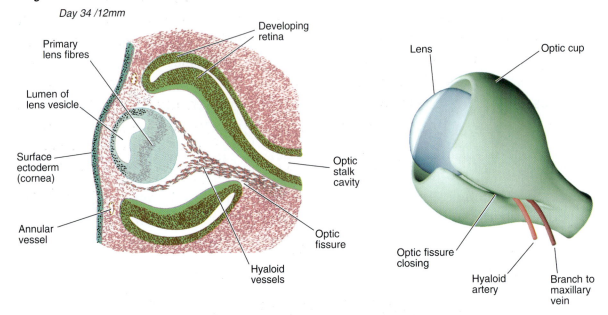

Fig. 18.18a HYALOID SYSTEM DEVELOPING VIA OPTIC FISSURE

Day 34 /12mm

Primary
lens fibres

Developing
retina

Lumen of
lens vesicle

Surface
ectoderm
(cornea)

Annular
vessel

Hyaloid
vessels

Optic
stalk
cavity

Optic
fissure

Fig.18.18b THE LENS IN THE OPTIC CUP

Lens

Optic cup

Optic fissure
closing

Hyaloid
artery

Branch to
maxillary
vein

**Fig. 18.19 HYALOID SYSTEM DEVELOPED, VESSELS IN PLACE IN PUPILLARY MEMBRANE,
OPTIC NERVE FORMED**

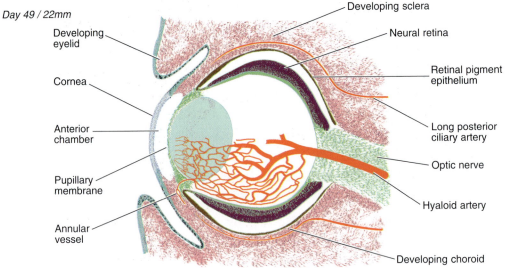

Day 49 / 22mm

Developing
eyelid

Cornea

Anterior
chamber

Pupillary
membrane

Annular
vessel

Developing sclera

Neural retina

Retinal pigment
epithelium

Long posterior
ciliary artery

Optic nerve

Hyaloid artery

Developing choroid

By the time the embryo is 5mm long (at about 4 weeks) the ophthalmic artery has developed and given off a branch, the hyaloid artery, which passes into the optic (embryonic) fissure in the lower surface of the optic cup. This develops within the growing eye to supply its anterior structures and, by links with vessels outside the cup, forms the annular vessels at the cup's anterior border. The hyaloid artery branches within the globe to surround the lens posteriorly, while the annular vessels extend outgrowths across the front of the lens to vascularize the pupillary membrane (week 6). The hyaloid system is fully developed at the 40mm (9 week) stage but then atrophies towards the end of week 12. Remnants of these vessels may be seen attached at the posterior pole of the adult lens (as Mittendorf's dot, see Fig.10.15).

Fig.18.20 HYALOID VESSELS DEGENERATING

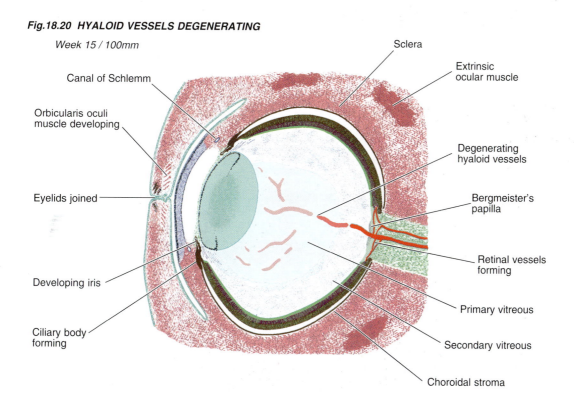

Week 15 / 100mm

Sclera

Extrinsic ocular muscle

Canal of Schlemm

Orbicularis oculi muscle developing

Degenerating hyaloid vessels

Eyelids joined

Bergmeister's papilla

Developing iris

Retinal vessels forming

Ciliary body forming

Primary vitreous

Secondary vitreous

Choroidal stroma

The two layers of neural ectodermal cells that form the back of the optic cup at the 5mm stage become the neural (inner) retina and the (outer) pigment epithelium. Pigmentation of the outer layer commences at about 28 days (6-7mm stage).

The neural retina develops from the inner neural ectodermal cell layer of the optic cup and by week 7 (the 20mm stage) has differentiated into an inner and outer neuroblastic layer. Receptor outer segments develop slowly from the initial appearance of cilia projecting from the cells of the outer neuroblastic layer at 4 weeks to the appearance of receptor processes at the fifth month and the differentiation of rod processes at month 7. By week 23 all the retinal layers are clearly defined, although the individual components continue to differentiate, while the foveal region continues to develop for some months after birth.

Fig.18.21 DEVELOPMENT OF THE RETINA

Day 32

Neural ectoderm

Day 40

Outer neuroblastic layer

Inner neuroblastic layer

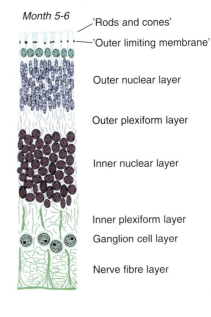

Month 5-6

'Rods and cones'

'Outer limiting membrane'

Outer nuclear layer

Outer plexiform layer

Inner nuclear layer

Inner plexiform layer

Ganglion cell layer

Nerve fibre layer

At the 15mm stage the retinal ganglion cells are producing axons which travel towards the optic stalk. The optic stalk had first appeared due to a constriction in the tissue between the forebrain cavity and the optic vesicle and had developed a groove in its lower surface to provide a route into the eye for the hyaloid artery and a route out for the nerve fibres of the retina. The retinal axons pass through the retina to fill and expand the groove so that the original connection between the optic vesicle and the forebrain is obliterated. (Only a small depression in the floor of the third ventricle then marks the origin of the optic stalk). By week 10 the hyaloid artery is surrounded by nerve fibres, and, as the artery atrophies, the space at the optic nerve head is filled with neuroglial cells forming Bergmeister's papilla (Fig.18.20) which may extend nearly halfway to the lens. As these glial cells degenerate in turn, the disc is left with a centrally excavated region which, in the adult, is the physiological cup (Bergmeister's papilla may be evident in the adult eye if these cells do not degenerate). The lamina cribrosa develops between the fourth and seventh months to bridge the hole in the sclera through which the optic nerve fibres emerged. Myelination of the optic nerve fibres commences at the chiasma at month 7-8 and normally stops on reaching the lamina cribrosa about one month after birth. Occasionally myelinated nerve fibres may be seen passing onto the surface of the retina, but, apart from enlarging the blind spot, this is a non-pathological congenital abnormality.

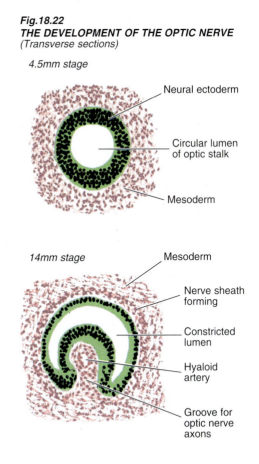

Fig.18.22
THE DEVELOPMENT OF THE OPTIC NERVE
(Transverse sections)

4.5mm stage

Neural ectoderm

Circular lumen of optic stalk

Mesoderm

14mm stage

Mesoderm

Nerve sheath forming

Constricted lumen

Hyaloid artery

Groove for optic nerve axons

Retinal vasculature develops from the degenerating hyaloid system during the fourth month. Buds appear at the optic disc which will become the upper and lower central retinal arteries. From these, vessels spread across the retina, with concurrent venous development, to reach the ora serrata during the eighth month.

Once the retinal ganglion cell axons have reached the proximal end of the optic stalk (at the 18mm stage), some axons start to decussate below the lower surface of the third ventricle so that by the end of the seventh week (22mm stage) the chiasma is forming. Continued axonal growth passes fibres round the diencephalon to meet the lateral geniculate bodies which have developed from cells in the dorsolateral wall of the thalamus. Fibres extend throughout the tracts and reach the lateral geniculate nucleus by the 48mm (10 week) stage, although the lamination of the lateral geniculate nucleus is not evident until about six months.

During the second month a layer of blood vessels forms between the retinal pigment epithelium and the developing sclera forming a primitive choriocapillaris. During the third and fourth months the outer vascular layers of the choroid are formed. The tissue contains pigment cells and appears dark brown in the adult eye but pigmented cells are not generally present in the foetal choroid until the seventh month.

The ciliary body and iris are relatively late in developing. At about 6 weeks (17mm stage) vessel loops from the hyaloid system extend across the anterior surface of the lens and, with the mesenchyme tissue, form a thin vascular membrane (Fig.18.19). The two layers of neural ectoderm at the rim of the optic cup extend to form the posterior layers of the iris. As these grow forward they are accompanied by mesenchymal tissue from the periphery of the cornea which will form the iris stroma. Late in month 3 the posterior layers of the iris begin to

Fig.18.23 THE ANTERIOR QUADRANT

Week 15 / 100mm

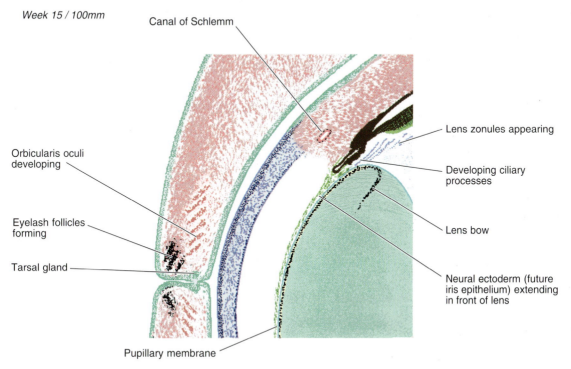

Canal of Schlemm

Lens zonules appearing

Developing ciliary processes

Orbicularis oculi developing

Eyelash follicles forming

Lens bow

Tarsal gland

Neural ectoderm (future iris epithelium) extending in front of lens

Pupillary membrane

differentiate, and the anterior (originally pigmented) layer loses its pigmentation. At the pupil margin, the iris sphincter muscle starts to form in this layer. Meanwhile the posterior layer (originally unpigmented) develops pigmentation and is fully pigmented by week 30. The dilator processes start to appear at the sixth month. The vascular pupillary membrane disappears at about week 32, although traces of the vessels may remain in the infant or adult eye (persistent pupillary membrane).

The development of the ciliary body matches that of the iris. At the 50mm stage (about week 11) the outer pigmented layer of the optic cup begins to fold into ridges, this causes the non-pigmented inner layer to fold and about 70-80 radial ciliary processes start to form. The neural crest mesenchyme cells start to differentiate into the smooth ciliary muscle between the epithelium and the sclera at about the same time. By week 20 the generally triangular section of the ciliary body is evident and the muscle fibres are anchored to the sclera at the scleral spur. The ciliary muscle continues to grow during the first year after birth.

The ciliary processes receive capillary-venous branches from the choroid at about 4 months. Later, after the major arterial circle has formed (at 6 months) recurrent vessels provide an artery to each process (at about 8 months).

Primary vitreous consisting of collagenous fibres, cells and vessels is present at the 13mm stage and the secondary (adult) vitreous is developed around the primary vitreous and the hyaloid system by week 13. During month 5 the zonular fibres appear linking the ciliary body to the crystalline lens.

Lid development commences at the 4 week (8mm) stage and the simple skin folds (Fig.18.19) are visible on the surface at the 20mm stage. As they grow they meet in front of the cornea at about week 8 and fuse along their edges at week 10. The eyelid stroma is mesenchymal in origin with the surface ectoderm providing the surface skin and conjunctival epithelium. The lid structures (eyelashes, muscles, glands) are formed and the lids separate at the beginning of the sixth month (160mm stage).

The lacrimal gland is formed by epithelial extensions of the conjunctival basal cells in orbital and palpebral groups at the upper fornix at week 7. These grow into cords whose centres develop a lumen during week 11 and, by the fifth month, the gland has developed and is divided by the levator tendon. The glands continue to develop for 2-3 years and, as they are not fully functional at birth, babies may cry a great deal but are initially unable to weep.

The lacrimal drainage system is produced from solid rods of tissue between the inner canthus and the nasal meatus. These branch towards the lid margin to form the canaliculi and upwards to start the development of the lacrimal sac at the 9 week (35mm) stage. The rods canalize and in general the lacrimal puncta are open at six months when the lids start to separate. The nasolacrimal canal opens into the nasal meatus shortly before birth but in some babies the canal is closed by a fold of mucous membrane. When present this generally resolves spontaneously with growth.

Because of rapid foetal development in the first few weeks maternal infection may produce serious eye defects. Probably the best known cause of ocular embryopathy is rubella (German measles) particularly if the infection is contracted in the first month of gestation. The virus inhibits cell division and cataract, uveitis, glaucoma, nystagmus and strabismus may result.

Post Natal Period

The globe is about 23mm diameter by age 3 and is adult size by about age 14-15.

The corneal periphery flattens and with-the-rule astigmatism may appear. The corneal epithelium thickens to 5 layers and the stroma becomes progressively more fibrous. The angle of the anterior chamber lengthens and widens during the first year. The lens continues to grow throughout life.

The ciliary muscle and the iris dilatator continue to develop for about the first 5 years. In white races pigmentation of the anterior border layer and stroma of the iris is absent at birth, so that the iris appears blue. The anterior border layer is covered in endothelium for the first year.

Retinal differentiation continues for some months after birth and the foveolar reflex is poor before 4 months. Retinal pigmentation is completed at about 6 months. The myelination of the radiations proceeds from the cortex and is completed at about 4 months.

The fixation reflex is present at birth. Static and statokinetic reflexes are present a few hours after birth and optokinetic nystagmus is demonstrable. Refixation (pursuit) reflex movements occur after a few weeks. Accommodation and convergence are present at 2 months.

It might seem that prematurity would result in hypermetropia, since there is normally (in about 73% of infants) 2.00 - 4.00D present at birth. However, a premature baby may have up to 20.00D of myopia that drops to a couple of dioptres at 6 months and then disappears. It also appears that myelination is accelerated by exposure to light and the premature child may have more myelination of the optic nerve than the full term infant of the same age. Prematurity tends to produce more heterotropia and lens abnormalities.

SUMMARY OF THE DEVELOPMENT OF THE EYE

Pre embryonic Period

Month 1   1-7mm
Optic vesicle
Lens pit
Embryonic fissure
Hyaloid vessels in fissure
Cup pigmentation

Embryonic period

Month 2   7-35mm
Fissure closes
Hyaloid system rapid development
Lens vesicle separates
    fibres fill lens/sutures commence
Primary vitreous
    secondary vitreous commenced
Cornea
    epithelium, endothelium develops
    collagen appears in stroma

Choriocapillaris forms
Retina
    neuroblastic layers
    ganglion cells/nerve fibres
    neuroglia
Muscle cone in place
Lid folds appear
    lashes forming
Lacrimal system initiated
    gland buds/drainage passages
Chiasma & LGB forming
Eye 1mm long

Foetal Period

Month 3   35-70mm
Hyaloid system regressing
Lens 2mm diameter/500 laminae
Cornea
   2mm diameter
   posterior limiting lamina forming
Sclera
   fibres at posterior pole
   Schlemm's canal initiated
Choroidal stroma developing
Retina
   plexiform layers
   synapses in IPL forming
   cone synapses
   macula growth moves ON nasally
Muscles insert into sclera
Lids fuse
   orbicularis developing
Optic tract developing
   visual cortex differentiating
Optic axes converge to 70º

Month 4   70-110mm
Cornea
   posterior limiting lamina formed
Scleral spur formed
   sclera forming lamina cribrosa
Cup growth producing cilary body
   iris sphincter initiated
   posterior pigment developing
   choroidal basal lamina forming
   major arterial circle formed
Retina
   vessels bud from hyaloid artery
Lid glands formed
Cranial nerves myelinating

Month 5   110-150mm
Cornea
   5.5mm diameter
   anterior limiting lamina formed
   nerve fibres in epithelial layer
Lens
   zonules in vitreous
Uvea
   precursors of SPCA's
   ciliary muscle joins scleral spur
Retina
   horizontal & amacrine cells
   rod synapses
   retinal vessels in nerve fibre layer
Optic nerve
   dural sheath forming
   Bergmeister's papilla complete
Globe 7mm

Month 6   150-200mm
Lid sensory system developing
Lens 5mm diameter
Uvea
   iris dilatator differentiating
   pupillary membrane atrophying
Aqueous forming
Retina
   macula differentiating
   outer segments differentiating
   Bergmeister's papilla complete
   ora serrata established
Optic tracts myelinating
Globe 10mm diameter

Month 7   200-230mm
Trabecular meshwork organised
Choroid pigmentation forming
Cilary muscle circular fibres present
Retina
   hyaloid artery closed
   foveal pit forming
   Bergmeister's papilla atrophies
Lids separating
Chiasma myelinating
ON myelination commences

Month 8   230-270mm
Lids fully separated
Ciliary circulation complete
Iris
   sphincter free in stroma
   innervation in place
Retina
   vessels at ora serrata
   ganglion cells two deep in fovea
Globe 15mm diameter

Month 9   270-330mm
Corneal epithelium 4 cells thick
Aqueous outflow initiated
Lens has 1450 lamellae
Ciliary muscle radial fibres present
Retina
   physiological cup develops
   structure complete, except fovea
Optic nerve
   myelination in orbital portion
Globe 17mm diameter

IPL	inner plexiform layer
LGB	lateral geniculate body
ON	optic nerve
SPCA	short posterior cilary artery

NOTE: Dimensions and timings are approximations only.

GLOSSARY

NOTE: This glossary is not intended to include all the terms that have been used in the text but to expand definitions of topics that may not be familiar to the reader.

Acinus: Rounded sac (literally - in the form of a berry growing in a cluster).

Active transport: The mechanism for moving materials through the cell membrane against the molecular concentration gradient, a process requiring the expenditure of energy which is provided by the breakdown of carbohydrates, proteins and lipids. Used, for example, to carry potassium ions into cells and sodium ions out. Amino acids are actively transported into cells to give an intracellular concentration up to twenty times higher than the extracellular concentration.

Adenoid tissue: Literally - glandular tissue. In the conjunctiva the term refers to the subepithelial lymphatic tissue. Increased activity in this layer produces the follicles (sac-like swellings) seen in viral infections and allergic reactions.

Alimentary tract: The gut, a tract for the digestion of food and absorption of nutrients.

Alveolus: Literally - a small cavity (cf. **Acinus**).

Amino acids: Organic compounds of carbon, hydrogen, oxygen and nitrogen forming the fundamental constituents of living matter.

Anastomosis: Joining of vessels. For example, the radial vessels of the iris anastomose to form the minor iridic circle (Fig.8.12).

Apical: Layer or structure remote from the basement membrane (cf. **Basal**).

Arrector muscle: The sympathetically innervated smooth muscles which lie in the same plane as, and attached to, the hair follicles on the side towards which the hair slopes. On contraction the skin above the origin of the muscle is depressed and that around the hair is elevated as the hair is pulled upright giving the appearance of "goose-flesh".

Avascular: Lacking vessels, usually refers to lack of blood vessels (cf. **Vascular**).

Basal: The layer adjacent to the basement membrane. Used also in basal lamina to mean the densely staining layer (50nm thick) of fine (4nm) fibrils next to the cell surface forming part of the cell basement membrane (cf. **Apical**).

Bone marrow: Soft pulp found in cavities in bone. Red marrow produces the cells of the vascular and lymphatic system, while the yellow marrow contains large numbers of fat cells. Both types are extremely vascular.

Brainstem: Part of the brain excluding the cerebral hemispheres and cerebellum. Consists of the midbrain, pons and medulla oblongata.

Carbohydrate: Compound of carbon and water molecules such as sugars, starch, cellulose. These form about 1% of the body weight and provide the most readily available source of chemical energy.

Cells: The basic living structural unit of the body, cells consist of living material (protoplasm) contained in a membrane (the plasma membrane or cell membrane). The protoplasm consists of a watery fluid or gel in which lies the membrane bound nucleus and the specialised organelles and inclusions. Living cells are motile (have the capacity for movement) and have the ability to reproduce themselves (for body growth or to heal a wound for example). With some special exceptions (e.g. muscle, nerve), cells have diameters between 5-50μm.

Circle of Willis (1621-75): An arterial circle formed by contributions from the anterior communicating, the anterior cerebral, the internal carotid, the posterior communicating and the posterior cerebral arteries.

Collagen: (See also page 17 and Fig.2.14). Collagen is formed by the synthesis of amino acids in the rough endoplasmic reticulum to give long polypeptide molecules. These move into the cisternae of the reticulum and link to form the pro- (or proto-) collagen molecule. When moved outside the cell these molecules are modified by cell enzymes to form tropocollagen filaments which link to form collagen fibrils.

Contralateral: On the opposite side (cf. **Ipsilateral**).

Cuticular (layer): In the choroid or ciliary body, this refers to the basement membrane of the pigment epithelium.

Deep: Structures lying within the tissue (cf. **Superficial**).

Diffusion: The process by which molecules move passively from a region of high concentration to a region of low concentration until equilibrium is reached. Since diffusion depends on random movement of molecules, collision with adjacent molecules slows down the process so that it is an impractical method for transporting substances over long distances.

Distal: Situated away from the centre of the body or CNS (cf. **Proximal**).

Electrolytes: Aqueous solutions of acids, bases or salts.

Endolymph: Fluid which fills the membranous labyrinth of the inner ear.

Enucleation: Removal of the globe from the orbit.

Fasciculus: Bundle of fibres.

Fenestrated: Having small openings or pores (up to 100nm diameter) closed by a fine diaphragm.

Follicles: Relatively avascular sac-like swelling due to lymphocyte hyperactivity as part of the immune response. The follicles contain lymphocytes, macrophages and plasma cells.

Ganglion: Collection of nerve cell bodies outside the central nervous system.

Glycoprotein: Component of ground substance formed of polysaccharide and protein. These molecules have stronger bonds than mucopolysaccharides and are found in the lens capsule and the posterior limiting lamina.

Histology: Study of tissues coined from the Greek word histos meaning a web.

Hydrophilic: Literally - water-loving. Molecules that form the gel of connective tissues have sites that bind water molecules. Water entering such gels produces swelling (oedema).

Hydrostatic pressure: The pressure exerted by a liquid. Contraction of the heart muscle generates a hydrostatic pressure in the capillaries which tends to push metabolites through the capillary walls into the extracellular fluid.

Intraocular pressure: Pressure within the globe created by the forces producing the aqueous humour and the forces resisting its escape. The value obtained depends on the method of measurement. Indentation (Schiøtz) tonometry gives a value of about 16mm Hg and applanation tonometry about 15mm Hg.

Ipsilateral: On the same side (cf. **Contralateral**).

Lagophthalmos: Literally - "Hare eye". A condition in which the lids fail to meet when lid closure is attempted. The cornea may dehydrate, resulting in keratitis. (Originally Lagophthalmus - The Physical Dictionary, 1657)

Lamella: Thin sheet or layer.

Lamina: Layer or sheet.

Lentiform nucleus: Part of the basal nuclei of the cerebral hemispheres. Together with the caudate nucleus it forms the corpus striatum, which receives and modifies information from most of the cerebral cortex, thalamus and brainstem nuclei. The modified information which is sent back to the thalamus and brainstem appears to influence manual dexterity.

Lesion: Damage, injury or disease affecting normal function.

Lumen: The cavity or space enclosed by the walls of a tube or sac.

Lysozyme: A bactericidal enzyme secreted by serous glands (lacrimal and salivary).

Meatus: Channel or passage.

Mesenchyme: Embryonic connective tissue consisting of amoeboid cells in mucopolysaccharide matrix. This develops into connective tissue, bone, cartilage, blood-forming tissue and the sheaths of nerves, muscle and bone.

Metabolites: Substances made by the body or taken from the environment. These are used as a source of building materials for the tissues, as a source of energy or a means of releasing energy.

Mucopolysaccharides: Component of ground substance formed by an amino-sugar polysaccharide (also called a glycosaminoglycan) molecule. These molecules have weaker bonding and are more slippery than glycoproteins.

Nucleus of origin: Site of the neural cell bodies whose axons form a motor or efferent cranial nerve.

Nystagmus: A repetitive eye movement which may be a smooth to and fro (pendular) oscillation or consist of a slow drift and a fast recovery phase (jerk nystagmus). Nystagmus is normal in response to vestibular and optokinetic stimuli but it may be induced pathologically by narcotics or fatigue.

Organ: Specialised structure within the body forming a functional unit, e.g. heart, kidney.

Organelles: Internal membrane systems of the cell (endoplasmic reticulum), membrane-bound structures (Golgi complex, lysosomes, mitochondria) and microtubules, microfilaments, centrioles and ribosomes. Their relationship to the cell could be compared with the relationship of organs to the whole body.

Osmotic pressure: The pressure that is produced as a result of there being a greater concentration of dissolved particles on one side of a membrane which allows the passage of the solvent (water, for example) but not the solute (the particles). The solvent will pass through the membrane until there are equal concentrations of the solute on both sides. This will give a net gain of water on the side which initially had the greater concentration. The osmotic pressure may be measured by opposing it with a hydrostatic pressure so that no water transfer occurs.

Papilla: (Plural - papillae) a mound of tissue.

Para-: By the side of, closer than Peri-.

Peri-: Surrounding, further out than Para-.

Phagocytosis: The method of ingestion and transport of solids by cells. The cell membrane envelops the material and forms a membrane-bound vesicle which may be carried to a site within the cell for breakdown by lysosomal enzymes.

Pinocytosis: A mechanism by which a cell draws fluid in from the extracellular area by infolding the cell membrane and trapping the fluid inside the cell.

Plexus: A network of interweaving fibres or vessels.

Polymerisation: Formation of large molecules from repeating sub-units.

Polypeptides: Combination of three or more amino acids.

Prickle cells: Epithelial cells which have processes (prickles) that project into indentations in the membrane of adjacent cells. Form the prickle cell layer of the epidermis.

Primate: Highest order of mammals, including man and monkey.

Process: When related to form means a projection from the surface of a cell or bone or from some structure such as the iris or ciliary body.

Prolapse: To slip down and forward out of place.

Proprioceptor: Neural receptor responding to movement, position and pressure. Includes sensory structures in muscles and joints and the vestibular receptors in the inner ear.

Protein: Complex organic molecules composed of amino acids. Protein molecules are very large, for example, the actin molecules found in muscle and many other cells, have a diameter of 5.5nm. Proteins form 17% of body weight.

Proximal: Situated towards the centre of the body or CNS. The point of origin of a nerve or muscle for example (cf. **Distal**).

Ramus: (Plural - rami). Nerve branches or fibres. Also process of a bone.

Recurrent: Turning back towards the origin.

Ret-: Prefix as in retina, rete, reticular, meaning net-like

Reticulo-endothelial system: A general term covering all cells and tissues with phagocytic properties. It is more appropriate to use the name mononuclear phagocyte system to group the phagocytic cells (excluding polymorphonuclear leucocytes) and to use lymphoreticular to describe the structures of the lymphatic system that produce cells for that system, effect immune response and which are involved in phagocytosis. Mononuclear cells are present in connective tissue, in nervous tissue as microglial cells, in the meninges as meningothelial cells and in blood and lymph. See also lymphocytes pages 17 and 27, the lymphatic system page 31.

Saccadic movement: Literally - a jerking movement. Term introduced by Javal (1839-1907). Rapid eye movement used to redirect the visual axis, either voluntarily or during the fast phase of nystagmus.

Scotoma: An area of the visual field in which vision is depressed relative to the surrounding field.

Sebaceous: Sebum producing.

Sebum: A fatty substance produced by holocrine glands such as the tarsal glands or the glands of hair follicles. Sebum lubricates the hair and skin, reduces drying and is bactericidal.

Secretion: The active transfer of materials produced by cells from inside the plasma membrane to the outside. The material may be moved to the cell surface in vesicles and then released (excytosis) or the cell may be destroyed to release the material (holocrine secretion of sebaceous glands).

Septum: A sheet of tissue separating two regions.

Stroma: (Also Substantia propria) The bulk or body of a structure, the tissue contained between the specialised surface layers.

Substantia propria: See **Stroma** above.

Superficial: Surface (cf. **Deep**).

Superficial origin: The point on the surface of the central nervous system at which a motor nerve emerges.

Synovial sheath: Membrane of connective tissue forming a bag filled with mucoprotein which lubricates and nourishes a joint. In the case of the superior oblique muscle it lubricates the tendon where it slides through the cartilagineous trochlea.

Tissue: The term tissue is used to describe collectively cells and their products involved in a particular function. Some tissues are merely composed of cell layers (epithelial, endothelial tissues) while in others the cells form only a small percentage of the tissue volume (bone, blood). Different tissue groups, engaged in co-operating to function in a special way, form organs.

Trabecula: A beam or bar shaped structure.

Transcellular: Literally - through a cell.

Tubercle: A small rounded projection on a bone (or the mass of cells characteristic of tuberculosis).

Vacuole: Large fluid-filled 'bubble' within a cell.

Varicosity: Swelling or distended part of an axon or dendrite, containing mitochondria or mitochondria and vesicles.

Vascular: Containing vessels, usually refers to a tissue containing blood vessels (cf. **Avascular**).

Venous pressure: Pressure in veins. In the intraocular veins, the pressure is about 2mm Hg above the intraocular (aqueous) pressure, while in the episcleral veins it is 2-3mm Hg below the mean intraocular pressure of 15mmHg.

Vesicle: Membrane-bound 'bubble' within a cell, usually containing fluid.

Viscosity: "Stickiness" of a fluid. Factor in determining the movement of particles in a fluid. Fluids formed of complex three dimensional molecules have a high viscosity e.g. ground substance of connective tissue.

BIBLIOGRAPHY

Babel, J., Bischoff, A. and Spoendlin, H. (1970). *Ultrastructure of the Peripheral Nervous System and Sense Organs*, George Thieme Verlag: Stuttgart.

Breinin, G. M. (1962). *The Electrophysiology of Extraocular Muscle*, University of Toronto Press: Toronto.

Brindley, G. S. (1970). *Physiology of the Retina and Visual Pathway* 2nd edition, Edward Arnold Ltd.

Carpenter, M. B. (1976). *Human Neuroanatomy* 7th edition, The Williams and Wilkins Co.: Baltimore.

Duke-Elder, S. and Wybar, K. C. (1961). *System of Ophthalmology* Vol. II, Henry Kimpton.

Duke-Elder, S. and Cook, C. (1963). *System of Ophthalmology* Vol. III, Normal and Abnormal Development, Part I, Embryology, Henry Kimpton.

Duke-Elder, S. (1968). *System of Ophthalmology* Vol. IV, Physiology of the eye and vision, Henry Kimpton.

Fine, B. S. and Yanoff, M. (1979). *Ocular Histology* 2nd edition, Harper and Row Inc.: Maryland.

Gardner, D. L. and Dodds, T. C. (1976). *Human Histology* 3rd edition, Churchill Livingstone.

Garven, H. S. D. (1965). *A Student's Histology* 2nd edition, E. and S. Livingstone Ltd.

Hogan, M. J., Alvarado, A. B. and Weddell, J. E. (1971). *Histology of the Human Eye*, W. B. Saunders Company: Philadelphia.

Hogan, M. J. and Zimmerman, L. E. (1962). *Ophthalmic Pathology,* 2nd edition, W. B. Saunders: Philadelphia.

Hunt, C. C. (1974). *Handbook of Sensory Physiology,* Vol III, Springer: Berlin.

Jacobiec, F. A. (1982). *Ocular Anatomy, Embryology and Teratology*, Harper and Row Inc.: Philadephia.

Koornneef, L. (1977). *Spatial Aspects of Orbital Musculo-fibrous Tissue in Man*, Swets and Zeitlinger: Amsterdam.

Leigh, R. J. and Zee, D. S. (1983). *The Neurology of Eye Movements*, F. A. Davis Company: Philadelphia.

Lockhart, R. D., Hamilton, G. F. and Fyfe, F. W. (1965) *Anatomy of the Human Body*, 2nd edition, Faber and Faber Ltd.

Marieb, E. N. (1992). *Human Anatomy and Physiology* 2nd edition, Benjamin/Cummings Publishing Co. Inc.: California.

Moses, R. A. (1970). *Adler's Physiology of the Eye* 5th edition, C. V. Mosby Co.: Saint Louis.

von Noorden, G. K. and Maumenee, A. E. (1967). *Atlas of Strabismus*, C. V. Mosby Co.: Saint Louis.

Oyster, C. W. (1999). *The Human Eye*, Sinauer Associates Inc.: Massachusetts

Rodieck, R. W. (1973). *The Vertebrate Retina*, W. H. Freeman and Co.: Sydney.

Shimizu, K. and Ujiie, K. (1978). *Structure of Ocular Vessels*, Igaku-Shoin Ltd.: Tokyo.

Spooner, J. D. (1957). *Ocular Anatomy*, Butterworths.

Warwick, R. (1976). *Eugene Wolff's Anatomy of the Eye and Orbit*, 7th edition, H. K. Lewis and Co. Ltd.

Williams, P. L., Warwick, R., Dyson, M. and Bannister, L. H. (1989). *Gray's Anatomy* 37th edition, Churchill Livingstone.

INDEX

401

Sphenoid bone 75, 77, **82**, 100
 greater wing 83, 100
 lesser wing 84, 100
 sinus 82, 83
Spherule, rod 157, 164
Sphincter pupillae 107, 132, 133, **134**
 contraction 134
 innervation 137, 329, 352
Spina recti lateralis 93, 208, 216
Spinal cord 45, **68**
Spinal nerves 68
Spindles, muscle **40**, 227, 228
Spinothalamic tract 70
Spiral ending 227
Spiral of Tillaux 209
Splenium **57**, 305
Spongy bone 24
Spur
 Fuchs 134, **135**
 Michel's 134, **135**
 scleral 122, **123**, 138, 140, 378
Squamous epithelium,
 simple **11**
 stratified **14**
Squamous suture 81
Squamous temporal bone **79**
Static reflex 357, 380
Statokinetic reflex 359, 360, 380
Stratified epithelium **14**, 112
Stratum corneum 236, 237
Stratum lucidum 236, 237
Striate area (cortex) 303, 356
Striated (striped) muscle 32, **33**
 contraction 35
Stroma 15, **389**
 choroid 147, **148**, 366
 ciliary body 141
 conjunctival 248
 corneal 111, **115**, 366, 370
 iris 132, **133**, 366
 scleral **126**, 366

Structural connective tissue 20
Styloid process 78
Stylomastoid foramen **80**, 340
Subarachnoid space **45**, 72
Subdural space 45
Sulcus 56
 calcarine **57**, 302, 303
 central 56
 external scleral **121**, 122, 251
 intermarginal 233, 245, 246, 249
 internal scleral 123
 lunate 302, 303
 orbitopalpebral 232
 parieto-occipital 57, 303
Summation 43
Superficial temporal
 artery 253, 312, 319, **320**
 vein 255, 322, 323, 324
Superior brachium 297, **298**, 309, 329, 352
Superior cervical ganglion 137, 260, 261, **348**, 349
Superior colliculus **59**, 297, 298, 309, 327, 328, 350, 354, 356
Superior oblique muscle 218
 action **219**, 220
Superior ophthalmic vein 71, 151, 209, 210, 218, 244, 255, 266, 321, 322, **323**
Superior orbital fissure 75, 77, **84**, 93, 101, 322, 327, 333, 337, 345
Superior rectus muscle 208, **210**
 action **210**, 211
Superior salivatory nucleus 267, 338, 340
Superior wall (roof) of orbit 92
Suprachoroid **147**, 148
Supraciliaris 138, **139**, 140
Supraciliary arch 80
Supraduction 205
Supra-orbital
 artery 253, 313, **317**, 318, 320

Supra-orbital (continued)
 nerve 259, 260, 343, 344, **345**
 notch 75, 80, 90, **92**, 100, 317, 345
 vein 255, **256**, 321, 322, 324
Supratrochlear
 artery 253, 313, **318**, 319
 nerve 259, **260**, 343, 344, 345
 vein 256, 322, 324
Surface ectoderm 365, 367, 368, 369, 372
Suspensory ligament of lens 199
Sutures, bone 73
Sutures, lens **198**, 199, 369
Sweat glands 235, 236, 237, **238**, 239, 349
Sympathetic nervous system 50
 ganglia **50**, 69
 orbital 261, 348, 349
 supply
  to choroid 151
  to ciliary body 146
  to eyelids 244, **260**, 261
  to iris 137
Synapse, 44
 transmitter substance 44
Synaptic ribbon 164, 166
Synergists 224
Synovial 218, 389

Tarsal,
 conjunctiva 249
 gland 235, 242, **245**, 246, 267, 377
 muscle 235, 242, **243**, 244
  innervation 244, 260, 261
 plate 235, **245**, 279, 280, 282
Tears
 constituents 268, 269
 drainage **269**, 275
 film 268
 functions 268, 269